Graded examples in

Matrices and Transformations

M. R. Heylings M.A., M.Sc.

Schofield & Sims Limited   Huddersfield

0 7217 2335 7

First printed 1984

Acknowledgements
The drawings on pages 44 and 113 by Sir D'Arcy Thompson,
On Growth and Form, are reproduced by permission of
Cambridge University Press.
The section of the Underground Map on page 122 is
reproduced by permission of London Transport.
The diagram of Hampton Court Maze on page 136 is
reproduced with the permission of the Controller of
Her Majesty's Stationery Office.

The series **Graded examples in mathematics**
comprises:

Fractions and Decimals	0 7217 2323 3
Answer Book	0 7217 2324 1
Algebra	0 7217 2325 x
Answer Book	0 7217 2326 8
Area and Volume	0 7217 2327 6
Answer Book	0 7217 2328 4
General Arithmetic	0 7217 2329 2
Answer Book	0 7217 2330 6
Geometry and Trigonometry	0 7217 2331 4
Answer Book	0 7217 2332 2
Negative Numbers and Graphs	0 7217 2333 0
Answer Book	0 7217 2334 9
Matrices and Transformations	0 7217 2335 7
Answer Book	0 7217 2336 5

In preparation:

Sets, Probability and Statistics	0 7217 2337 3
Answer Book	0 7217 2338 1
Revision of Topics	0 7217 2339 x
Answer Book	0 7217 2340 3

Designed by Graphic Art Concepts, Leeds
Printed in England by Pindar Print Limited, Scarborough, North Yorkshire

Author's Note

This series has been written and produced in the form of eight topic books, each offering a wealth of graded examples for pupils in the 11–16 age range; plus a further book of revision examples for fifth formers.

There are no teaching points in the series. The intention is to meet the often heard request from teachers for a wide choice of graded examples to support their own class teaching. The contents are clearly labelled for easy use in conjunction with an existing course book; but the books can also be used as the chief source of material, in which case the restrictions imposed by the traditional type of mathematics course book are removed and the teacher is free to organise year-by-year courses to suit the school. Used in this way, the topic-book approach offers an unusual and useful continuity of work for the class-room, for homework or for revision purposes.

The material has been tested over many years in classes ranging from mixed ability 11-year-olds to fifth formers taking public examinations. Some sections are useful for pupils of above average ability while other sections suit the needs of the less able, though it is for the middle range of ability that the series is primarily intended.

Contents

Symmetry

Transformations

Topology

Matrices

Transformations and Matrices

Symbols

=	is equal to
≠	is not equal to
≃	is approximately equal to
<	is less than
≤	is less than or equal to
≮	is not less than
>	is greater than
≥	is greater than or equal to
≯	is not greater than
⇒	implies
⇐	is implied by
→	maps onto
∈	is a member of
∉	is not a member of
⊂	is a subset of
⊄	is not a subset of
∩	intersection (or overlap)
∪	union
A'	the complement (or outside) of set A
$\mathscr{E}$	The Universal set
∅ or { }	the empty set
(x, y)	the co-ordinates of a point
$\begin{pmatrix} x \\ y \end{pmatrix}$	the components of a vector

The Greek alphabet

A	α	alpha
B	β	beta
Γ	γ	gamma
Δ	δ	delta
E	ε	epsilon
Z	ζ	zeta
H	η	eta
Θ	θ	theta
I	ι	iota
K	κ	kappa
Λ	λ	lambda
M	μ	mu
N	ν	nu
Ξ	ξ	xi
O	o	omicron
Π	π	pi
P	ρ	rho
Σ	σ, ς	sigma
T	τ	tau
Y	υ	upsilon
Φ	ϕ, φ	phi
X	χ	chi
Ψ	ψ	psi
Ω	ω	omega

Symmetry

Line symmetry
Rotational symmetry
Axes and planes of symmetry

Line symmetry

Part 1 Pinpricks

1 Fold a sheet of paper and make a straight crease.
Use a ruler to draw the shape shown here on one side of the crease.
Pin prick through the corners of the shape; unfold the paper and join the pin-holes on the other side.

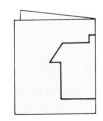

2 Repeat with these shapes, where the coloured line is the crease in the paper.

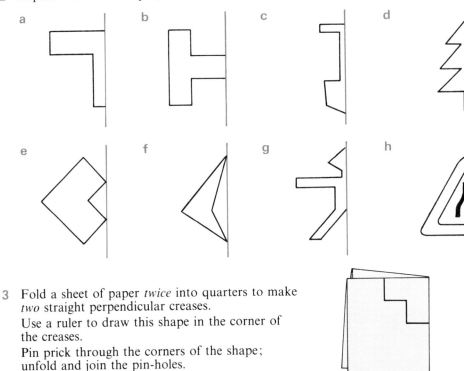

3 Fold a sheet of paper *twice* into quarters to make *two* straight perpendicular creases.
Use a ruler to draw this shape in the corner of the creases.
Pin prick through the corners of the shape; unfold and join the pin-holes.

4 Repeat with these shapes, where the coloured lines give the two creases.

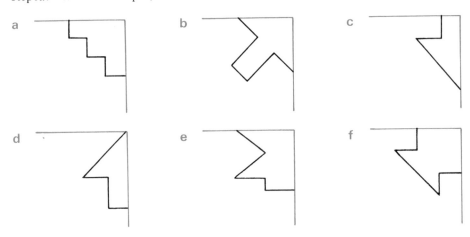

Line symmetry

Part 2 Paper cut-outs

1 Fold a sheet of paper to make a straight crease.

  a Cut across the crease along the dotted lines shown in this diagram.

    Name the shape you have made when you unfold the paper.

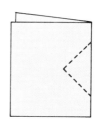

Repeat for these diagrams, where the dotted lines show where to cut and the coloured line gives the crease.

Unfold and name the shapes you have made.

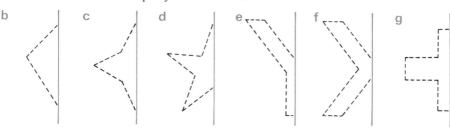

2 Fold a sheet of paper once.

  Can you cut across the crease to make a hole in the shape of

  a a rectangle   b a square   c an isosceles triangle
  d a rhombus (diamond)   e a right-angled triangle?

3 Fold a sheet of paper *twice* into quarters with *two* perpendicular creases.

  a Cut in the corner of the creases along the dotted lines of this diagram.

    Unfold and name the shape you have made.

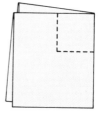

Repeat for these diagrams. Name each shape you make when you unfold the paper.

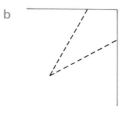
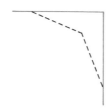
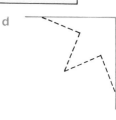

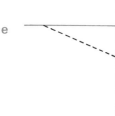
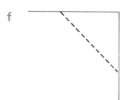
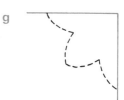

4 Fold a sheet of paper *twice* into quarters.

  Can you cut in the corner of the creases to make a hole in the shape of

  a a rectangle   b a cross   c a circle
  d a four-petalled flower   e a six-petalled flower?

Line symmetry

5　Fold a sheet of paper twice, but slant the second crease as shown in this diagram. Make *one* straight cut across the corner. You will make one of these shapes.

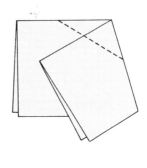

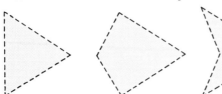

Can you alter the position of the cut to make the other two shapes of hole?

6　Fold a rectangular piece of paper *three* times as shown, so that all the creases meet at a point to make an angle of 45°.

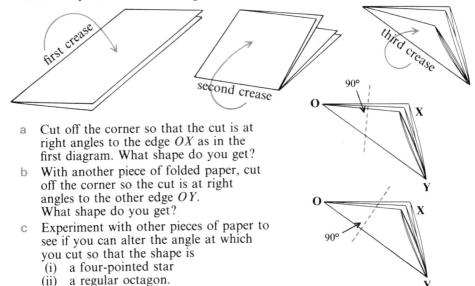

a　Cut off the corner so that the cut is at right angles to the edge *OX* as in the first diagram. What shape do you get?

b　With another piece of folded paper, cut off the corner so the cut is at right angles to the other edge *OY*. What shape do you get?

c　Experiment with other pieces of paper to see if you can alter the angle at which you cut so that the shape is
　(i)　a four-pointed star
　(ii)　a regular octagon.

7

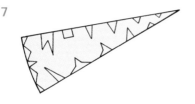

A **doily** is a paper mat placed on a plate when serving cakes.
Make one by folding a circle of diameter 20 cm four times through its centre into sixteenths.
Cut pieces of your own design out of the two radii—this diagram shows a possible design.
Finally, open it out.

8　Paper decorations can be made from a strip of paper about 1 m long and 10 cm wide.
Start at one end and fold forward and backwards in 10-cm strips like the zigzag of a concertina.
Finally, fold the whole concertina in half along the dotted line as shown in this diagram.

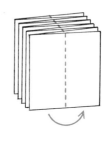
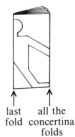

last　　all the
fold　concertina
　　　folds

Now draw half the shape you want—half a man is shown here—and cut it out.
Carefully unfold the concertina to see your shapes all joined together.

Part 3 Line symmetry

1 Plane figures have a **line of symmetry** if one half of the figure will reflect onto the other half.
Copy these shapes and draw their lines of symmetry.
If any shape has no line of symmetry, then say so.
You might find a small mirror useful.

2 Copy only the letters of the alphabet, as printed here, which have lines of symmetry. Draw the lines of symmetry on them.

A B C D E F G H I J K L M N
O P Q R S T U V W X Y Z

3 Some letters can be printed in a different way.
Copy these letters and draw their lines of symmetry.

Line symmetry

4 For each of these arrow shapes, decide which of the lettered lines are lines of symmetry.

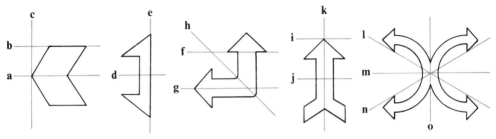

5 How many lines of symmetry has a perfectly round letter O?

6 Copy each of these shapes. If they have any lines of symmetry, draw the lines on them.

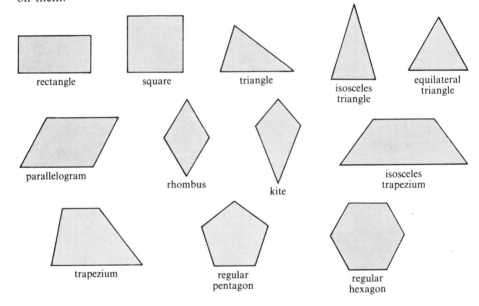

rectangle   square   triangle   isosceles triangle   equilateral triangle

parallelogram   rhombus   kite   isosceles trapezium

trapezium   regular pentagon   regular hexagon

7 Copy only those numbers printed here which have lines of symmetry. Draw the lines of symmetry on them.

0 1 2 3 4 5 6 7 8 9

8 Write each of these words and numbers just as they are printed here. Draw any lines of symmetry on them; if there are none, then say so.

a **mum**   b **dud**   c **bid**   d **noon**   e **onion**

f **CODE**   g **BOOK**   h **NONE**   i **TOOT**   j **OXO**

k **1313**   l **6006**   m **1881**   n **916**   o **808**

Line symmetry

9 Copy these diagrams which are all incomplete.
The dotted lines are lines of symmetry. Use them to complete each diagram.
You might find a mirror useful.

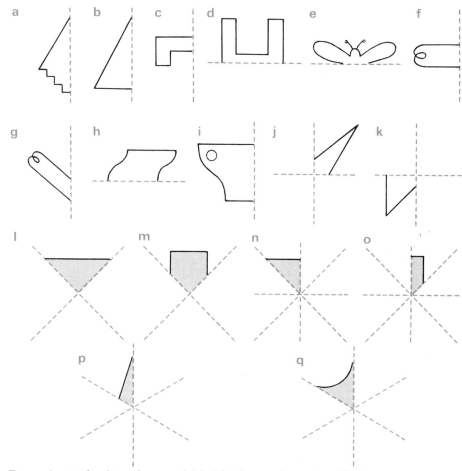

10 For each set of points, draw and label both axes from 0 to 10
plot the points and join them in order to give part of a shape
and draw the lines of symmetry given and complete the shape.

	Points	Lines of symmetry
a	(4, 4), (3, 6), (3, 3), (2, 3), (2, 8), (3, 8), (4, 6)	$x = 4$
b	(4, 2), (1, 2), (1, 3), (3, 7), (1, 7), (1, 8), (4, 8), (4, 7), (2, 3), (4, 3)	$x = 4$
c	(2, 5), (2, 9), (6, 9), (6, 7), (4, 7), (4, 6), (6, 6), (6, 5)	$y = 5$
d	(3, 3), (1, 5), (2, 6), (3, 5), (6, 8), (5, 9), (6, 10), (8, 8)	$y = x$
e	(2, 2), (2, 9), (6, 9), (6, 7), (5, 7), (5, 8), (3, 8), (3, 3)	$y = x$
f	(2, 5), (2, 9), (3, 9), (3, 6), (5, 6)	$x = 5$ and $y = 5$
g	(4, 5), (4, 7), (2, 7), (2, 9), (5, 9)	$x = 5$ and $y = 5$
h	(3, 3), (2, 4), (3, 5), (1, 9)	$y = x$ and $x + y = 10$
i	(3, 5), (1, 7), (2, 8)	$\begin{cases} x = 5 \text{ and } y = 5 \\ y = x \text{ and } x + y = 10 \end{cases}$

13

Line symmetry

11   Say whether these statements are *true* or *false*.

a   A square has only two lines of symmetry.

b   An isosceles triangle has just one line of symmetry.

c   The diagonal of any rectangle is a line of symmetry.

d   The diamond shape on a playing-card has just one line of symmetry.

e   The club shape on a playing-card has three lines of symmetry.

f   A semicircle has just one line of symmetry.

g   Only one letter in the word **SYMMETRY** has no lines of symmetry.

h   An equilateral triangle has three lines of symmetry.

i   A quarter of a circle has two lines of symmetry.

j   The line joining the midpoints of the opposite sides of any parallelogram is a line of symmetry.

12   Draw a quadrilateral which has

a   only two lines of symmetry, both passing through opposite corners

b   only two lines of symmetry, with neither passing through any corners

c   no lines of symmetry

d   just one line of symmetry (there are two possible shapes—draw one of each type)

e   four lines of symmetry.

Rotational symmetry

1   If a shape fits on top of itself as it rotates about a point, then it has **rotational symmetry** (or **point symmetry**). The number of times it fits onto itself during a full turn is the *order* of its rotational symmetry.
Copy and complete this table by looking at the shapes below.
You might find a sheet of tracing paper useful.

Shape	a	b	c	d	e	---	q	r
Has it rotational symmetry?								
If *yes*, what is the order of the rotational symmetry?								

2   Look at the letters of the alphabet printed in question **2** on page 11.
Copy only those letters which have rotational symmetry.
Mark with a cross the centre of the rotational symmetry.

3   Look at the shapes in question **6** on page 12.
Copy only those shapes which have rotational symmetry.
Mark with a cross the centre of the rotational symmetry; and write the *order* of the symmetry.

Rotational symmetry

4   Copy only those words and numbers which have rotational symmetry.

a **mum**   b **bud**   c **dud**   d **dib**   e **dip**

f **NOON**   g **ONION** h **bob**   i **pod**   j **oxo**

k **818**   l **6009**   m **1961**   n **303**   o **90806**

5   For each set of points, draw and label both axes from 0 to 10.
Plot and join the points in order, to give part of a shape which has rotational symmetry.
Take the point (5, 5) as the centre of the symmetry each time; and complete the rest of the shape using the order of symmetry given.
Tracing paper might be useful.
a   (4, 4), (2, 4), (2, 9), (3, 9), (3, 6), (4, 6)   order 4
b   (6, 6), (6, 8), (4, 10), (2, 10), (2, 8), (4, 8), (4, 6)   order 4
c   (4, 5), (2, 7), (5, 10), (5, 8), (4, 7), (5, 6)   order 4
d   (4, 5), (4, 8), (0, 8), (4, 10), (6, 6), (6, 5)   order 2
e   (4, 5), (4, 7), (7, 8), (10, 8), (10, 6), (9, 6), (9, 7), (7, 7), (6, 5)   order 2
f   (5, 6), (9, 2), (9, 1), (7, 1), (8, 2), (7, 3), (5, 3), (5, 4)   order 2

6   Copy these diagrams, each of which is only *part* of a shape.
Use the dot as the centre of rotational symmetry, and complete the shape using the given order of rotational symmetry.
Tracing paper might be useful.

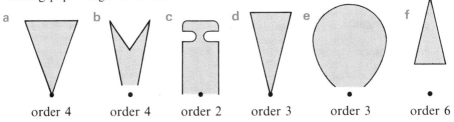

a   b   c   d   e   f

order 4   order 4   order 2   order 3   order 3   order 6

7   Copy each of these shapes; and then add *one extra* limb so that they each have rotational symmetry.

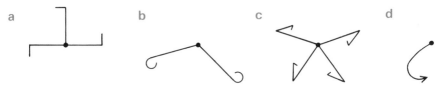

a   b   c   d

Axes and planes of symmetry

1 If a solid object fits on itself as it rotates about an axis, then this axis is an **axis of symmetry**. The number of times it fits on itself during a full turn is the *order* of the rotational symmetry.

State the order of the rotational symmetry for each of these solids about the axes shown.

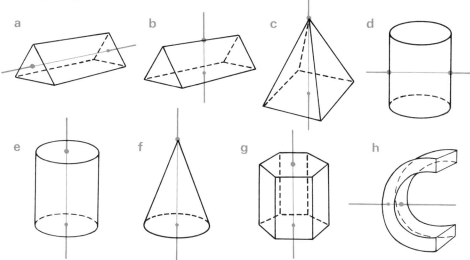

2 Which of these objects have axes of rotational symmetry?

a	a saucer	b	a rugby ball	c	a spoon
d	a fork	e	a paintbrush	f	a house brick
g	a chess-board	h	a car tyre	i	a grand piano
j	a milk bottle	k	a chair	l	a square floor-tile

3 Each of these objects has an axis of rotational symmetry.
What is the order of the rotational symmetry?

a	a rectangular bar of chocolate	b	a sharpened hexagonal pencil
c	a tennis racket	d	a square-based pyramid

4 Copy or trace these solids and draw *all* their axes of symmetry.

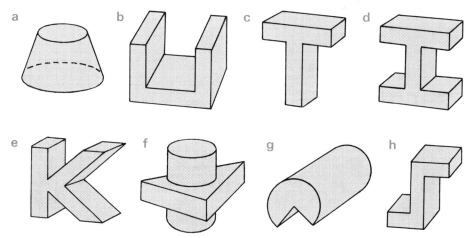

17

Axes and planes of symmetry

5   This octahedron is made from two
    square-based pyramids.
    Copy or trace it, and draw its
    five axes of symmetry.

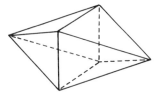

6   a   How many axes of
        symmetry has this
        cuboid?

    b   This cuboid has a square cross-section. It has
        more axes of symmetry than the cuboid in **a**.
        How many has it?

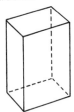

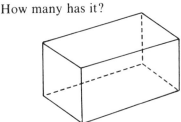

    c   A cube has many
        axes of symmetry.
        Three of them are
        shown here.
        How many are
        there altogether?

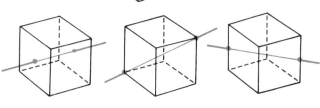

7   A solid object has a **plane of symmetry** if one half of
    the object reflects onto the other half.
    This drawing of a chair shows that the chair has a
    plane of symmetry.

    Which of the shaded planes in these diagrams are
    planes of symmetry?

a

b

c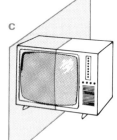

d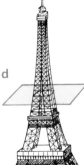

e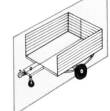

f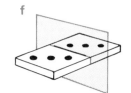

g

Axes and planes of symmetry

8 How many planes of symmetry has
  a a bath   b a cup   c a 3-pin plug
  d a grand piano   e a bed   f a door
  g a rolling-pin   h a sharpened   i a typewriter
                              hexagonal pencil
  j a cricket bat   k a 3-legged stool   l a dustbin?

9 Name the objects described here, all of which have a plane of symmetry.
  a something to put the post through
  b something that fits on ears and nose
  c something to cook in
  d something to put a key into
  e something to climb up
  f something to wear on the head
  g something to get light from
  h something to pull splinters out with

10 These objects have each been drawn twice to show two planes of symmetry.
    What is the total number of planes of symmetry for each object?

a    b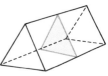

c 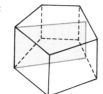 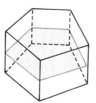   d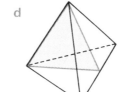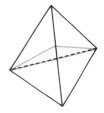

11 A cube has many planes of
    symmetry. Here are two
    of them.
    How many are there altogether?

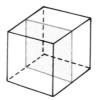 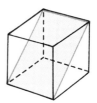

12 Copy or trace these solids and draw on them all their planes of symmetry.

a   b 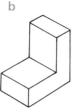   c 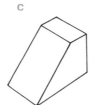   d   e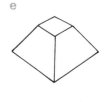

Transformations

Reflections

Rotations

Shears

Vectors

Translations

Stretches

Enlargements

Similarity

Combining transformations

Reflections

Part 1

1   You often see this word printed in reverse on certain vehicles.
   a   How would it be seen by the driver of a car when he looks in his mirror with this vehicle behind him?
   b   How should the word FIRE be painted on the front of a fire engine?
   c   How should the word POLICE be painted on the front of a police car?

2   The words EMERGENCY and DANGEROUS are painted on the fronts of two vehicles like this:

   ＥＭＥＲＧＥＮＣＹ   ＳＵＯＲＥＧＮＡＤ

   But there is one mistake in each word. Which two letters have been painted incorrectly?

3   Here is a sentence reflected in the coloured line. How many letters of the reflection are incorrect, and which are they?

   LEWIS CARROL WROTE "THROUGH THE LOOKING GLASS".

4   a   Write your name in capital letters as it would appear if you saw it in a mirror. Check your attempt using a mirror.
   b   This sentence is written as if in a mirror. What does it say?

   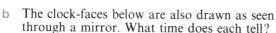

   c   Which of these words can be reflected in a mirror and stay unchanged?

   COOK   BEECH   CHICK   NOOSE   TOOT   MINIM   MUM

5

 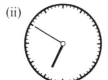

   The lettered star is reflected in the coloured line. Which letters should appear in the numbered positions?

6   a   A boy looks in a mirror and sees the clock as in this diagram. What time is it?

   b   The clock-faces below are also drawn as seen through a mirror. What time does each tell?

   (i)   (ii)   (iii)   (iv)

 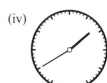

   c   Draw your own clock-faces like these to show the following times when seen through a mirror:
   (i) 4 o'clock   (ii) 10 past 3   (iii) 5 to 2   (iv) a quarter to 7.

Reflections

7   Which *one* of the five unshaded shapes could be a reflection of the shaded shape?

a   b   c   d   e

8   These eight triangles labelled *A* to *H*
    can be reflected onto each other in
    the lines numbered from 1 to 4.
    Which triangle is the reflection of
    a   triangle *A* in line 2
    b   triangle *A* in line 3
    c   triangle *D* in line 4
    d   triangle *F* in line 3
    e   triangle *B* in line 1?
    Find the line which will reflect
    f   triangle *H* onto triangle *G*
    g   triangle *H* onto triangle *C*
    h   triangle *E* onto triangle *B*
    i   triangle *E* onto triangle *H*
    j   triangle *A* onto triangle *F*.

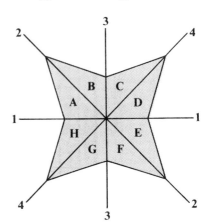

9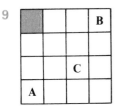

    Copy this diagram and shade the square shown.
    On your diagram draw three mirror lines which will
    reflect the shaded square onto
    a   square *A*   b   square *B*   c   square *C*.

10 Copy this diagram and shade the triangle shown.
    On your diagram draw three mirror lines which will
    reflect the shaded triangle onto
    a   triangle *X*   b   triangle *Y*   c   triangle *Z*.

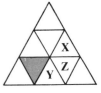

11 a   This dice and domino are both
        reflected in a mirror. What
        scores should there be in the
        lettered positions?
    b   The dice and domino below are
        now reflected in the corner of
        two mirrors. What scores should
        there be in the lettered
        positions?

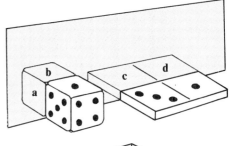

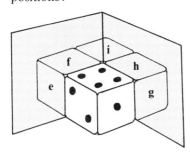

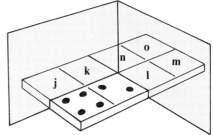

Reflections

12 The Ace of Spades is placed in front of one mirror and then in the corner of two mirrors. In which of the lettered corners of the reflections will you see the letter *A*?

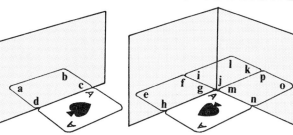

13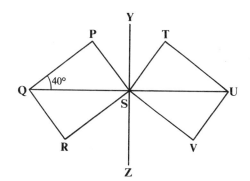

The two triangles *ABC* and *BDE* are reflected in the line *BC*.
Which line is equal in length to

a   *AB*   b   *AF*   c   *FD*
d   *FG*   e   *GE*   f   *BD*?

Which angle is equal to

g   ∠*AFB*   h   ∠*FDG*   i   ∠*GCE*
j   ∠*FBE*   k   ∠*FGE*   l   ∠*ABC*?

If *ABW* is a straight line, what is the size of
m   ∠*ABC*   n   ∠*WBC*?

14 The right-angled triangle *XYZ* is reflected in the line *MN* so that ∠*MXY* = 50°.
If ∠*XZY* = 30°, find

a   ∠*YXZ*   b   ∠*NXZ*
c   ∠*NXV*   d   ∠*WVX*
e   ∠*WXM*   f   ∠*VXZ*.

15

The right-angled triangles *KLM* and *JML* are reflected in the line *KM*.
If ∠*KLJ* = 40° and ∠*JLM* = 30°, find the sizes of

a   ∠*LJM*   b   ∠*LKM*   c   ∠*JNM*
d   ∠*JNK*   e   ∠*MJN*   f   ∠*JKN*.

16 The rectangle *PQRS* is reflected in the line *YZ* so that the diagonal *QS* and its reflection *US* form a straight line.
Which side reflects onto

a   *ST*   b   *TU*
c   *SV*   d   *UV*?

If ∠*PQS* = 40°, find

e   ∠*PSQ*   f   ∠*PSY*
g   ∠*YST*   h   ∠*TSU*
i   ∠*RSZ*   j   ∠*VSZ*.

Reflections

17

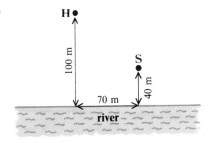

A rider on horseback at point *H* wants to reach the stable *S* by the shortest possible route, but he has to let his horse drink at the river bank before he reaches *S*.

Decide which point of the river bank he should aim for, by drawing this diagram using a scale of 1 cm for 10 metres.

18 On the snooker table, the white ball *W* has to hit the pink ball *P* without hitting the black ball *B* which is in the way.

At which point on each of the four cushions could the white ball be aimed?

Draw your own diagram, and show all your construction lines.

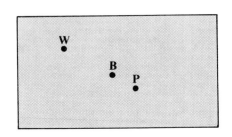

19

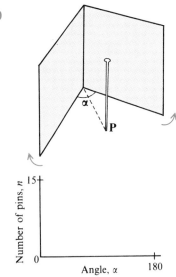

Two mirrors are placed edge to edge at an angle α as shown in this diagram. A pin *P* stands symmetrically on the bisector of angle α. The mirrors are turned about their common edge, keeping the pin symmetrically between them, so that angle α increases from 0° to 180°.

a Count the number of pins you can see for various angles α (including the actual pin itself), though for small values of α this will be difficult.

Enter your results in a table like this:

Angle, α	Number of pins, *n*

b Draw a graph of your results on axes as shown. Following the pattern of the results, can you *predict* the number of pins for small values of α, and so extend your graph?

Part 2 Reflections on a grid

1 L_1, L_2 and L_3 are three straight lines.

Which points are reflections of

a *B* in L_1 b *A* in L_1
c *N* in L_1 d *M* in L_1
e *K* in L_2 f *R* in L_2
g *Q* in L_2 h *E* in L_2
i *J* in L_2 j *P* in L_3
k *D* in L_3 l *N* in L_3
m *E* in L_3 n *F* in L_3
o *H* in L_3 p *A* in L_3?

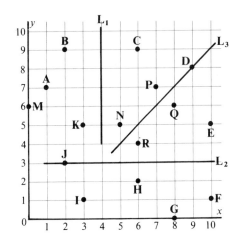

Reflections

2 Copy the diagram alongside with the lines L and M.

Reflect each of the object points A to J in both lines.

Copy and complete this table.

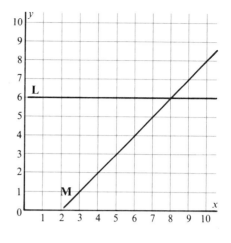

	Object point	Image in line L	Image in line M
A	(6, 5)		
B	(4, 4)		
C	(3, 2)		
D	(2, 4)		
E	(7, 5)		
F	(7, 2)		
G	(9, 4)		
H	(9, 8)		
I	(10, 8)		
J	(8, 6)		

3 Draw axes, labelling the x-axis from -7 to 7 and the y-axis from 0 to 7.
   a Plot the points (0, 5), (5, 5), (3, 7), (0, 7) and join them in this order.
      Reflect the shape in the y-axis.
   b Plot these points to make a square: (2, 1), (3, 1), (3, 2), (2, 2).
      Plot these points to make another square: (2, 3), (3, 3), (3, 4), (2, 4).
      Reflect both these squares in the y-axis.
   c Plot these four points to make a rectangle: (0, 0), (1, 0), (1, 2), (0, 2).
      Reflect this rectangle in the y-axis.
   d Join the points (4, 5) and (4, 0) with a straight line.
      Reflect this line in the y-axis.

4 Draw axes, labelling the x-axis from -6 to 6 and the y-axis from 0 to 15.
   a Plot these four points: (3, 9), (5, 11), (3, 13) and (1, 11). Join them together to make a square.
      Reflect this square in the y-axis.
   b Plot these four points on the same diagram: (2, 5), (4, 7), (2, 9), (0, 7).
      Join them together to make a square and reflect this square in the y-axis.
   c Plot these four points on the same diagram: (3, 3), (1, 5), $(-1, 3)$, (1, 1).
      Join them together to make a square and reflect this square in the y-axis.

5 Draw and label both axes from 0 to 8.
   Plot the points (6, 1), (7, 8) and (2, 3); and join them to make a triangle.
   Draw the line $x = 4$ and reflect the triangle in this line.

6 Copy this diagram of six kites onto squared paper.

   Reflect each kite in the straight line L.

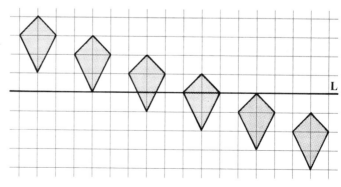

25

Reflections

7 For each of these three parts, draw a new diagram with both axes labelled from 0 to 10.
   a Join these points in order to make a capital letter L: (1, 5), (1, 10), (3, 10), (3, 7), (5, 7), (5, 5), (1, 5).
      Reflect the shape in the line $y = x$.
   b Join these points in order to make another capital letter L: (1, 4), (1, 9), (3, 9), (3, 6), (5, 6), (5, 4), (1, 4).
      Reflect the shape in the line $y = x$.
   c Draw another capital L by joining the points (1, 2), (1, 7), (3, 7), (3, 4), (5, 4), (5, 2), (1, 2); and reflect it in the line $y = x$.

8 Copy this shape with the axes onto squared paper.
   Reflect it in the x-axis.
   Reflect it in the y-axis.
   Make another reflection to complete the last quarter of the diagram.

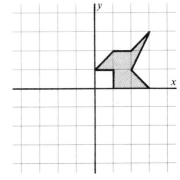

9 Copy each of the following words, MATHS, WORK, PAM, TOM, FIT and CUP, onto squared paper as they are drawn here.
   Reflect each word in the straight line given, drawing the reflection in a different colour.

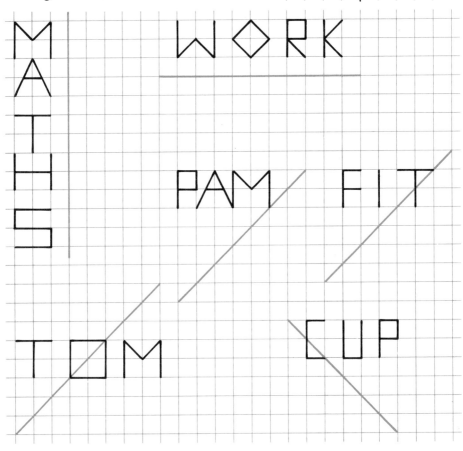

Reflections

10 Draw axes, labelling both from -6 to $+6$.
Plot these points to make a triangle: (2, 1), (5, 1), (5, 3).
Label this triangle with the letter A.
Reflect triangle A in the line $y = x$.   Label your image with the letter B.
Reflect triangle B in the y-axis.   Label this image with the letter C.
Reflect triangle C in the line $y = -x$. Label this image with the letter D.
Reflect triangle D in the x-axis.   Label this image with the letter E.
Reflect triangle E in the line $y = x$.   Label your image with the letter F.
Continue the process until you arrive back at triangle A.

Part 3   Lines of reflection

1 Draw and label both axes from 0 to 10.
Draw these three object shapes and their images by joining the points in order.
Each image is a reflection of its object. Find and draw the line of the reflection.

	Object shape	Image shape
a	(3, 8), (3, 10), (2, 9), (0, 10), (2, 8)	(5, 8), (5, 10), (6, 9), (8, 10), (6, 8)
b	(8, 9), (10, 10), (10, 7), (9, 7), (9, 8)	(8, 3), (10, 2), (10, 5), (9, 5), (9, 4)
c	(1, 3), (1, 5), (3, 5), (3, 4)	(2, 2), (4, 2), (4, 4), (3, 4)

2 Draw and label both axes from 0 to 10.
Draw these three object shapes and their images after reflection.
Find and draw the three lines of reflection.

	Object shape	Image shape
a	(8, 6), (10, 6), (9, 10)	(8, 8), (10, 8), (9, 4)
b	(4, 4), (8, 2), (7, 2), (6, 1)	(6, 4), (2, 2), (3, 2), (4, 1)
c	(1, 9), (4, 10), (3, 5)	(5, 5), (6, 8), (1, 7)

3 Draw and label both axes from 0 to 10.
The image shapes are reflections of the object shapes. Draw them and find their
lines of reflection.

	Object shape	Image shape
a	(5, 5), (9, 2), (4, 1), (6, 3)	(5, 5), (1, 2), (6, 1), (4, 3)
b	(2, 7), (2, 10), (4, 10), (4, 9), (3, 9), (3, 7)	(2, 7), (5, 7), (5, 9), (4, 9), (4, 8), (2, 8)
c	(6, 7), (8, 10), (8, 7), (9, 7), (8, 6)	(9, 10), (6, 8), (9, 8), (9, 7), (10, 8)

4 Each object and image pair here will require its own diagram with axes labelled
from 0 to 10.
Draw them and find their lines of reflection.

	Object shape	Image shape
a	(5,0), (10, 5), (10, $2\frac{1}{2}$)	(3, 4), (10, 5), (8, $6\frac{1}{2}$)
b	(4, 3), ($4\frac{1}{2}$, $6\frac{1}{2}$), ($6\frac{1}{2}$, 8)	(0, 5), ($2\frac{1}{2}$, $7\frac{1}{2}$), ($2\frac{1}{2}$, 10)
c	(5, 0), (10, 2.5), (10, 5), (7.5, 5)	(1.4, 4.8), (5.2, 8.9), (7.6, 8.2), (6.9, 5.8)
d	(5, 7.5), (2.5, 10), (2.5, 7.5), (0, 5)	(5.8, 6.9), (8.9, 5.2), (6.5, 4.5), (4.8, 1.4)

Reflections

5   Draw and label the x-axis from -10 to 10 and the y-axis from 0 to 10.
    Join the points $(5, 0)$, $(5, 5)$, $(10, 0)$, $(10, 5)$ in order to make a letter N.
    This letter N is reflected and its image found by joining the points $(-4, 3)$,
    $(-1, 7)$, $(-8, 6)$, $(-5, 10)$.
    Find and draw the line of this reflection.

6   Draw and label both axes from 0 to 14.
    An object shape with corners $(5, \frac{1}{2})$, $(10, \frac{1}{2})$, $(10, 5\frac{1}{2})$, $(7\frac{1}{2}, 5\frac{1}{2})$ is reflected onto
    its image with corners $(1, 8\frac{1}{2})$, $(4, 12\frac{1}{2})$, $(8, 9\frac{1}{2})$, $(6\frac{1}{2}, 7\frac{1}{2})$.
    Find and draw the line of reflection.

7   Draw and label the x-axis from -10 to 10 and the y-axis from 0 to 10.
    An arrow with corners $(-5, 0)$, $(-7, 2)$, $(-6, 2)$, $(-6, 5)$, $(-4, 5)$, $(-4, 2)$,
    $(-3, 2)$ is reflected so that its image has corners $(4, 3)$, $(4.4, 5.8)$, $(3.6, 4.8)$,
    $(1.8, 7.6)$, $(0.2, 6.4)$, $(2, 4)$, $(1.2, 3.4)$.
    Draw the line of reflection.

Part 4   Successive reflections

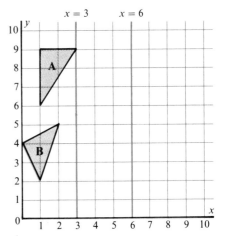

1   This diagram shows two triangles A
    and B and two lines $x = 3$ and $x = 6$.

    Copy the diagram.

    a   Find the image A' of A after
        reflection in the line $x = 3$.
    b   Find the image A'' of A' after
        reflection in the line $x = 6$.
    c   Find the image B' of B after
        reflection in the line $x = 3$.
    d   Find the image B'' of B' after
        reflection in the line $x = 6$.

For each problem in this exercise, diagrams will be needed with both axes labelled
from 0 to 10.

2   Draw the triangle C $(2, 0)$, $(4, 1)$, $(1, 2)$ and the parallelogram D $(8, 0)$, $(10, 2)$,
    $(8, 3)$, $(6, 1)$.
    Find the images C' and D' of C and D after a reflection in the line $y = 4$.
    Find the images C'' and D'' of C' and D' after a reflection in the line $y = 6$.

3   The line L joins $(0, 4)$ to $(6, 10)$; and the line M joins $(0, 4)$ to $(10, 4)$.
    Draw a letter F by joining these points in order: $(1, 6)$, $(1, 10)$, $(3, 10)$, $(3, 9)$,
    $(2, 9)$, $(2, 8)$, $(3, 8)$, $(3, 7)$, $(2, 7)$, $(2, 6)$.
    Transform F onto F' by reflecting it in the line L.
    Transform F' onto F'' by reflecting F' in the line M.

4   Draw the shape S $(6, 1)$, $(7, 1)$, $(7, 6)$, $(5, 4)$, $(6, 4)$ and its image S' after a
    reflection in the line $y = x$.
    S' is now reflected onto S'' using the line $y = x + 4$. Draw S''.

5   The shape A $(3, 10)$, $(5, 10)$, $(5, 9)$, $(4, 7)$, $(3, 7)$, $(4, 9)$, $(3, 9)$ is transformed
    onto A' by a reflection in the line $x + y = 10$. Draw both A and A'.
    A' is now reflected in the line $y = x$ onto A''. Draw A''.

Reflections

6 The shape P (6, 10), (4, 8), (7, 4), (9, 6), (5, 8) is reflected in the line $y = 5$ onto its image P'.
   P' is now reflected in the line $x = 5$ onto a new image P''.
   Draw P, P' and P'' on one diagram.

7 The shape S (9, 0), (9, 3), (10, 3), (10, 4), (9, 4), (9, 5), (8, 5), (8, 4), (7, 4) is reflected in the line $y = x$ onto its image S'.
   S' is now reflected in the line $y = 6$ onto S''.
   S'' is reflected in the line $x + y = 5$ onto S'''.
   Draw the shape S and its three images on one diagram.

Part 5 Letters for reflections

1 P represents a reflection in line P.
   Q represents a reflection in line Q.
   R represents a reflection in line R.

   Which points on this diagram are the images of these reflected points?

   a P(A)   b Q(A)   c P(D)
   d R(D)   e Q(G)   f R(G)
   g Q(C)   h P(J)   i R(I)
   j P(I)

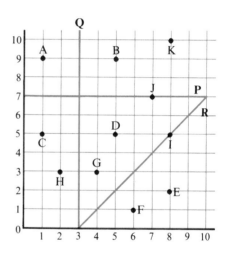

2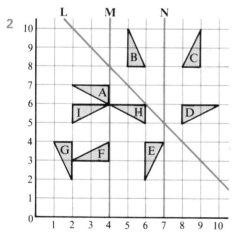

L, M and N represent reflections in the lines L, M and N.

Copy and complete the following.
a N(C) = ...   b M(H) = ...
c N(H) = ...   d M(E) = ...
e L(B) = ...   f L(E) = ...
g L(A) = ...   h L(F) = ...

3 Draw and label both axes from 0 to 16.
   Draw the square with corners (5, 2), (5, 9), (12, 9), (12, 2).
   K represents a reflection in the left-hand side of the square; L a reflection in the top side of the square; M a reflection in the right-hand side of the square; and N a reflection in the bottom side of the square.
   Shape A has corners (1, 4), (1, 5), (3, 5), (4, 4).   Draw A and K(A).
   Shape B has corners (10, 10), (11, 12), (9, 12).   Draw B and L(B).
   Shape C has corners (15, 3), (15, 6), (13, 6), (13, 3). Draw C and M(C).
   Shape D has corners (9,0), (9, 1), (6, 1), (6, 0).   Draw D and N(D).
   Draw a cross at (10, 8) and name the shape you have constructed.

Reflections

4 Draw and label both axes from 0 to 10.
P represents a reflection in the line $y = 3$; and **Q** represents a reflection in the line $y = 6$.
Draw these two lines.
A is the point (1, 2). Plot A, **P**(A) and **QP**(A).
B is the point (3, 1). Plot B, **P**(B) and **QP**(B).
C is the point (5, 10). Plot C, **Q**(C) and **PQ**(C).
D is the point (7, 9). Plot D, **Q**(D) and **PQ**(D).
E is the point (9, 4). Plot E, **P**(E) and **QP**(E).

5 Draw and label both axes from 0 to 10.
M represents a reflection in the line $x = 5$; and **N** represents a reflection in the line $y = 5$.
Draw these two lines.
The shape A has corners (1, 7), (1, 9), (4, 9), (2, 8), (2, 7). Draw A and its images **M**(A), **NM**(A), **MNM**(A) and **NMNM**(A).

6 Draw and label both axes from 0 to 10.
P represents a reflection in the line joining the points (1, 5) and (6, 10).
Q represents a reflection in the line joining the points (1, 5) and (10, 5).
R represents a reflection in the line joining the points (1, 5) and (6, 0).
Draw the shape X (3, 7), (1, 7), (1, 9), (5, 9); and also draw its images **P**(X), **QP**(X) and **RQP**(X).

7 Draw and label both axes from 0 to 10.
U represents a reflection in the line $y = x$; and **V** represents a reflection in the line $x + y = 10$.
The quadrilateral Q has corners (1, 4), (1, 7), (4, 8), and (2, 4). Draw Q and its images **V**(Q), **UV**(Q), **VUV**(Q) and **UVUV**(Q).

8 Draw and label the x-axis from 0 to 16 and the y-axis from 0 to 10.
A reflection in the line $x = 4$ is represented by **M**; and a reflection in the line $x = 8$ is represented by **N**.
The shape S has corners (1, 4), (3, 4), (3, 8) and (2, 7).
Draw S and its images **M**(S), **N**(S) and **NM**(S).
Draw the line in which **N**(S) must be reflected to map onto **NM**(S), and write its equation.

Rotations

Part 1

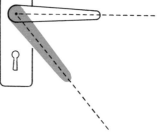

1   Use your protractor to measure the angle through which this door handle turns when opening the door.

2

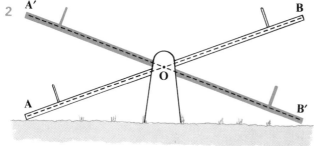

A see-saw rotates about the axis O. The diagram shows the two positions when each end is touching the ground.

Use your protractor to find the maximum angle through which the see-saw rotates.

3   A car travelling along a road goes round a bend.
Use your protractor to find the angle through which it has turned.

4

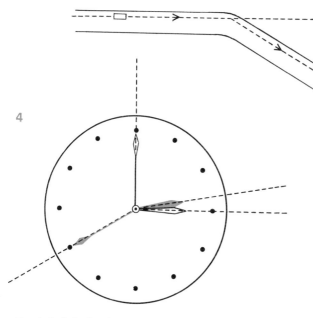

This clock face shows the hands at 3 o'clock and also 20 minutes earlier.

What angle has

a   the minute-hand

b   the hour-hand

rotated through in this time?

Either use your protractor or calculate your answers.

5   A lady's fan is made from ten sectors, each with a central angle of 20°.

The fan is closed by rotating sector F clockwise.

After how many degrees of rotation will sector F be in the position of

a   sector G b   sector H

c   sector I d   sector J

e   sector K?

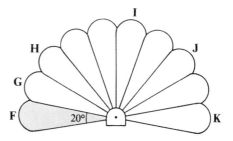

31

Rotations

6 These two cog-wheels could be used in a ratchet. Their designs are based on the two triangles T and A which can be rotated about one corner to map onto the other triangles.

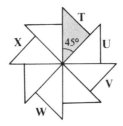 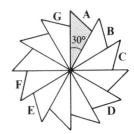

Through how many degrees clockwise must triangle T rotate to be in the position of

a triangle U b triangle V c triangle W d triangle X?

Through how many degrees clockwise must triangle A rotate to be in the position of

e triangle B f triangle C g triangle D h triangle E
i triangle F j triangle G?

7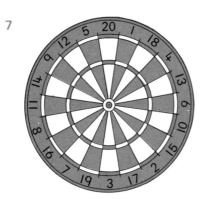

The face of a dartboard is divided into twenty numbered sectors, each making an angle of $\frac{360}{20} = 18°$ at the centre.

Through what angle and direction would the 20 sector have to be rotated clockwise to become

a the 1 sector   b the 18 sector
c the 6 sector   d the 3 sector
e the 19 sector   f the 11 sector
g the 14 sector   h the 5 sector?

8 Three regular hexagons are arranged with points P, Q, R and S at the corners shown in this diagram.

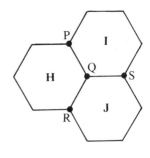

a Hexagon H can be rotated onto hexagon I in two ways. Write the angle, the direction and the centre of each rotation.

b Hexagon I can be rotated onto hexagon J in two ways. Write the angle, the direction and the centre of each rotation.

c Repeat for hexagon J rotating onto hexagon H.

9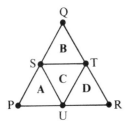

The equilateral triangle with corners P, Q and R is divided into four smaller equilateral triangles A, B, C and D.

Find the angle, the direction and the centre of the rotation which maps triangle A onto

a triangle C b triangle B c triangle D.

There are *two* possible answers in each case. Give the details for *both* possibilities.

Rotations

10 This pattern of eight squares is formed by rotating square *S* clockwise about corner *O*.

What angle of rotation is needed to map square *S* onto

a square *T* b square *U*
c square *V* d square *W*
e square *X* f square *Y*
g square *Z*?

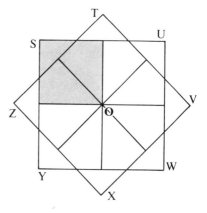

11 Which *one* of the uncoloured shapes could be rotated onto the coloured shape?

a   (i)   (ii)   (iii) (iv)

b   (i) (ii) (iii) (iv)

c   (i)   (ii)   (iii)   (iv)

12 Cog *A* has 30 teeth and cog *B* has 10 teeth.

a If *B* rotates clockwise, in which direction does *A* rotate?

b How many degrees does *A* rotate if *B* rotates one full turn?

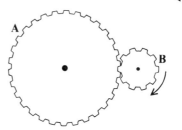

13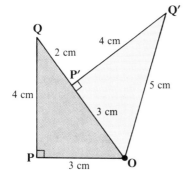

Draw this diagram of the two right-angled triangles *OPQ* and *OP'Q'* accurately, using a ruler and protractor.

Triangle *OPQ* can be rotated clockwise about *O* onto triangle *OP'Q'*. Use compasses to draw the path along which *P* moves. Also draw the path of *Q* as it moves to *Q'*.

Use your protractor to find the angle of the rotation.

Rotations

14 Draw each of these diagrams accurately.

In each diagram, one shape can rotate about point O onto the other shape.

Use your compasses to draw the paths along which each lettered point moves to its image point.

Use your protractor to find the angle of rotation and say whether the direction of the rotation is clockwise or anticlockwise.

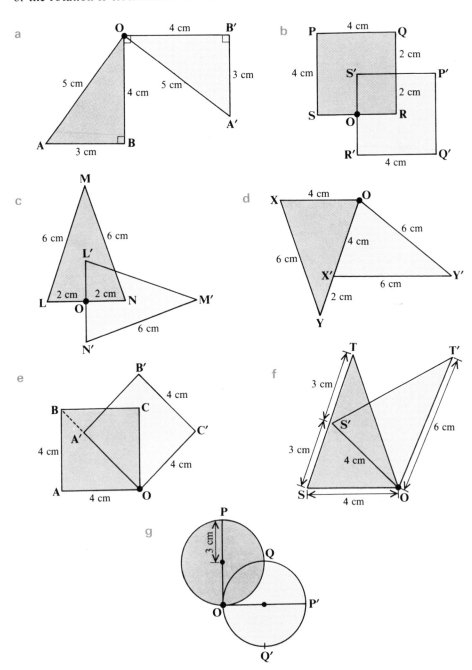

Rotations

Part 2   Polar paper

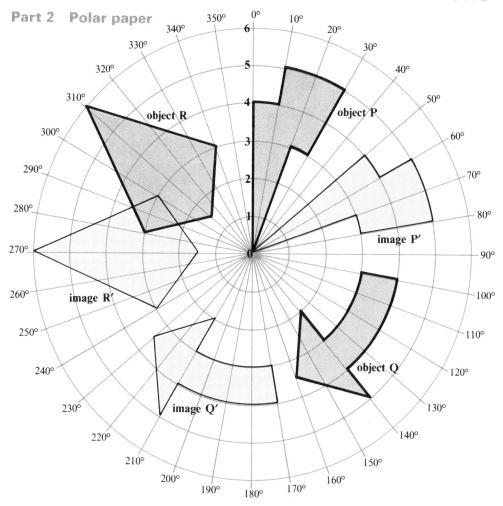

1   This diagram shows three object shapes and their images after rotations about
the centre point *O*.
Write for each object and its image
a   the angle of rotation   b   the direction of rotation.

2   Label a sheet of polar paper with circles from 0 to 10 and radii from 0° to 350°.
Plot these points and join them in order to draw four object shapes and image
shapes.
Describe the rotations which have taken place by writing
(i) the angle of rotation   and   (ii) the direction of rotation.

	Object shape	Image shape
a	(9, 10°), (6, 20°), (5, 0°)	(9, 40°), (6, 50°), (5, 30°)
b	(3, 70°), (8, 70°), (8, 100°), (7, 100°), (7, 80°), (3, 80°)	(3,120°), (8, 120°), (8, 150°), (7, 150°), (7, 130°), (3, 130°)
c	(2, 220°), (5, 240°), (5, 230°), (9, 220°), (5, 210°), (5, 200°)	(2, 180°), (5, 200°), (5, 190°), (9, 180°), (5, 170°), (5, 160°)
d	(0, 0°), (9, 330°), (9, 290°), (7, 310°), (7, 290°), (5, 310°)	(0, 0°), (9, 300°), (9, 260°), (7, 280°), (7, 260°), (5, 280°)

35

Rotations

3 Label another sheet of polar paper as in **2** above.
Plot these points and join them in order to make object shapes and image shapes.
Describe each rotation by finding the angle and direction of rotation.

	Object shape	Image shape
a	(8, 20°), (7½, 60°), (6, 30°), (3, 80°), (4, 350°)	(8, 50°), (7½, 90°), (6, 60°), (3,110°), (4, 20°)
b	(6, 220°), (7, 220°), (7½, 200°), (9, 200°), (8, 190°), (5, 200°), (6½, 200°)	(6, 130°), (7, 130°), (7½, 110°), (9, 110°), (8, 100°), (5, 110°), (6½, 110°)
c	(3, 160°), (10, 160°), (8, 140°), (8, 150°), (4, 150°), (4, 140°)	(3, 330°), (10, 330°), (8, 310°), (8, 320°), (4, 320°), (4, 310°)
d	(4, 300°), (8, 290°), (9, 260°), (7, 260°), (6, 280°), (4, 280°)	(4, 280°), (8, 270°), (9, 240°), (7, 240°), (6, 260°), (4, 260°)

4 Label a sheet of polar paper as before.
Draw the four object shapes by joining the given points in order with straight lines.
Rotate each object shape as described, and draw its image.
What shape do the combined images make, and what should be drawn at the point (7, 20°)?
Object a: (2, 140°), (8, 140°), (10, 130°), (8, 150°), (2, 150°)
            is rotated anticlockwise about (0, 0°) through 60°.
Object b: (2, 220°), (3, 220°), (4, 200°), (5, 170°)
            is rotated anticlockwise about (0, 0°) through 140°.
Object c: (8, 280°), (7, 230°), (5, 230°), (4, 280°)
            is rotated clockwise about (0, 0°) through 160°.
Object d: (10, 325°), (8, 325°), (6, 310°), (4, 320°), (5, 340°), (7, 340°)
            is rotated clockwise about (0, 0°) through 50°.

5 Label a sheet of polar paper as before.
Draw these four object shapes by joining the given points in order with straight lines.
Rotate each object shape as described and draw its image.
What shape do the combined images make, and what should be drawn at the point (6½, 345°)?
Object a: (5, 300°), (8, 300°), (8, 310°), (7, 320°), (5, 320°), (4, 310°)
            is rotated clockwise about (0, 0°) through 50°.
Object b: (5, 210°), (6, 210°), (7, 180°), (8, 160°), (5, 180°)
            is rotated anticlockwise about (0, 0°) through 120°.
Object c: (3, 240°), (5, 280°), (8, 260°), (7, 230°), (5, 230°), (4, 220°), (0, 0°), (1, 310°) is rotated clockwise about (0, 0°) through 140°.
Object d: (2, 140°), (2½, 140°), (3, 130°), (5, 130°), (3, 150°), (4, 150°), (5, 140°), (8, 140°), (7, 130°), (5, 120°), (3, 120°)
            is rotated anticlockwise about (0, 0°) through 150°.

6 Label a sheet of polar paper as before.
Join these points in order with straight lines to give four object shapes which are then rotated as described.
Draw their images, and describe the shape which these images make.
What should be drawn at the point (9, 15°)?
Object a: (9, 170°), (8, 150°), (8, 175°)
            is rotated anticlockwise about (0, 0°) through 160°.
Object b: (4, 250°), (5, 250°), (7, 260°), (8, 280°), (8, 300°), (7, 290°), (5½, 290°)
            is rotated clockwise about (0, 0°) through 140°.
Object c: (5, 165°), (5, 220°), (4½, 230°), (6, 220°), (5½, 220°), (5½, 175°)
            is rotated anticlockwise about (0, 0°) through 105°.
Object d: (4, 330°), (5, 330°), (9, 320°), (9½, 315°), (9, 310°), (8, 315°)
            is rotated clockwise about (0, 0°) through 60°.

Rotations

Part 3 On a square grid

1 Copy each of these letters onto squared paper.
Trace each one and rotate it clockwise through 90° about point *O*.
Draw each image on the same diagram.

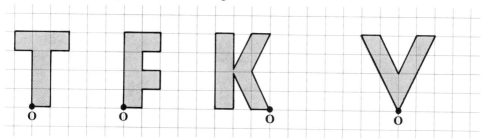

2 Each triangle in this question needs its own diagram with axes labelled from 0 to 8.
Draw the triangle given here. Rotate it clockwise through 90° about the given point, and draw its image. Tracing paper will be useful.

	Triangle	Centre of rotation
a	(0, 2), (0, 7), (3, 2)	(3, 2)
b	(1, 4), (1, 7), (6, 7)	(4, 3)
c	(2, 2), (2, 7), (5, 2)	(3, 4)
d	(1, 6), (4, 6), (4, 1)	(4, 4)

3 a Draw and label both axes from 0 to 10.
On them, draw the right-angled triangle (1, 1), (1, 7), (7, 7).
Rotate it clockwise through 45° about the point (1, 1), and draw its image.
  b On a new diagram, with axes labelled as before, draw the same right-angled triangle. Now rotate it clockwise through 45° about the point (4, 4), and draw its image.

4 Each part of this question will need a new diagram with both axes labelled from 0 to 8.
Draw the equilateral triangle with corners (4, 4), (2, $7\frac{1}{2}$), (0, 4).
Use tracing paper to help you draw the image of this triangle after a clockwise rotation of
  a 60° about the point (4, 4)   b 60° about the point (2, 4)
  c 120° about the point (2, 4)   d 180° about the point (2, 5.2).

5 Draw and label both axes from −6 to 6 and on them draw the object shape with corners (5, 0), (2, 3), (3, 6), (0, 2), (2, 0).
On the same diagram, draw the image of this shape after a clockwise rotation about the origin through
  a 90°   b 180°   c 270°.

6 a Draw and label both axes from −8 to 8, and on them draw the object shape with corners (8, 2), (1, 2), (6, 8), (5, 5).
On the same diagram, draw three images of this shape after clockwise rotations about the point (0, 0) through
  (i) 90°   (ii) 180°   (iii) 270°.
  b Draw the same object shape on new axes. Draw three images of this shape after clockwise rotations about the point (2, 1) through
  (i) 90°   (ii) 180°   (iii) 270°.
  c Repeat these instructions again, but now take the point (3, 2) as the centre of the three rotations.

37

Rotations

7   Answer this question *yes* or *no* for each part.
Is a clockwise rotation through $\alpha°$ equivalent to an anticlockwise rotation through $\beta°$ about the same point, when
a $\alpha = 40°$, $\beta = 320°$ b $\alpha = 120°$, $\beta = 240°$
c $\alpha = 200°$, $\beta = 140°$ d $\alpha = 160°$, $\beta = 220°$
e $\alpha = 270°$, $\beta = 90°$ f $\alpha = 180°$, $\beta = 180°$?

8   Draw all the shapes, whose corners are given below, on one diagram with both axes labelled from 0 to 20.
Use tracing paper to rotate each shape as described in the table, and draw each image on the diagram.
Discover what all these images have given you.

Shape	Corners	Centre of rotation	Clockwise angle of rotation
Square	(2, 13), (2, 15), (4, 15), (4, 13)	(4, 11)	90°
Rectangle	(2, 9), (1, 9), (1, 11), (2, 11)	(1, 2)	90°
Triangle	(12, 11), (13, 10), (16, 14)	(11, 10)	180°
Quadrilateral	(14, 4), (14, 5), (18, 6), (19, 2)	(13, 1)	270°
Quadrilateral	(15, 6), (14, 10), (19, 10), (19, 9)	(13, 5)	270°
Straight line	(5, 16), (9, 16)	(7, 14)	180°
L-shape	(2, 7), (2, 2), (3, 2)	(4, 4)	180°

Part 4   Finding centres of rotation

There are three methods:
a   using tracing paper   b   by paper folding   c   by geometric construction.

Tracing paper

1   Trace each object shape, then find the point about which the tracing paper must rotate so that the object maps onto its image.
Write the centre, the angle and the direction of each rotation.

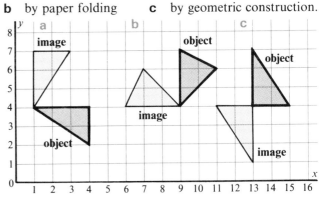

2   Use tracing paper to find the centre, the angle and the direction of each of these rotations which map an object letter onto its image.
(Heavy lines show the object and light lines show its image.)

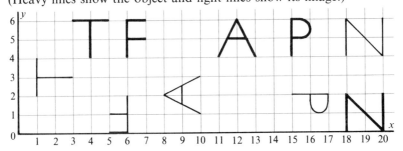

Rotations

3 Each part of this problem requires its own diagram with both axes labelled from 0 to 8.

Draw the object and image shapes, and use tracing paper to find the centre, angle and direction of each rotation.

	Object shape	Image shape
a	(3, 3), (7, 3), (7, 1)	(1, 3), (1, 7), (3, 7)
b	(5, 2), (7, 7), (7, 3)	(3, 8), (1, 3), (1, 7)
c	(7, 1), (3, 1), (3, 5), (5, 5), (5, 3), (7, 3)	(2, 2), (2, 6), (6, 6), (6, 4), (4, 4), (4, 2)
d	(1, 1), (3, 5), (7, 4)	(5, 1), (1, 3), (2, 7)
e	(4, 6), (4, 2), (1, 1), (0, 4)	(2, 2), (2, 6), (5, 7), (6, 4)
f	(1, 2), (1, 7), (6, 7), (2, 5)	(5, 8), (5, 3), (0, 3), (4, 5)
g	(3, 2), (1, 7), (3, 6), (2, 6)	(1, 4), (6, 6), (5, 4), (5, 5)
h	(1, 1), (1, 6), (3, 1)	$(2\frac{1}{2}, 4\frac{1}{2})$, (6, 8), (4, 3)

4 The square (1, 2), (1, 6), (5, 6), (5, 2) can be rotated onto the square (7, 2), (7, 6), (11, 6), (11, 2) in three different ways.

Find the centre, angle and direction for each of the three possible rotations.

Paper folding

5 The diagram below shows three object and image pairs, with objects drawn heavy and images light.

By looking at the direction around the perimeter of the shapes, find which *one* of these three images cannot be obtained by a rotation of its object.

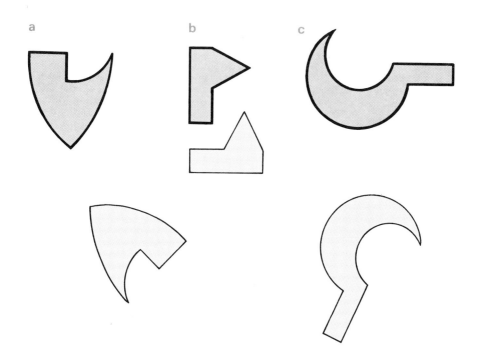

a   b   c

Rotations

6   a   b   c

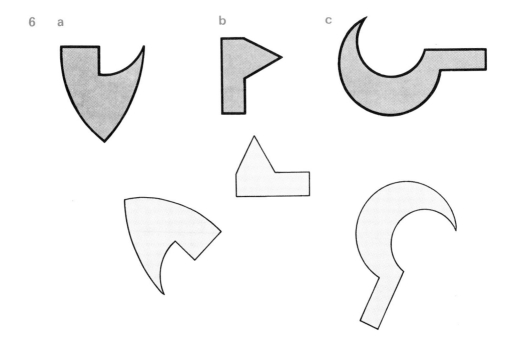

Find the centre of each rotation on the above diagram, as follows.

Trace each object and image pair.

Concentrate on one corner of the object and the corresponding corner of the image.

Fold the tracing paper so that these two corners are on top of each other. Crease the tracing paper along the fold.

Repeat for another pair of points on object and image.

The centre of the rotation is where the two creases intersect.

(You can check your result in two ways:
(i) by repeating with a third crease for a third pair of points
(ii) by rotating the tracing paper on the diagram here with a pencil on the centre of rotation.)

7   Draw these object and image pairs on axes labelled from 0 to 8.

Trace each object and its image; and then, by folding the tracing paper, find the centre of each rotation.

Remember to check your results.

	Object shape	Image shape
a	(2, 3), (1, 7), (4, 6)	(2, 5), (6, 6), (5, 3)
b	(2, 1), (8, 3), (6, 8)	(8, 1), (6, 7), (1, 5)
c	(1, 2), (2, 7), (4, 7), (6, 3)	(1, 8), (6, 7), (6, 5), (2, 3)
d	(3, 4), (2, 8), (0, 3), (2, 5)	(7, 6), (3, 5), (8, 3), (6, 5)

By construction

All these next problems are designed to be done on A4 squared paper, ruled in 2 mm squares. A ruler, protractor, pencil and compasses will be needed. Label both axes using a scale of 2 cm per unit in all problems, with the x-axis labelled from 0 to 9 and the y-axis from 0 to 10.

Rotations

8   Draw a circle, centre $C(4, 5)$ and radius 5 units. (You may not be able to fit all of it on your squared paper.)

   a   Point $A(9, 5)$ is rotated about centre C along the circle until it is mapped onto point $A'(4, 10)$. Plot and label point A and its image; draw the line AA' and use compasses to construct its perpendicular bisector.

   b   Point $B(8, 8)$ is rotated about centre C until it maps onto point $B'(1, 9)$. Plot and label point B and its image; draw the line BB' and construct its perpendicular bisector.

   c   What do you notice about the point where the two perpendicular bisectors cross? Your construction is equivalent to the paper-folding exercise in problems **6** and **7**, where the creases are equivalent to these perpendicular bisectors.

   d   To find the angle of rotation, join both A and A' to C and measure angle ACA' with a protractor. Check your answer by joining B and B' to C and measuring angle BCB'.

9   a   Point $A(7, 1)$ maps onto point $A'(4, 6)$ under a rotation. Draw and label the line AA' and construct its perpendicular bisector.

   b   Point $B(8, 4)$ maps onto point $B'(1, 7)$ under the same rotation. Draw and label line BB' and construct its perpendicular bisector.

   c   Label the centre of the rotation C. Use compasses to draw the arc of the circle from A and A' and also the arc from B to B'.

   d   The line AC rotates onto its image $A'C$. Draw these lines and use a protractor to measure the angle of rotation. Check your answer by drawing lines BC and $B'C$ and measuring angle BCB'.

10   a   Point $A(2, 2)$ rotates onto point $A'(4.6, 3.5)$. Draw and label the line AA' and construct its perpendicular bisector.

   b   Point $B(7, 3)$ rotates onto point $B'(6.2, 8.3)$. Draw and label the line BB' and construct its perpendicular bisector.

   c   Label the centre of the rotation C. Use compasses to draw the two arcs along which A moves to A' and B moves to B'.

   d   Join A and A' to C and measure the angle of rotation ACA'. Check your answer by drawing and measuring angle BCB'.

   e   Measure the length of AC, and taking π as 3.14, calculate the length of the arc AA'. Measure the length of BC and calculate the length of the arc BB'. Give both answers to 2 significant figures.

11   a   Triangle $L(5, 1)$, $M(8, 2)$, $N(8, 5)$ is mapped onto triangle $L'(4.8, 3.4)$, $M'(6.2, 6.3)$, $N'(4.1, 8.4)$ under a rotation. Draw both triangles and shade them in *lightly*.

   b   Construct the perpendicular bisector of the line MM'; and also that for the line NN'. Label the centre of the rotation C.

   c   The line CM rotates onto CM'. Use your protractor to find the angle of rotation. Check your answers by measuring angle LCL'.

   d   Draw the three arcs along which the three corners of the triangle move under this rotation. Measure the length of MC and calculate the length of arc MM' (to 2 significant figures).

12   a   Triangle $P(6, 4)$, $Q(5, 1)$, $R(3, 2)$ rotates onto triangle $P'(0, 8)$, $Q'(3, 7)$, $R'(2, 5)$. Draw both triangles and construct the perpendicular bisectors of the lines PP' and RR'. Label the centre of the rotation C.

   b   Measure the angle through which the line CR rotates onto CR'. Check your answer by measuring angle PCP'.

   c   Draw the three arcs along which the corners of the triangle move under the rotation. Measure the length of CQ and calculate the length of arc QQ'.

Rotations

13 a The quadrilateral $K(5, 6)$, $L(5, 7)$, $M(3, 8)$, $N(2, 6)$ maps onto $K'(6, 3)$, $L'(5, 3)$, $M'(4, 1)$, $N'(6, 0)$ under a rotation. Draw the quadrilateral and its image, and construct the perpendicular bisectors of KK' and NN' to find the centre of the rotation C.

b The line CL rotates onto CL'. Measure the angle of rotation LCL', and check your answer by measuring angle NCN'.

c Draw the path of L as it rotates onto L' and calculate the distance it travels.

14 a The quadrilateral $P(6, 2)$, $Q(5, 7)$, $R(1, 8)$, $S(0, 4)$ rotates onto $P'(7, 7)$, $Q'(2, 6)$, $R'(1, 2)$, $S'(5, 1)$. Draw both the quadrilateral and its image, and find the centre of the rotation C by constructing two perpendicular bisectors of your choice.

b Draw the line CP and its image, and find the angle of rotation. Also measure the angle between side SP and its image $S'P'$. What do you notice about this angle?

c Draw the path along which P moves to P' and calculate the distance which P travels.

15 a $L(6, 5)$, $M(8, 8)$, $N(1, 7)$ are the corners of a triangle which map onto $L'(6.7, 6.7)$, $M'(3.2, 6.0)$, $N'(8.8, 1.7)$ under a rotation. Draw the triangle and its image and use ruler and compasses to find the centre of the rotation C by constructing two perpendicular bisectors.

b Draw the line CN and its image, and measure the angle of rotation.

c Draw the paths of the three corners of the triangle under the rotation, and calculate the distance which point N moves.

Part 5 Letters for rotations

1

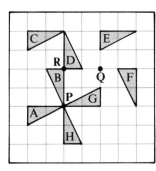

P, **Q** and **R** represent clockwise rotations of a quarter-turn about the points P, Q and R respectively.

A to H denote the eight triangles shown in this diagram.

Say whether these statements are *true* or *false*.

a $P(G) = H$	b $P(A) = B$	c $P(B) = G$
d $P^2(H) = B$	e $P^2(G) = H$	f $P^2(A) = G$
g $Q(F) = G$	h $Q(G) = E$	i $Q(D) = E$
j $Q^2(E) = G$	k $Q^2(D) = F$	l $Q^2(F) = B$
m $Q^3(F) = E$	n $P^3(G) = B$	o $R^2(B) = D$

2 Find the image triangles for these transformations.

a $P(H)$	b $Q(E)$	c $Q(H)$	d $P(C)$
e $P^2(B)$	f $Q^2(G)$	g $R^2(D)$	h $R^2(G)$
i $QP(B)$	j $PQ(F)$	k $QR^2(B)$	l $PR^2(D)$
m $QR^2(C)$	n $R^2Q(H)$	o $QR^2P(A)$	

3 Each of these parts needs a diagram with both axes labelled from 0 to 10.

a **P** and **Q** both represent clockwise rotations of 90°; with **P** having point (5, 4) as centre, and **Q** point (8, 7) as centre.
S is the shape (5, 7), (9, 7), (9, 8), (8, 8), (8, 9).
On one diagram, draw S, **P**(S) and **QP**(S).
Use tracing paper to find and describe the single rotation which maps S directly onto **QP**(S).

b   **L** and **M** both represent anticlockwise rotations of 90°; with **L** having point (1, 6) as centre, and **M** point (7, 6) as centre.
Q is the quadrilateral with corners (3, 1), (1, 2), (3, 5), (2, 2).
On one diagram, draw Q, **L**(Q) and **ML**(Q).
Use tracing paper to find and describe the single rotation which maps Q directly onto **ML**(Q).

c   **A** and **B** both represent clockwise rotations of 90°; with **A** having point (1, 5) as centre, and **B** point (7, 2) as centre.
T is the triangle (1, 6), (1, 10), (3, 10).
On one diagram, draw T, **A**(T) and **BA**(T).
Use tracing paper to find and describe the single rotation which maps T directly onto **BA**(T).

d   **R** and **S** both represent clockwise rotations of 45°; with **R** having a centre (1, 6) and **S** a centre (7, 2).
Q is the quadrilateral with corners (1, 10), (1, 6), (4, 9), (4, 10).
Draw Q, **R**(Q) and **SR**(Q).
Find and describe the single rotation which maps Q onto **SR**(Q).

e   **U** and **V** both represent clockwise rotations of 60°; with **U** having a centre (2, 3), and **V** a centre (10, 3).
T is the triangle (6, 10), (6, 3), (2, 3).
Draw T, **U**(T) and **VU**(T).
Find and describe the single rotation which maps T onto **VU**(T).

4   **R** represents a clockwise rotation of a quarter-turn about the point (5, 5).
S is the shape (4, 6), (6, 6), (5, 7), (9, 9), (4, 9).
On axes labelled from 0 to 10, draw S, **R**(S), $\mathbf{R}^2$(S) and $\mathbf{R}^3$(S).
What can you say about $\mathbf{R}^4$(S)?

5   **Q** represents an anticlockwise rotation of a quarter-turn about the point (5, 5).
T is the shape (5, 6), (5, 8), (4, 9), (2, 9), (0, 10), (4, 10), (6, 8), (6, 5).
On axes labelled from 0 to 10, draw T, **Q**(T), $\mathbf{Q}^2$(T) and $\mathbf{Q}^3$(T).
What can you say about $\mathbf{Q}^4$(T)?

In the following problems, **Q** represents a rotation of 90° clockwise about the origin; **H** a half-turn about the origin; **R** a rotation of 270° clockwise about the origin; and **I** the identity transformation.

6   Without drawing any diagrams, say which of these statements are *true* and which are *false*.

a $\mathbf{Q}^2 = \mathbf{H}$ b $\mathbf{Q}^3 = \mathbf{R}$ c $\mathbf{H}^2 = \mathbf{I}$ d $\mathbf{H}^3 = \mathbf{R}$

e $\mathbf{Q}^4 = \mathbf{I}$ f $\mathbf{R}^2 = \mathbf{I}$ g $\mathbf{Q}^6 = \mathbf{H}$ h $\mathbf{Q}^8 = \mathbf{I}$

i $\mathbf{H}^3 = \mathbf{H}$ j $\mathbf{Q}^8 = \mathbf{I}$ k $\mathbf{QH} = \mathbf{R}$ l $\mathbf{QR} = \mathbf{I}$

m $\mathbf{RH} = \mathbf{Q}^5$ n $\mathbf{QHQ} = \mathbf{R}$ o $\mathbf{HRQ} = \mathbf{H}$ p $\mathbf{QRQ} = \mathbf{Q}$

7   The *inverse* of a rotation is another rotation about the *same* centre, through the *same* angle, but in the *opposite* direction.
For example, **Q** is a clockwise rotation of 90° about the origin; so the inverse of **Q** (written as $\mathbf{Q}^{-1}$) is an *anticlockwise* rotation of 90° about the origin.
Without drawing any diagrams, say which of these statements are *true* and which are *false*.

a $\mathbf{Q}^{-1} = \mathbf{R}$ b $\mathbf{H}^{-1} = \mathbf{H}$ c $\mathbf{R}^{-1} = \mathbf{H}$ d $\mathbf{H}^{-2} = \mathbf{I}$

e $\mathbf{Q}^{-2} = \mathbf{H}$ f $\mathbf{Q}^{-1}\mathbf{Q} = \mathbf{I}$ g $\mathbf{R}^{-1}\mathbf{R} = \mathbf{Q}$ h $\mathbf{Q}^{-1}\mathbf{R} = \mathbf{H}$

8   Simplify each of these and write as a *single* transformation.

a $\mathbf{H}^4$ b $\mathbf{Q}^5$ c $\mathbf{R}^2$ d $\mathbf{Q}^{-3}$

e $\mathbf{Q}^{-4}$ f $\mathbf{R}^{-2}$ g $\mathbf{Q}^{-1}\mathbf{H}$ h $\mathbf{Q}^{-2}\mathbf{H}$

i $\mathbf{Q}^{-1}\mathbf{HQ}$ j $\mathbf{Q}^{-1}\mathbf{HQ}^2$ k $\mathbf{Q}^{-2}\mathbf{R}$ l $\mathbf{R}^{-1}\mathbf{Q}^3$

Shears

Part 1

A shear is a transformation in which layers of an object move sideways over each other.

For example, a bolt which has its head pulled sideways will eventually snap or **shear off**.

Rock in the earth's surface can be subject to forces which make layers of the rock slide or **shear** across each other.

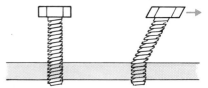

Earlier this century, Sir d'Arcy Thompson showed that the shape of certain fish or the skeletons of some animals can be transformed from one to another. These two diagrams show how the shape of one fish (*Argyropelecus olfersi*) can be transformed to that of another fish (*Sternoptyx diaphana*) by a shear.

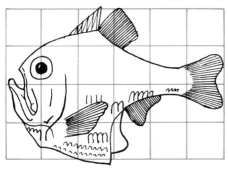 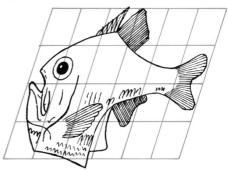

1　Six books are placed in a pile with book *AB* at the bottom and book *XY* at the top.

The pile is pushed sideways and held so that *AB* does not move and *XY* moves to X′Y′.

Copy these two diagrams and draw the missing books in their final positions.

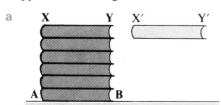 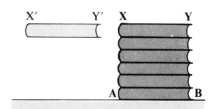

2　Many sheets of thin paper, such as a pack of cards, are placed in a pile. The pile is pushed sideways and held so that the bottom *AB* does not move and the top *XY* moves to X′Y′.

Copy these two diagrams and draw the final positions of the missing sheets.

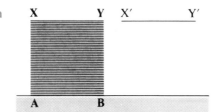 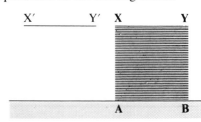

Shears

3 These four shapes are each sheared so that *AB* does not move and points *X* and *Y* move to X′ and Y′. We say that *AB* is the **invariant line**.

Copy each diagram and draw the final position of each shape.

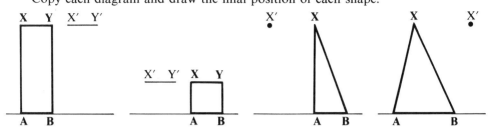

4 Copy each of these object shapes on squared paper.

Each object is sheared with the line *AB* invariant.
Use the given image-points to complete each image after the shear has taken place.

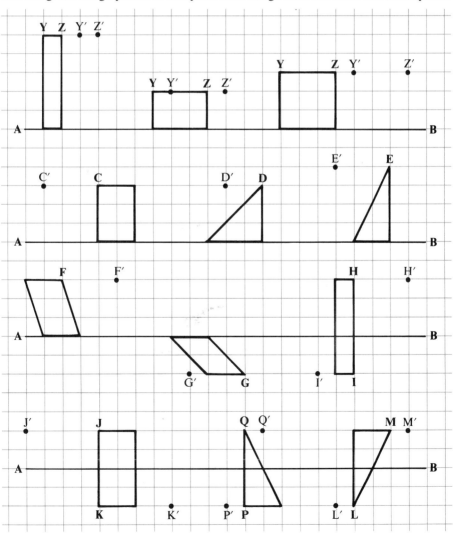

45

Shears

5 The line AZ is sheared into three different positions AZ', AZ'' and AZ''' with the line AB invariant.

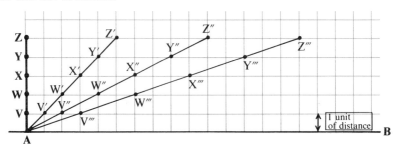

Use the diagram to count how far the labelled points move under these three shears. Copy this table and enter your results.

Point	Distance of point from AB	Distance moved by point as $AZ \to AZ'$	Distance moved by point as $AZ \to AZ''$	Distance moved by point as $AZ \to AZ'''$
V	1	1	2	
W	2	2		
X	3			
Y				
Z				

Note the following.

For $AZ \to AZ'$, the distance any point moves equals its distance from AB. This is called a *shear factor of 1*.

For $AZ \to AZ''$, the distance any point moves is twice its distance from AB. This is called a *shear factor of 2*.

For $AZ \to AZ'''$, the distance any point moves is three times its distance from AB. This is called a *shear factor of 3*.

6 What are the shear factors for these object and image shapes? (Heavy lines show the object and light lines show its image.)

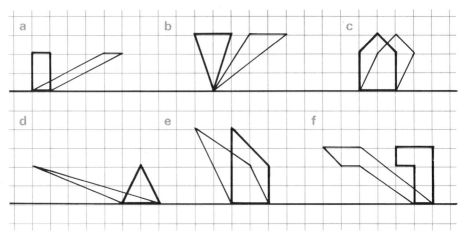

Shears

7 Copy each of these shapes onto squared paper, and shear them to the right using the shear factor given.

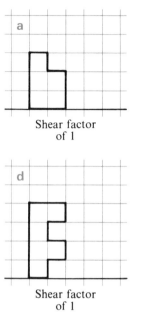

a

Shear factor
of 1

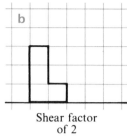

b

Shear factor
of 2

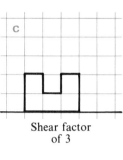

c

Shear factor
of 3

d

Shear factor
of 1

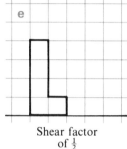

e

Shear factor
of $\frac{1}{2}$

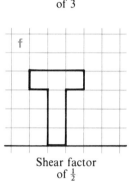

f

Shear factor
of $\frac{1}{2}$

8 Copy each of these shapes onto squared paper, and shear them to the left using the shear factor given.

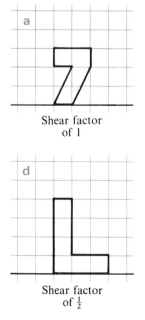

a

Shear factor
of 1

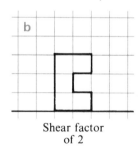

b

Shear factor
of 2

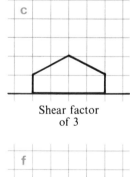

c

Shear factor
of 3

d

Shear factor
of $\frac{1}{2}$

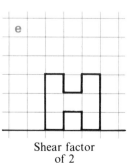

e

Shear factor
of 2

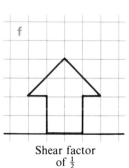

f

Shear factor
of $\frac{1}{2}$

47

Shears

9 Draw and label both axes from 0 to 20. All these shapes are to be drawn onto the one diagram.

a Draw the rectangle (2, 0), (4, 0), (4, 4), (2, 4).
Shear it so that the x-axis is invariant
and the point $(4, 4) \rightarrow (8, 4)$ using a shear factor of 1.

b Draw the shape (10, 0), (13, 0), (13, 2), (12, 2), (12, 4), (10, 4).
Shear it so that the x-axis is invariant
and the point $(10, 4) \rightarrow (14, 4)$ using a shear factor of 1.

Draw the line $y = 6$.

c Draw the arrow (2, 6), (2, 8), (1, 8), (3, 10), (5, 8), (4, 8), (4, 6).
Shear it so that the line $y = 6$ is invariant
and the point $(3, 10) \rightarrow (11, 10)$ using a shear factor of 2.

d Draw the steps (12, 6), (12, 10), (13, 10), (13, 9), (14, 9), (14, 8), (15, 8), (15, 7), (16, 7), (16, 6).
Shear it so that the line $y = 6$ is invariant
and the point $(12, 10) \rightarrow (20, 10)$ using a shear factor of 2.

Draw the line $y = 12$.

e Draw the kite (2, 12), (1, 14), (2, 18), (3, 14).
Shear it so that the line $y = 12$ is invariant
and the point $(2, 18) \rightarrow (5, 18)$ using a shear factor of $\frac{1}{2}$.

f Draw the arrow (6, 12), (10, 12), (9, 13), (11, 15), (9, 17), (7, 15), (6, 16).
Shear it so that the line $y = 12$ is invariant
and the point $(9, 17) \rightarrow (11\frac{1}{2}, 17)$ using a shear factor of $\frac{1}{2}$.

g Draw the face (15, 12), (14, 17), (18, 18), (19, 15), (18, 15), (18, 14), (17, 14), (18, 13), (16, 12).
Shear it so that the line $y = 12$ is invariant
and the point $(18, 18) \rightarrow (21, 18)$ using a shear factor of $\frac{1}{2}$.

10 Draw and label both axes from 0 to 20. All these shapes are to be drawn onto the one diagram.
Draw each object shape and shear it as described in the table.

	Object shape		Invariant line	One object point and its image	Shear factor
a	Rectangle	(0, 2), (0, 4), (4, 4), (4, 2)	y-axis	$(4, 2) \rightarrow (4, 6)$	1
b	Trapezium	(0, 9), (0, 11), (2, 11), (4, 9)	y-axis	$(4, 9) \rightarrow (4, 13)$	1
c	Pentagon	(0, 14), (4, 14), (4, 16), (2, 16), (0, 18)	y-axis	$(4, 14) \rightarrow (4, 18)$	1
d	Arrow	(6, 10), (8, 8), (8, 9), (10, 9), (10, 11), (8, 11), (8, 12)	$x = 6$	$(10, 11) \rightarrow (10, 19)$	2
e	Letter W	(6, 3), (6, 2), (7, 1), (8, 2), (9, 1), (10, 2), (10, 3), (9, 2), (8, 3), (7, 2), (6, 3)	$x = 6$	$(10, 3) \rightarrow (10, 7)$	1
f	Letter L	(14, 18), (15, 18), (15, 15), (17, 15), (17, 14), (14, 14)	$x = 14$	$(15, 18) \rightarrow (15, 19\frac{1}{2})$	$1\frac{1}{2}$
g	Letter M	(14, 2), (15, 2), (15, 5), (17, 3), (19, 5), (19, 2), (20, 2), (20, 6), (19, 6), (17, 4), (15, 6), (14, 6)	$x = 14$	$(15, 2) \rightarrow (15, 3\frac{1}{2})$	$1\frac{1}{2}$

Shears

11 a Draw and label both axes from 0 to 12.
Draw the rectangle (1, 7), (1, 11), (7, 11), (7, 7), and label it *R*.
Shear it so that the line $x = 1$ is invariant and the point (7, 7) maps onto (7, 1) using a shear factor of 1. Label the image *S*.
Shear *S* so that the line $x = 7$ is invariant and the point (1, 7) maps onto (1, 1) using a shear factor of 1. Label the image *T*.
Find the areas of *R*, *S* and *T*. What do you notice?

b Draw and label both axes from 0 to 10.
Draw the shape (1, 5), (1, 9), (7, 9), (7, 7), (5, 5), and label it *R*.
Shear it with the line $x = 1$ invariant and the point (5, 5) mapping onto (5, 1) using a shear factor of 1. Label the image *S*.
Shear *S* with the line $y = 1$ invariant and the point (7, 3) mapping onto (9, 3) using a shear factor of 1. Label the image *T*.
Find the areas of *R*, *S* and *T*. What do you notice?

12 a The coloured rectangle can be sheared onto each of the five parallelograms.

What is the area of the rectangle and the area of each parallelogram?

b The coloured right-angled triangle can be sheared onto each of the five other triangles. What is the area of each of the triangles?

c What can you say about the areas of an object and its image under a shear?

Part 2   More shears

1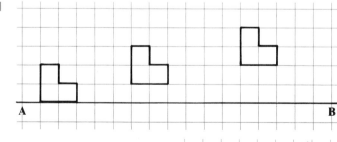

Copy this diagram of three L-shapes onto squared paper.

Take *AB* as the invariant line and shear each shape to the right using a shear factor of 1.

2 Copy this diagram of five rectangles onto squared paper.

Take *AB* as the invariant line and shear each rectangle using a shear factor of 1 in the direction of the arrows.

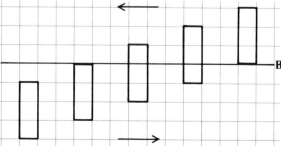

Shears

3 a Draw and label both axes from 0 to 10.
Draw the line $y = 5$.
Draw a letter F by joining the points (2, 3), (2, 8), (5, 8), (5, 7), (3, 7), (3, 6), (5, 6), (5, 5), (3, 5), (3, 3) in order.
Shear this shape using a shear factor of 1 so that the line $y = 5$ is invariant and the point (5, 8) maps onto (8, 8).

  b Draw and label both axes from 0 to 10.
Draw the line $y = 5$.
Draw a letter M by joining the points (3, 3), (3, 8), (4, 8), (6, 6), (8, 8), (9, 8), (9, 3), (8, 3), (8, 7), (6, 5), (4, 7), (4, 3) in order.
Shear this shape using a shear factor of 1 so that the line $y = 5$ is invariant and the point (3, 8) maps onto (0, 8).

  c Draw and label both axes from 0 to 10.
Draw the line $x = 5$.
Draw an arrow by joining the points (4, 5), (7, 8), (6, 9), (9, 9), (9, 6), (8, 7), (5, 4) in order.
Transform this shape using a shear with the line $x = 5$ invariant and a shear factor of 1, so that the point (4, 5) maps onto (4, 6).

  d Draw and label both axes from 0 to 10.
Draw the line $x = 5$.
Draw a letter V by joining these points in order:
(1, 7), (2, 7), ($3\frac{1}{2}$, 4), (5, 7), (6, 7), (4, 3), (3, 3).
Transform this shape under a shear with shear factor 1 such that the line $x = 5$ is invariant and the point (6, 7) maps onto (6, 8).

4 Copy this diagram onto squared paper.

Mark the points R, S and T, and their images R′, S′ and T′ under a shear having the line $y = x$ invariant.

Find the shear factor and complete the three image shapes.

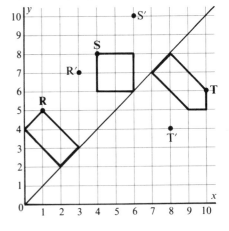

5 Draw and label both axes from 0 to 16.
Draw the line $y = x$ and use this as the invariant line for the following shears.

  a Draw the letter L by joining the points (2, 2), (0, 4), (1, 5), (2, 4), (3, 5), (4, 4) in order.
Shear the shape so that the point (0, 4) maps onto (2, 6).

  b Draw the letter F by joining the points (6, 6), (2, 10), (4, 12), (5, 11), (4, 10), (5, 9), (6, 10), (7, 9), (6, 8), (7, 7) in order.
Shear the shape so that the point (2, 10) maps onto (6, 14).

  c Draw the letter T by joining the points (9, 9), (11, 7), (12, 8), (13, 7), (10, 4), (9, 5), (10, 6), (8, 8) in order.
Shear the shape so that the point (10, 4) maps onto (7, 1).

Shears

6 Draw and label both axes from 0 to 10.
  Draw the line $y = x$ and use it as the invariant line.
  Draw the rectangle (1, 7), (2, 8), (7, 3), (6, 2).
  Transform this rectangle using a shear under which the point (1, 7) maps onto
  $(2\frac{1}{2}, 8\frac{1}{2})$.

7 Draw and label both axes from 0 to 12.
  Draw the line joining (10, 0) to (0, 10) and use it as the invariant line.
  Draw a letter Z by joining the points (2, 8), (2, 9), (5, 9), (5, 8), (3, 4), (5, 4),
  (5, 3), (2, 3), (2, 4), (4, 8) in order.
  Transform this shape using a shear under which the point (5, 3) maps onto (6, 2).

8 Draw a circle of radius 5 units and centre (5, 5) on an x-axis labelled from 0 to
  18 and a y-axis labelled from 0 to 10.
  Shear the circle with a shear factor of 1 and with the x-axis invariant so that the
  point (5, 10) maps onto (15, 10).

9 a Draw and label both axes from -8 to 8.
    Use compasses to draw a circle of radius 5 units and centre the origin. Shear
    this circle with a shear factor of 1 and the x-axis invariant, so that the point
    (3, 4) maps onto the point (7, 4).
    Note that points *above* the x-axis will shear to the right, and points *below*
    the x-axis will shear to the left.
    Take π as 3.14 and calculate the area of the circle.
    Write the area of the image.
  b Draw the same circle on new axes, and also draw the line $y = x$.
    Take $y = x$ as the invariant line and shear the circle with a shear factor of 1,
    so that the point (3, 4) maps onto the point $(3\frac{1}{2}, 4\frac{1}{2})$.
    What is the area of the image?
  c What is the mathematical name for the shape of both these images?

10 a Draw the invariant line $y = \frac{1}{2}x$ on an x-axis labelled from 0 to 14 and a
    y-axis from 0 to 7.
    Draw the square S (2, 1), (1, 3), (3, 4), (4, 2) and the parallelogram P (6, 3),
    (8, 4), (13, 4), (11, 3).
    Shear both S and P using a shear factor of 2 so that S moves to the right
    and P to the left.
  b Draw the line $y = 2x$ on an x-axis labelled from 0 to 10 and a y-axis from 0
    to 12.
    Draw the L-shaped object (5, 10), (7, 9), (6, 7), (8, 6), (10, 10), (6, 12) and
    shear it with a shear factor of $1\frac{1}{2}$ taking the line $y = 2x$ invariant, so that the
    point (8, 6) maps onto (5, 0).

Part 3   Finding the invariant line

1 In each of these diagrams, a transformation maps line AB onto line $A'B'$.
  Which of the transformations could be shears?

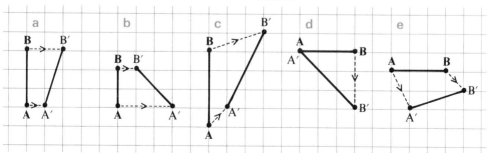

Shears

2 For each part, draw and label new axes from 0 to 4.
The line AB maps onto $A'B'$ under a shear.
Draw AB and $A'B'$ and construct the invariant line of the shear.

	a	b	c	d	e	f
A	(0, 4)	(1, 3)	(1, 0)	(4, 1)	(2, 0)	(0, 2)
B	(2, 2)	(1, 1)	(2, 1)	(2, 1)	(1, 1)	(1, 3)
A'	(3, 4)	(2, 3)	(1, 4)	(4, 3)	(4, 2)	(2, 0)
B'	(3, 2)	(4, 1)	(2, 3)	(2, 2)	(2, 2)	(2, 2)

3 Draw each object and image shape on axes labelled from 0 to 8.
Find and draw the invariant line of the shear, and write its equation.
   a *Object* (1, 4), (1, 7), (2, 7), (2, 4)   *Image* (3, 4), (6, 7), (7, 7), (4, 4)
   b *Object* (2, 5), (2, 6), (4, 6), (4, 5)   *Image* (4, 5), (5, 6), (7, 6), (6, 5)
   c *Object* (1, 4), (1, 7), (3, 4)   *Image* (4, 4), (7, 7), (6, 4)
   d *Object* (1, 6), (1, 5), (4, 5), (4, 6)   *Image* (1, 3), (1, 2), (4, $3\frac{1}{2}$), (4, $4\frac{1}{2}$)
   e *Object* (3, 8), (3, 6), (5, 6), (5, 8)   *Image* (3, 6), (3, 4), (5, 2), (5, 4)
   f *Object* (5, 7), (5, 5), (7, 7)   *Image* (5, 4), (5, 2), (7, 1)

4 A letter T is formed by joining (1, 5) to (3, 5), and (2, 5) to (2, 3). It is sheared
so that its image is made by joining (5, 5) to (7, 5), and then (6, 5) to (4, 3).
Draw a diagram to show the letter T and its image. Construct the invariant line
and write its equation.

5 A letter I is formed by joining (5, 7) to (7, 7), and (5, 5) to (7, 5), and (6, 7) to (6, 5).
Its image under a shear is made by joining (0, 7) to (2, 7), and (2, 5) to (4, 5),
and (1, 7) to (3, 5).
Draw a diagram to show the object and image. Construct the invariant line and
write its equation.

6 By joining (9, 4) to (9, 1) to (11, 1), make an L-shape.
Under a shear its image is made by joining (7, 4) to (1, 1) to (3, 1).
Draw a diagram to find the invariant line and its equation.

7 Join (4, 6) to (6, 6), and (5, 6) to (5, 4) to make a letter T.
It is transformed under a shear so that its image is made by joining (4, 4) to
(6, 2), and (5, 3) to (5, 1).
Draw a diagram to find the invariant line and its equation.

8 For each part, draw new axes, labelling the x-axis from 0 to 8 and the y-axis
from 0 to 12.
Each object is sheared onto its image. Draw both object and image shapes and
construct the invariant line.
   a *Object* (3, 3), (1, 5), (2, 6), (4, 4)   *Image* (5, 5), (7, 11), (8, 12), (6, 6)
   b *Object* (5, 5), (3, 7), (6, 6)   *Image* (6, 6), (6, 10), (7, 7)
   c *Object* (3, 7), (1, 7), (1, 5), (3, 5)   *Image* (4, 6), (3, 5), (4, 2), 5, 3)
   d *Object* (4, 4), (4, 3), (2, 3), (2, 6)   *Image* ($5\frac{1}{2}$, $5\frac{1}{2}$), (5, 4), (4, 5), ($5\frac{1}{2}$, $9\frac{1}{2}$),
              (5, 6), (5, 4)   (7, 8), (6, 5)

9 Two points and their images provide sufficient information to fix the position of
the invariant line of a shear.
For each part below, draw and label both axes from 0 to 8.
Plot the points and images given, and construct the invariant lines.
   a (2, 6) → (6, 6)   b (1, 5) → (3, 7)   c (1, 4) → (7, 4)
      (2, 4) → (4, 4)   (3, 3) → (4, 4)   (4, 1) → (1, 1)
   d (2, 3) → (2, 7)   e (0, 4) → (4, 8)   f (3, 1) → (1, 3)
      (6, 5) → (6, 1)   (6, 4) → (4, 2)   (3, 7) → (4, 6)

Vectors

Part 1 Introduction

1 A quantity having a *direction* as well as a *size* is called a **vector**. But a quantity which has only a size and has *no* direction is called a **scalar**.
   Say whether a *vector* or *scalar* quantity is involved in each of these statements.
   a A car is travelling due north at 100 km/h on the motorway.
   b 840 people attended a concert last night in the Town Hall.
   c A motor boat sailed 15 km on a bearing of 065°.
   d A sheet of paper has an area of 250 cm².
   e A cricket ball is thrown vertically upwards at a speed of 12 m/s.
   f The temperature in the classroom is 18°C.

2 In which of these situations are vector quantities involved?
   a laying a pipeline across open country
   b measuring the volume of a glass beaker
   c flying an aircraft between two cities
   d rowing a barge on a canal
   e counting the people at a football match
   f investigating the airflow in a wind-tunnel

3 Which of these are *vector* quantities and which are *scalar* quantities?
   a velocity   b area   c force   d volume
   e weight   f mass   g perimeter   h acceleration

4 A vector can be represented by an arrow. Which of these two diagrams shows vectors of the same size but in different directions; and which diagram shows vectors with the same directions but different sizes?

a    b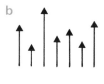

5

The route taken by a boat from Newport to Flaxmouth is shown on this map by five vectors, labelled **a** to **e**. The scale of the map is 1 cm = 10 km. Copy and complete this table.

Vector	Distance km	Direction, or bearing
a		
b		
c		
d		
e		

6 The six legs of a journey which a yacht makes from Saltbay to Cleehead are described by the six vectors in this table.

Vector	a	b	c	d	e	f
Distance, km	60	40	20	30	40	25
Direction	due N	due E	due S	due E	due S	due W

   a Draw the route accurately using a scale of 1 cm = 10 km.
   b Give the size and direction of the vector which an aeroplane would use to go directly from Saltbay to Cleehead.

53

Vectors

7

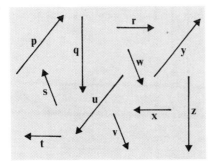

Two vectors are equal if they have the *same* size and the *same* direction. A vector is the negative of another vector if it has the *same* size but the *opposite* direction.
Say whether these statements are *true* or *false*.

a	$p = y$	b	$v = w$	c	$v = x$
d	$x = t$	e	$y = -u$	f	$r = -t$
g	$s = w$	h	$v = -s$	i	$z = y$
j	$u = -p$	k	$r = x$	l	$w = r$

8   A knight on a chess-board starts from the coloured square on this diagram.
The vector shows one possible move.
Copy the diagram and label with the number 1 all squares which the knight can reach in *one* move.
Label with the number 2 all squares which it can reach in *two* moves.
Continue to label squares with 3, 4, ... until all the squares are labelled.
What do you notice about the numbers
   a   on the black squares   b   on the white squares?

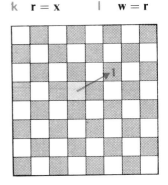

Part 2   Components of vectors

1   Write the components of each vector in this diagram.
For example, $a = \begin{pmatrix} 2 \\ 3 \end{pmatrix}$.

2   A vector can also be labelled with a capital letter at each end.
Write the components of these vectors.
For example, $AB = \begin{pmatrix} 4 \\ 2 \end{pmatrix}$.

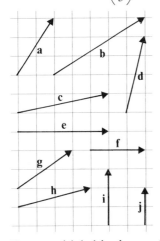

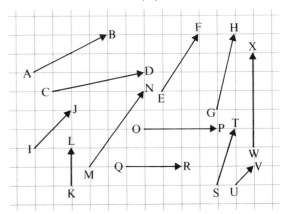

3   Draw and label both axes from 0 to 10.
For each pair of points, draw the vector from the first point to the second, and write its components.

a	A(1, 6)	B(4, 10)	b	C(1, 4)	D(4, 5)	c	E(6, 6)	F(7, 9)
d	G(8, 7)	H(10, 7)	e	I(9, 4)	J(9, 6)	f	K(2, 0)	L(4, 3)
g	M(6, 1)	N(6, 5)	h	P(7, 2)	Q(10, 2)	i	R(8, 0)	S(10, 1)
j	T(0, 9)	U(1, 10)						

Vectors

4 The two components of a vector are positive or negative as given below.

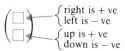

{ right is + ve
{ left is − ve

{ up is + ve
{ down is − ve

Write the components of each of these vectors, starting with the vector **a** and working alphabetically.

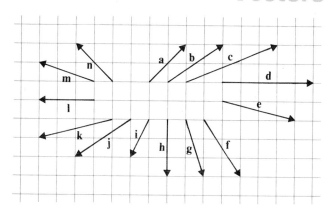

5 Draw and label both axes from 0 to 10.
Draw the vectors which join each first point to the second, and write their components.

a	A(1, 1)	B(3, 4)	b	C(1, 5)	D(4, 6)	c	E(1, 8)	F(4, 7)
d	G(2, 10)	H(5, 7)	e	I(4, 5)	J(5, 0)	f	K(6, 10)	L(6, 8)
g	M(9, 10)	N(7, 7)	h	P(10, 8)	Q(7, 6)	i	R(10, 5)	S(6, 5)
j	T(10, 3)	U(6, 4)	k	V(7, 0)	W(6, 3)	l	X(10, 1)	Y(8, 2)

6 Draw and label both axes from 0 to 10.
Draw and label an arrow for each vector, starting at the given point.
Copy and complete the final row of the table.

Starting point	P(7, 1)	M(10, 6)	I(7, 8)	C(3, 8)	U(2, 4)	E(3, 4)	S(3, 6)
Vector	$PQ = \begin{pmatrix} 3 \\ 4 \end{pmatrix}$	$MN = \begin{pmatrix} -3 \\ 4 \end{pmatrix}$	$IJ = \begin{pmatrix} -6 \\ 2 \end{pmatrix}$	$CD = \begin{pmatrix} -3 \\ -3 \end{pmatrix}$	$UV = \begin{pmatrix} -1 \\ -4 \end{pmatrix}$	$EF = \begin{pmatrix} 3 \\ -2 \end{pmatrix}$	$ST = \begin{pmatrix} 5 \\ -1 \end{pmatrix}$
End point							

7 This map shows a group of islands served by four airstrips W, X, Y and Z. Five of the islands also have jetties A to E.

Write the components of the vector which gives the direct route of a boat sailing from

a B to D   b B to E
c A to D   d A to C
e C to E   f D to E
g E to A   h D to C.

Write the components of the vector which gives the route taken by an aeroplane flying directly from

i Z to Y   j Y to X
k Y to W   l W to X
m X to Z   n Z to X
o W to Z   p Z to W.

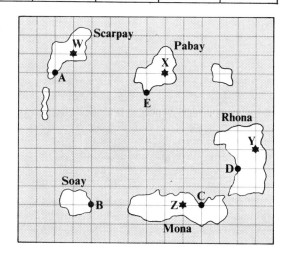

55

Vectors

Part 3 Equal, multiple and negative vectors

1 Say whether these statements
are *true* or *false*.

a $\mathbf{a} = \mathbf{c}$ b $\mathbf{a} = \mathbf{b}$
c $\mathbf{a} = \mathbf{l}$ d $\mathbf{a} = -\mathbf{l}$
e $\mathbf{i} = \mathbf{k}$ f $\mathbf{i} = \mathbf{h}$
g $\mathbf{i} = \mathbf{d}$ h $\mathbf{i} = -\mathbf{d}$
i $\mathbf{c} = -\mathbf{l}$ j $\mathbf{f} = \mathbf{j}$
k $\mathbf{b} = \mathbf{n}$ l $\mathbf{b} = \mathbf{f}$
m $\mathbf{b} = -\mathbf{f}$ n $\mathbf{n} = \mathbf{f}$
o $\mathbf{k} = \mathbf{m}$ p $\mathbf{k} = -\mathbf{d}$
q $\mathbf{a} = \mathbf{e}$ r $\mathbf{j} = -\mathbf{n}$

2

A cuboid with a square cross-section
has vectors along its edges as shown.
Say whether these statements are
true or *false*.

a $\mathbf{a} = \mathbf{b}$ b $\mathbf{a} = -\mathbf{c}$ c $\mathbf{h} = \mathbf{g}$
d $\mathbf{h} = \mathbf{i}$ e $\mathbf{i} = -\mathbf{g}$ f $\mathbf{e} = \mathbf{f}$
g $\mathbf{e} = \mathbf{d}$ h $\mathbf{a} = \mathbf{i}$ i $\mathbf{h} = \mathbf{c}$
j $\mathbf{f} = -\mathbf{d}$

3 By looking at both the length
and the direction of these vectors,
say whether these statements
are *true* or *false*.

a $\mathbf{c} = 2\mathbf{a}$ b $\mathbf{l} = 2\mathbf{a}$
c $\mathbf{g} = 3\mathbf{d}$ d $\mathbf{j} = 2\mathbf{d}$
e $\mathbf{f} = 2\mathbf{e}$ f $\mathbf{m} = 2\mathbf{b}$
g $\mathbf{i} = 2\mathbf{h}$ h $\mathbf{n} = \frac{1}{2}\mathbf{h}$
i $\mathbf{k} = \frac{1}{2}\mathbf{h}$ j $\mathbf{i} = -4\mathbf{k}$
k $\mathbf{e} = -\frac{1}{2}\mathbf{f}$ l $\mathbf{l} = -\mathbf{c}$
m $\mathbf{n} = \mathbf{k}$ n $\mathbf{b} = \frac{1}{2}\mathbf{m}$
o $\mathbf{d} = \frac{1}{3}\mathbf{g}$

4 Write the vectors
$\mathbf{t}, \mathbf{u}, \mathbf{v}, \mathbf{w}, \mathbf{x}, \mathbf{y}$ and $\mathbf{z}$
in terms of the vector $\mathbf{a}$.

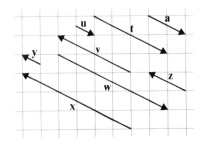

5 Write the vectors
$\mathbf{b}, \mathbf{c}, \mathbf{d}, \mathbf{e}, \mathbf{f}, \mathbf{g}$ and $\mathbf{h}$
in terms of the vector $\mathbf{a}$.

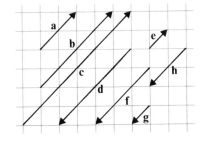

Vectors

Part 4   Addition and subtraction

1   These diagrams show vectors being added by placing them tip to tail. The resultant vector is shown by a double arrow. Copy these equations and use the diagrams to complete them.

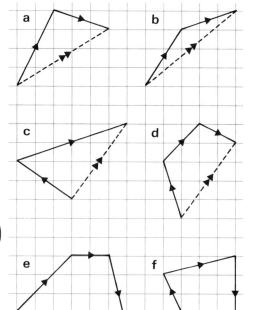

a $\begin{pmatrix} 2 \\ 4 \end{pmatrix} + \begin{pmatrix} 3 \\ -1 \end{pmatrix} = \begin{pmatrix} \\ \end{pmatrix}$

b $\begin{pmatrix} 2 \\ 3 \end{pmatrix} + \begin{pmatrix} \\ \end{pmatrix} = \begin{pmatrix} \\ \end{pmatrix}$

c $\begin{pmatrix} -3 \\ 2 \end{pmatrix} + \begin{pmatrix} \\ \end{pmatrix} = \begin{pmatrix} \\ \end{pmatrix}$

d $\begin{pmatrix} -1 \\ 3 \end{pmatrix} + \begin{pmatrix} \\ \end{pmatrix} + \begin{pmatrix} \\ \end{pmatrix} = \begin{pmatrix} \\ \end{pmatrix}$

e $\begin{pmatrix} 3 \\ 3 \end{pmatrix} + \begin{pmatrix} \\ \end{pmatrix} + \begin{pmatrix} \\ \end{pmatrix} = \begin{pmatrix} \\ \end{pmatrix}$

f $\begin{pmatrix} \\ \end{pmatrix} + \begin{pmatrix} 4 \\ 1 \end{pmatrix} + \begin{pmatrix} \\ \end{pmatrix} = \begin{pmatrix} \\ \end{pmatrix}$

2   Draw your own diagrams to illustrate these vector additions.

a $\begin{pmatrix} 1 \\ 3 \end{pmatrix} + \begin{pmatrix} 2 \\ 2 \end{pmatrix} = \begin{pmatrix} 3 \\ 5 \end{pmatrix}$ b $\begin{pmatrix} 4 \\ 2 \end{pmatrix} + \begin{pmatrix} 1 \\ 3 \end{pmatrix} = \begin{pmatrix} 5 \\ 5 \end{pmatrix}$ c $\begin{pmatrix} 3 \\ 1 \end{pmatrix} + \begin{pmatrix} 2 \\ -4 \end{pmatrix} = \begin{pmatrix} 5 \\ -3 \end{pmatrix}$

d $\begin{pmatrix} 5 \\ -2 \end{pmatrix} + \begin{pmatrix} 1 \\ 4 \end{pmatrix} = \begin{pmatrix} 6 \\ 2 \end{pmatrix}$ e $\begin{pmatrix} 3 \\ -1 \end{pmatrix} + \begin{pmatrix} 2 \\ -3 \end{pmatrix} = \begin{pmatrix} 5 \\ -4 \end{pmatrix}$ f $\begin{pmatrix} -1 \\ 4 \end{pmatrix} + \begin{pmatrix} 3 \\ 1 \end{pmatrix} = \begin{pmatrix} 2 \\ 5 \end{pmatrix}$

g $\begin{pmatrix} 3 \\ 1 \end{pmatrix} + \begin{pmatrix} 1 \\ -4 \end{pmatrix} + \begin{pmatrix} -2 \\ 1 \end{pmatrix} = \begin{pmatrix} 2 \\ -2 \end{pmatrix}$ h $\begin{pmatrix} 5 \\ -3 \end{pmatrix} + \begin{pmatrix} 1 \\ 4 \end{pmatrix} + \begin{pmatrix} -2 \\ -1 \end{pmatrix} = \begin{pmatrix} 4 \\ 0 \end{pmatrix}$

i $\begin{pmatrix} 1 \\ 4 \end{pmatrix} + \begin{pmatrix} 3 \\ -2 \end{pmatrix} + \begin{pmatrix} 1 \\ -5 \end{pmatrix} + \begin{pmatrix} -5 \\ 3 \end{pmatrix} = \begin{pmatrix} 0 \\ 0 \end{pmatrix}$ j $\begin{pmatrix} 6 \\ -2 \end{pmatrix} + \begin{pmatrix} -9 \\ -2 \end{pmatrix} + \begin{pmatrix} 1 \\ 7 \end{pmatrix} + \begin{pmatrix} 2 \\ -3 \end{pmatrix} = \begin{pmatrix} 0 \\ 0 \end{pmatrix}$

3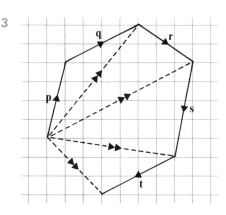

Use the diagram to write the components of the resultant of each of these vector additions.

a   **p** + **q**

b   **p** + **q** + **r**

c   **p** + **q** + **r** + **s**

d   **p** + **q** + **r** + **s** + **t**

Vectors

4 The vectors **a** to **e** are given in this diagram.
   Draw them tip-to-tail to find the resultant of each of these vector additions.

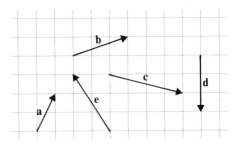

   a **a + b**   b **a + c**   c **a + e**
   d **b + c**   e **b + d**   f **c + d**
   g **a + b + c**   h **e + b + d**
   i **c + d + e**   j **a + c + d**

5 Without drawing any diagrams, find the resultant of these vector additions.

a $\begin{pmatrix} 2 \\ 3 \end{pmatrix} + \begin{pmatrix} 4 \\ 1 \end{pmatrix}$

b $\begin{pmatrix} 5 \\ 3 \end{pmatrix} + \begin{pmatrix} -2 \\ 1 \end{pmatrix}$

c $\begin{pmatrix} 3 \\ 4 \end{pmatrix} + \begin{pmatrix} -3 \\ -2 \end{pmatrix}$

d $\begin{pmatrix} 1 \\ 3 \end{pmatrix} + \begin{pmatrix} -4 \\ -3 \end{pmatrix}$

e $\begin{pmatrix} 2 \\ 0 \end{pmatrix} + \begin{pmatrix} -5 \\ -4 \end{pmatrix}$

f $\begin{pmatrix} 1 \\ -2 \end{pmatrix} + \begin{pmatrix} 4 \\ -3 \end{pmatrix}$

g $\begin{pmatrix} -4 \\ -2 \end{pmatrix} + \begin{pmatrix} -1 \\ 2 \end{pmatrix}$

h $\begin{pmatrix} 3 \\ -2 \end{pmatrix} + \begin{pmatrix} -4 \\ 5 \end{pmatrix}$

i $\begin{pmatrix} 0 \\ 2 \end{pmatrix} + \begin{pmatrix} -3 \\ 0 \end{pmatrix}$

j $\begin{pmatrix} 2 \\ 3 \end{pmatrix} + \begin{pmatrix} 4 \\ -1 \end{pmatrix} + \begin{pmatrix} -6 \\ 2 \end{pmatrix}$

k $\begin{pmatrix} 4 \\ 5 \end{pmatrix} + \begin{pmatrix} -1 \\ 2 \end{pmatrix} + \begin{pmatrix} -2 \\ -6 \end{pmatrix}$

6 Find the value of each letter in these additions.

a $\begin{pmatrix} y \\ z \end{pmatrix} + \begin{pmatrix} 4 \\ 4 \end{pmatrix} = \begin{pmatrix} 5 \\ 7 \end{pmatrix}$

b $\begin{pmatrix} x \\ w \end{pmatrix} + \begin{pmatrix} 3 \\ 0 \end{pmatrix} = \begin{pmatrix} 7 \\ 4 \end{pmatrix}$

c $\begin{pmatrix} u \\ 4 \end{pmatrix} + \begin{pmatrix} 2 \\ v \end{pmatrix} = \begin{pmatrix} 2 \\ 9 \end{pmatrix}$

d $\begin{pmatrix} 5 \\ 8 \end{pmatrix} + \begin{pmatrix} s \\ t \end{pmatrix} = \begin{pmatrix} 4 \\ 6 \end{pmatrix}$

e $\begin{pmatrix} 7 \\ r \end{pmatrix} + \begin{pmatrix} q \\ -2 \end{pmatrix} = \begin{pmatrix} 1 \\ 4 \end{pmatrix}$

f $\begin{pmatrix} 4 \\ 0 \end{pmatrix} + \begin{pmatrix} -3 \\ p \end{pmatrix} = \begin{pmatrix} n \\ -3 \end{pmatrix}$

g $\begin{pmatrix} 8 \\ n \end{pmatrix} + \begin{pmatrix} m \\ -5 \end{pmatrix} = \begin{pmatrix} 6 \\ 7 \end{pmatrix}$

h $\begin{pmatrix} 2 \\ j \end{pmatrix} + \begin{pmatrix} 6 \\ 7 \end{pmatrix} + \begin{pmatrix} k \\ -4 \end{pmatrix} = \begin{pmatrix} 5 \\ 5 \end{pmatrix}$

i $\begin{pmatrix} 3 \\ -4 \end{pmatrix} + \begin{pmatrix} j \\ 9 \end{pmatrix} + \begin{pmatrix} -2 \\ h \end{pmatrix} = \begin{pmatrix} 1 \\ 4 \end{pmatrix}$

7 Simplify without drawing any diagrams.

a $\begin{pmatrix} 2 \\ 4 \end{pmatrix} + 2\begin{pmatrix} 1 \\ 2 \end{pmatrix}$

b $\begin{pmatrix} 3 \\ 2 \end{pmatrix} + 3\begin{pmatrix} 0 \\ 2 \end{pmatrix}$

c $2\begin{pmatrix} -1 \\ 0 \end{pmatrix} + \begin{pmatrix} 2 \\ 5 \end{pmatrix}$

d $\begin{pmatrix} 1 \\ 4 \end{pmatrix} + 2\begin{pmatrix} 3 \\ 2 \end{pmatrix}$

e $\begin{pmatrix} -4 \\ 3 \end{pmatrix} + 3\begin{pmatrix} 2 \\ 0 \end{pmatrix}$

f $\begin{pmatrix} 8 \\ -9 \end{pmatrix} + 4\begin{pmatrix} -2 \\ 3 \end{pmatrix}$

g $\begin{pmatrix} 12 \\ -5 \end{pmatrix} + 3\begin{pmatrix} -3 \\ 2 \end{pmatrix}$

h $4\begin{pmatrix} 2 \\ 1 \end{pmatrix} + \begin{pmatrix} 2 \\ -4 \end{pmatrix}$

i $6\begin{pmatrix} 1 \\ 3 \end{pmatrix} + \begin{pmatrix} -7 \\ -10 \end{pmatrix}$

j $4\begin{pmatrix} 2 \\ 3 \end{pmatrix} + 2\begin{pmatrix} 1 \\ 6 \end{pmatrix}$

k $3\begin{pmatrix} 4 \\ 2 \end{pmatrix} + 2\begin{pmatrix} -5 \\ -3 \end{pmatrix}$

l $8\begin{pmatrix} 2 \\ -1 \end{pmatrix} + 3\begin{pmatrix} -5 \\ 3 \end{pmatrix}$

Vectors

8 Given that $a = \begin{pmatrix} 2 \\ 3 \end{pmatrix}$, $b = \begin{pmatrix} 4 \\ 0 \end{pmatrix}$, $c = \begin{pmatrix} -2 \\ 1 \end{pmatrix}$, $d = \begin{pmatrix} 3 \\ -5 \end{pmatrix}$ and $e = \begin{pmatrix} -2 \\ -3 \end{pmatrix}$

find the values of

a $\quad a + b$	b $\quad 2a + b$	c $\quad 2a - b$	d $\quad 3a + c$
e $\quad 3a + d$	f $\quad a + e$	g $\quad b + 2c$	h $\quad c + d$
i $\quad 2c + d$	j $\quad 2a + 3b$	k $\quad 5a + 2b$	l $\quad 3c + e$
m $\quad 2d + 3e$	n $\quad b + \frac{1}{2}a$	o $\quad \frac{1}{2}c + \frac{1}{2}a$.	

9 These vectors add to give the zero vector $\begin{pmatrix} 0 \\ 0 \end{pmatrix}$.
Find the unknown lettered components.

a $\begin{pmatrix} 2 \\ 5 \end{pmatrix} + \begin{pmatrix} x \\ y \end{pmatrix} = \begin{pmatrix} 0 \\ 0 \end{pmatrix}$ b $\begin{pmatrix} 3 \\ 1 \end{pmatrix} + \begin{pmatrix} x \\ y \end{pmatrix} = \begin{pmatrix} 0 \\ 0 \end{pmatrix}$ c $\begin{pmatrix} -2 \\ 7 \end{pmatrix} + \begin{pmatrix} x \\ y \end{pmatrix} = \begin{pmatrix} 0 \\ 0 \end{pmatrix}$

d $\begin{pmatrix} x \\ y \end{pmatrix} + \begin{pmatrix} -3 \\ 4 \end{pmatrix} = \begin{pmatrix} 0 \\ 0 \end{pmatrix}$ e $\begin{pmatrix} 2 \\ 3 \end{pmatrix} + \begin{pmatrix} 7 \\ 4 \end{pmatrix} + \begin{pmatrix} x \\ y \end{pmatrix} = \begin{pmatrix} 0 \\ 0 \end{pmatrix}$

f $\begin{pmatrix} 8 \\ -1 \end{pmatrix} + \begin{pmatrix} 3 \\ -6 \end{pmatrix} + \begin{pmatrix} x \\ y \end{pmatrix} = \begin{pmatrix} 0 \\ 0 \end{pmatrix}$ g $\begin{pmatrix} 2 \\ 8 \end{pmatrix} + \begin{pmatrix} 3 \\ -4 \end{pmatrix} + \begin{pmatrix} x \\ y \end{pmatrix} = \begin{pmatrix} 0 \\ 0 \end{pmatrix}$

h $\begin{pmatrix} x \\ y \end{pmatrix} + \begin{pmatrix} 7 \\ 5 \end{pmatrix} + \begin{pmatrix} -3 \\ -8 \end{pmatrix} = \begin{pmatrix} 0 \\ 0 \end{pmatrix}$

10 To subtract one vector from a other, we add the negative of the vector.
That is, we use the fact that
$a - b = a + (-b)$.
Copy and complete these equations by looking at the diagram.

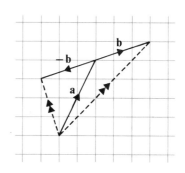

(i) $a + b = \begin{pmatrix} \cdots \\ \cdots \end{pmatrix}$

(ii) $a - b = \begin{pmatrix} \cdots \\ \cdots \end{pmatrix}$

11 Use these diagrams to write the components of the resultants of the vectors below.

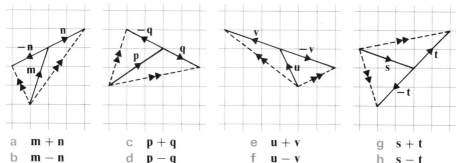

a $\quad m + n$	c $\quad p + q$	e $\quad u + v$	g $\quad s + t$
b $\quad m - n$	d $\quad p - q$	f $\quad u - v$	h $\quad s - t$

Vectors

12 Without drawing any diagrams, subtract these vectors.

a $\begin{pmatrix} 7 \\ 5 \end{pmatrix} - \begin{pmatrix} 2 \\ 3 \end{pmatrix}$
b $\begin{pmatrix} 6 \\ 9 \end{pmatrix} - \begin{pmatrix} 1 \\ 7 \end{pmatrix}$
c $\begin{pmatrix} 5 \\ 3 \end{pmatrix} - \begin{pmatrix} 4 \\ 3 \end{pmatrix}$

d $\begin{pmatrix} 8 \\ 2 \end{pmatrix} - \begin{pmatrix} 5 \\ 3 \end{pmatrix}$
e $\begin{pmatrix} 7 \\ 4 \end{pmatrix} - \begin{pmatrix} 9 \\ 4 \end{pmatrix}$
f $\begin{pmatrix} 0 \\ 1 \end{pmatrix} - \begin{pmatrix} 3 \\ 3 \end{pmatrix}$

g $\begin{pmatrix} 0 \\ 2 \end{pmatrix} - \begin{pmatrix} 6 \\ 5 \end{pmatrix}$
h $\begin{pmatrix} -1 \\ 0 \end{pmatrix} - \begin{pmatrix} 3 \\ 7 \end{pmatrix}$
i $\begin{pmatrix} -1 \\ -2 \end{pmatrix} - \begin{pmatrix} 4 \\ 5 \end{pmatrix}$

j $\begin{pmatrix} -2 \\ -3 \end{pmatrix} - \begin{pmatrix} 8 \\ 1 \end{pmatrix}$
k $\begin{pmatrix} 2 \\ -2 \end{pmatrix} - \begin{pmatrix} 6 \\ 6 \end{pmatrix}$
l $\begin{pmatrix} -4 \\ 4 \end{pmatrix} - \begin{pmatrix} 4 \\ 4 \end{pmatrix}$

13 Given that $\mathbf{p} = \begin{pmatrix} 8 \\ 6 \end{pmatrix}$, $\mathbf{q} = \begin{pmatrix} 0 \\ 5 \end{pmatrix}$, $\mathbf{r} = \begin{pmatrix} 1 \\ 3 \end{pmatrix}$, $\mathbf{s} = \begin{pmatrix} -1 \\ 0 \end{pmatrix}$ and $\mathbf{t} = \begin{pmatrix} -2 \\ -5 \end{pmatrix}$

find the values of

a $\mathbf{p} - \mathbf{q}$ b $\mathbf{p} - \mathbf{r}$ c $\mathbf{p} - 2\mathbf{r}$ d $2\mathbf{p} - 3\mathbf{q}$
e $\mathbf{s} - \mathbf{q}$ f $\mathbf{s} - \mathbf{r}$ g $\mathbf{s} - \mathbf{p}$ h $3\mathbf{s} - \mathbf{r}$
i $\mathbf{t} - \mathbf{q}$ j $\mathbf{t} - \mathbf{r}$ k $\mathbf{t} - 2\mathbf{r}$ l $\mathbf{p} - 2\mathbf{q}$
m $\mathbf{s} - 2\mathbf{r}$ n $\mathbf{r} - \mathbf{p}$ o $3\mathbf{r} - 2\mathbf{q}$.

Part 5 Geometric problems

1 In this parallelogram, V and Y are the
midpoints of their sides.
If $\mathbf{XY} = \mathbf{a}$ and $\mathbf{XU} = \mathbf{b}$, write these
vectors in terms of **a** and **b**.

a **YZ**   b **UV**   c **YV**   d **ZW**
e **XZ**   f **UW**   g **UX**   h **YX**
i **VY**   j **ZY**   k **WU**   l **ZX**

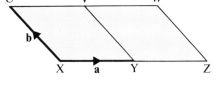

2

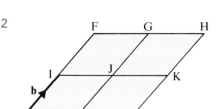

The midpoints of the sides of the large
parallelogram are joined to form four equal
smaller parallelograms.
Given that $\mathbf{LM} = \mathbf{a}$ and $\mathbf{LI} = \mathbf{b}$, write these
vectors in terms of **a** and **b**.

a **MN**   b **IJ**   c **GH**   d **MJ**
e **NK**   f **NH**   g **FG**   h **FH**
i **IK**   j **LF**   k **IL**   l **JM**
m **NM**   n **HG**   o **HF**   p **GM**

3 L, M and N are the midpoints of the sides
of triangle PQR.
If $\mathbf{PN} = \mathbf{a}$ and $\mathbf{PL} = \mathbf{b}$, write these vectors
in terms of **a** and **b**.

a **NR**   b **PR**   c **LQ**   d **PQ**
e **LM**   f **NM**   g **RN**   h **RP**
i **LP**   j **QP**   k **MN**   l **NP**

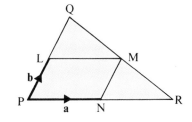

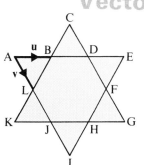

4 This star is formed from two overlapping
   equilateral triangles AEI and CGK which
   cut each other's sides in thirds.
   If **AB** = **u** and **AL** = **v**, find these vectors in
   terms of **u** and **v**.

   a **AD**   b **AE**   c **LJ**   d **DF**
   e **CF**   f **CG**   g **LI**   h **KJ**
   i **KG**   j **DB**   k **EB**   l **JL**
   m **IA**   n **GC**   o **EA**   p **DF**

5

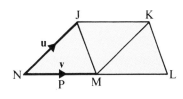

   M is the midpoint of the side LN of the
   trapezium JKLN.
   If P is the midpoint of NM, and **NJ** = **u**
   and **NM** = **v**, express each of these vectors
   in terms of **u** and **v**.

   a **MK**   b **JK**   c **ML**   d **NL**
   e **NP**   f **PM**   g **PL**   h **KM**
   i **KJ**   j **PN**   k **LN**   l **LP**

6 Points P and Q cut the side XY of triangle
   XYZ in thirds. Similarly for points R, S, T,
   U on sides YZ and ZX.
   If **XY** = **a** and **YZ** = **b** and **ZX** = **c**, express
   the following vectors in terms of **a**, **b** and **c**.

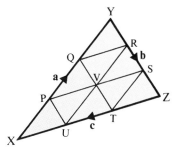

   a **XP**   b **YR**   c **ZT**   d **PQ**
   e **XQ**   f **YS**   g **TX**   h **UV**
   i **UR**   j **QV**   k **QT**   l **RQ**
   m **SP**   n **TS**   o **PU**   p **SV**

7 Write an expression for the vector **z** using the other vectors in each of these
   diagrams.

   a   b   c

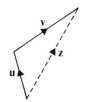   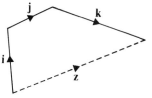   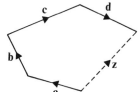

8 Write **y** and **z**   9 Write **x**, **y** and **z**   10 Write the vectors
   in terms of **a** and **b**.   in terms of   **OM** and **OL**
                                  a, **b**, **c** and **d**.   in terms of **a** and **b**.

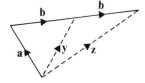   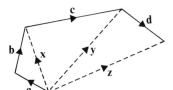   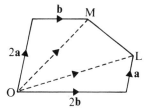

61

Vectors

11 Find expressions for **z** in terms of the other vectors in each of these diagrams, and simplify your answers.

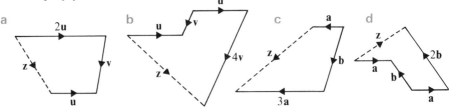

a   b   c   d

12 Write the vectors **CD** and **DC** in terms of **i** and **j**.

13 Write the vectors **PO** and **PQ** in terms of **p** and **q**.

14 Write the vectors **PR** and **OR** in terms of **p** and **q**.

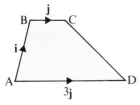 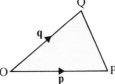 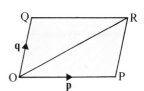

15 P is the midpoint of the side BC of the parallelogram ABCD, in which **DA** = **u** and **DC** = **v**.
Write the following vectors in terms of **u** and **v**.

a   **AB**   b   **CB**   c   **CP**   d   **BP**
e   **DB**   f   **DP**

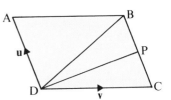

16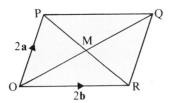

The diagonals of the parallelogram OPQR intersect at M.
Write the following vectors in terms of **a** and **b**.

a   **PQ**   b   **OQ**   c   **OM**   d   **MQ**
e   **RO**   f   **RP**   g   **RM**   h   **MP**

17 P and Q are the midpoints of two sides of the square ABCD as shown.
Given **AP** = **u** and **AQ** = **v**, express the following vectors in terms of **u** and **v**.

a   **QB**   b   **AB**   c   **AD**   d   **CD**
e   **PA**   f   **PQ**   g   **DA**   h   **DB**

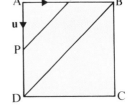

18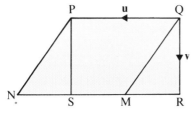

PQRS is a rectangle and PQMN is a parallelogram where M is the midpoint of SR.
If **QP** = **u** and **QR** = **v**, find the following vectors in terms of **u** and **v**.

a   **PS**   b   **RS**   c   **MS**   d   **RM**
e   **QM**   f   **PN**   g   **NM**   h   **MN**

Vectors

19

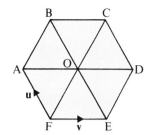

O is the centre of the hexagon in which
FA = **u** and **FE** = **v**.
Express the following vectors in terms of
u and **v**.

a	**EO**	b	**EB**	c	**BC**	d	**AD**
e	**FO**	f	**AB**	g	**FC**	h	**BE**

20 O is the origin, and the position vectors of
points A and B are **a** and **b**.
M is the midpoint of AB and has a position
vector **m**.
Find the following vectors in terms of **a** and **b**.

a **BO**   b **BA**   c **BM**   d **OM**

Simplify your answer for part **d**.

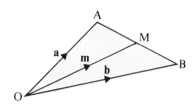

21

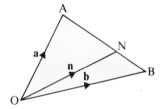

a, **b** and **n** are the position vectors of A, B
and N and NB is one third of AB.
Find the following vectors in terms of
a and **b**.

a **BO**   b **BA**   c **BN**   d **ON**

Simplify your answer for part **d**.

22 M and N are the midpoints of sides OA and
OB of triangle OAB.
The position vectors of M and N are **m** and **n**.
Express the following vectors in terms of **m**
and **n**.

a **MO**   b **MN**   c **AM**

d **AO**   e **AB**

f   What do your answers for **MN** and **AB**
tell you about the lengths MN and AB?

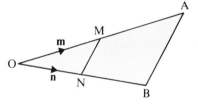

23

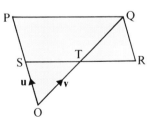

PQRS is a parallelogram.
S and T are the midpoints of OP and OQ
where **OS** = **u** and **OT** = **v**.
Express the following vectors in terms of **u** and **v**.

a **OP**   b **TQ**   c **PS**   d **QR**

e **TR**   f **SO**   g **ST**

h   What do your answers for **TR** and **ST**
tell you about point T?

24 The position vectors of P, Q and R are **p**, **q**
and **r** as shown in this cuboid.
Express the following vectors in terms of
p, **q** and **r**.

a **RD**   b **OD**   c **DB**   d **OB**

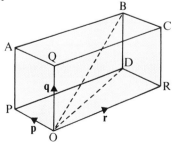

Vectors

25 This wedge has **AB = u**, **AD = v** and **BE = w**.
Express the following vectors in terms of **u**, **v** and **w**.

a **EF**　　b **AE**　　c **DF**　　d **AF**

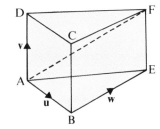

26

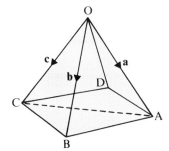

This pyramid shows the position vectors of A, B and C as **a**, **b** and **c**.
Express the following vectors in terms of these position vectors.

a **CO**　　b **CB**　　c **BO**　　d **BA**
e **DA**　　f **AD**　　g **OD**

27 This diagram shows a rectangular octahedron.

a By looking at the diagram, write down which edge is equal and parallel to
(i) edge AB　　(ii) edge AD
(iii) edge AE　　(iv) edge AC.

b Given that **AB = u**, **BC = v** and **CD = w**, express the following vectors in terms of **u**, **v** and **w**.
(i) **DF**　　(ii) **AC**　　(iii) **EF**
(iv) **AD**　　(v) **BF**

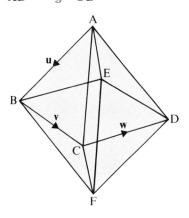

Part 6 Applications with forces and velocities

A *force* has a magnitude (or size) and acts in a given direction; so force is a vector and can be represented by an arrow.

A *velocity* also has a magnitude and a direction; so velocity is a vector. The magnitude (or size) of a velocity is called the *speed*—speed alone has no direction and so it is not a vector.

1 A large ocean-going liner is being pulled by three tugs which exert forces T_1, T_2 and T_3.
The directions of the arrows give the directions of the forces, and their lengths give the size of the forces to a scale of 1 cm = 1 unit of force.

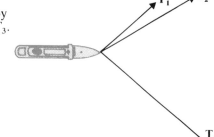

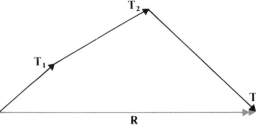

To find the resultant force of the three tugs on the liner, the arrows are drawn tip-to-tail as shown. Use a ruler to find the magnitude (or size) of the resultant force R.

Vectors

2 Find the magnitude of the resultant force for each of these sets of forces (where 1 cm = 1 unit of force). The easiest way to draw the arrows tip-to-tail is to draw them on tracing paper, one by one, moving the tracing paper parallel to each arrow after you have drawn it.

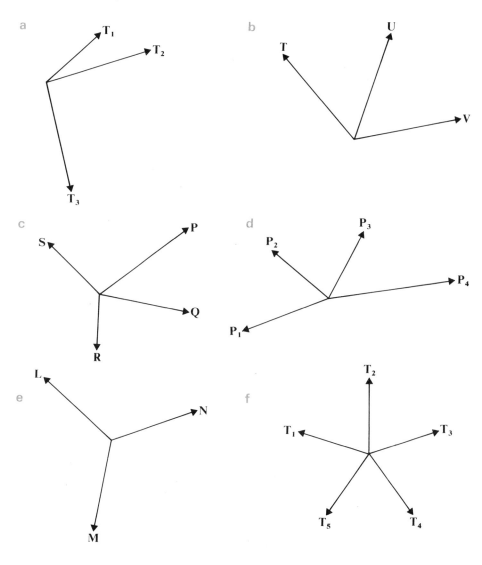

3 This plan view of a moving car shows the forward force P exerted by the engine, the total frictional force F and the wind resistance W.

Use tracing paper to find the resultant force acting on the car.
What is
a its magnitude
b the angle it makes with the direction of force P?

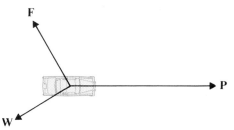

Vectors

4   A rowing-boat is being pulled to the quayside
    by a force P. The wind and tide also exert
    forces on the boat of W and T.

    Taking 1 cm as 1 unit of force, find the
    resultant force acting on the boat.

    What is
    a   its magnitude
    b   the angle it makes with the direction of
        force P?

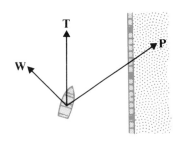

5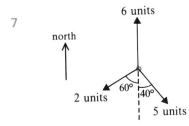
    A swimmer exerts a force F of 4 units due
    north when the tide is running north-east.
    The force T of the tide on the swimmer is
    5 units.

    Draw your own scale diagram to find the
    magnitude of the resultant force on the
    swimmer, and the direction (bearing) of the
    resultant.

6   A fisherman's float is held by a horizontal
    tension T of 5 units in the fishing line,
    against the current of the river which exerts
    a force C of 6 units. The angle between the
    two forces is 40° as shown.

    Find, by accurate drawing, the resultant
    force on the float; and write its magnitude
    and the angle it makes with the current.

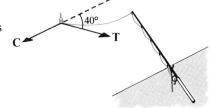

7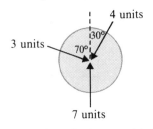
    The top of a telegraph pole has three
    horizontal wires fixed to it with the tensions
    and directions shown.

    Draw a scale diagram to find the resultant
    of these three tensions and write its
    magnitude and its bearing.

8   Three small children push a circular table on
    castors with the forces and directions given
    in this diagram.

    Use a scale diagram to find the resultant
    force acting on the table and write its
    magnitude.

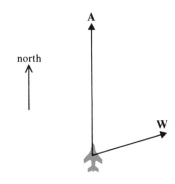

9   The *air speed* of an aeroplane is the speed it has
    when flying in *still* air. When a wind is blowing,
    its actual speed is found by adding the vector
    for its air speed A to the vector for the wind
    speed W.

    The arrows on this diagram give the magnitude
    and directions of the velocities where
    1 cm = 100 km/h.

    Use tracing paper to find
    a   its true speed
    b   the bearing on which it actually flies.

Vectors

10 Use tracing paper to find
  (i) the actual speed
  (ii) the bearing of the flight, for each of these aeroplanes.
      The arrows are drawn to a scale of 1 cm = 100 km/h.

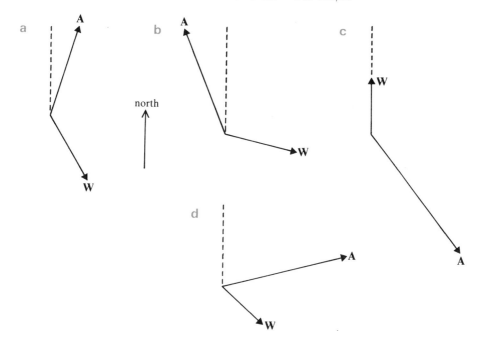

11 A swimmer aims to swim straight across a river at a speed S of 5 km/h; but a current C of 4 km/h flows at right angles to him.
Draw your own diagram, using a scale of 1 cm = 1 km/h, to find
  a the actual speed of the swimmer
  b the angle which he makes with his intended direction.

12 The same swimmer with a speed S of 5 km/h as before crosses the same river, flowing with a speed C of 4 km/h. This time he aims upstream at an angle of 53° as shown.
Draw another diagram to find his actual speed and the direction in which he moves.

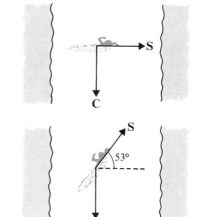

13

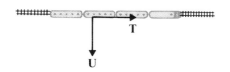

A train has a speed T of 100 km/h on a straight track, when one of its passengers throws an apple core through a window at right angles to the track with a speed U of 30 km/h.
Draw a diagram to find the actual speed of the apple core and the angle which its motion makes with the track.

Vectors

14 A ship is steaming at a steady speed
    S of 12 km/h. A passenger P walks
    across the deck at a speed T of
    5 km/h at an angle of 60° as shown.
    Find the actual speed of the
    passenger, and the angle which his
    actual speed makes with the motion
    of the ship.

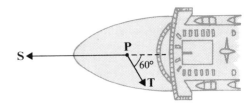

15

A ship steams due north at a speed S
of 30 km/h, when a wind is blowing
from the north-west at a speed W
of 50 km/h.

Find the speed at which the smoke
issues from its funnel, and the bearing
on which the smoke begins to move.

16 An aeroplane can maintain a steady speed of 200 km/h when flying in still air.
    On one particular flight, it steers a course due north, but is then blown off
    course by a westerly wind of 100 km/h.
    Find, by accurate drawing, the actual speed of the plane and the bearing on
    which it flies. (Use a scale of 1 cm = 20 km/h.)

17 Another aeroplane flies with an air speed of 160 km/h on a bearing of 065°
    when a wind of 50 km/h starts to blow from the east.
    Find the new speed of the plane and the new bearing on which it flies.

18 The wind is blowing a raft on the sea due east at a speed of 8 km/h when a tide
    starts to run to the south-east at a speed of 5 km/h.
    Find the new speed of the raft and the bearing on which it now sails.

Translations

Part 1 Translating points

1 Points A, B, C, D are all mapped
onto their images by the same
translation.
Points W, X, Y, Z are all
mapped by a different
translation.
Write the vectors which describe
these two translations.

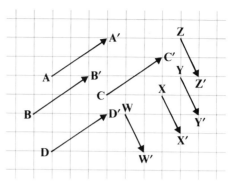

2 Draw and label both axes from 0 to 10.
Plot and label these points and translate each one using the vector $\begin{pmatrix} 3 \\ -1 \end{pmatrix}$.
Write the co-ordinates of their images.
  a P(4, 2)   b Q(1, 7)   c R(6, 4)   d S(3, 9)   e T(7, 1)   f U(2, 3)

3 Draw and label both axes from 0 to 10.
Each object point maps onto its image point under a translation given by the
vector.
Plot the object points and draw the vectors. Copy and complete the empty row
of this table.

	a	b	c	d	e	f	g	h	i	j
Object point	(0, 6)	(3, 7)	(7, 8)	(6, 6)	(8, 4)	(7, 4)	(5, 4)	(3, 3)	(3, 4)	(3, 5)
Vector	$\begin{pmatrix} 2 \\ 4 \end{pmatrix}$	$\begin{pmatrix} 4 \\ 3 \end{pmatrix}$	$\begin{pmatrix} 3 \\ 0 \end{pmatrix}$	$\begin{pmatrix} 4 \\ -1 \end{pmatrix}$	$\begin{pmatrix} 2 \\ -3 \end{pmatrix}$	$\begin{pmatrix} 0 \\ -3 \end{pmatrix}$	$\begin{pmatrix} -2 \\ -3 \end{pmatrix}$	$\begin{pmatrix} -3 \\ -2 \end{pmatrix}$	$\begin{pmatrix} -3 \\ 1 \end{pmatrix}$	$\begin{pmatrix} -1 \\ 2 \end{pmatrix}$
Image point	....	....	....	....	....	....	....	....	....	....

4 Draw and label both axes from 0 to 10.
Find the vectors which translate each of these object points onto their images.
  a A(1, 5) A′(4, 9)   b B(5, 7) B′(10, 9)   c C(3, 5) C′(7, 5)
  d D(8, 6) D′(10, 1)   e E(6, 4) E′(6, 1)   f F(5, 3) F′(1, 2)

5 The ship anchored off Coral Island
has to sail round the island to reach
the sunken treasure.
Write a list of vectors to describe its
journey.

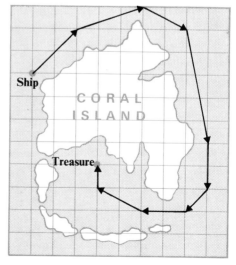

Translations

6   This map shows some of the capital
cities of EEC countries.

Key   O   Brussels
A   Amsterdam
B   Bonn
C   Copenhagen
D   Dublin
L   London
P   Paris
R   Rome

Imagine an aircraft leaving the EEC
headquarters in Brussels and going
on a journey of several stages given
by these vectors.

List the cities visited on each
journey.

a $\begin{pmatrix} 1 \\ 2 \end{pmatrix} + \begin{pmatrix} 3 \\ 3 \end{pmatrix}$ b $\begin{pmatrix} 2 \\ 0 \end{pmatrix} + \begin{pmatrix} 2 \\ 5 \end{pmatrix}$

c $\begin{pmatrix} 2 \\ 0 \end{pmatrix} + \begin{pmatrix} 1 \\ -7 \end{pmatrix}$ d $\begin{pmatrix} -2 \\ 1 \end{pmatrix} + \begin{pmatrix} -4 \\ 2 \end{pmatrix}$ e $\begin{pmatrix} -6 \\ 3 \end{pmatrix} + \begin{pmatrix} 5 \\ -5 \end{pmatrix}$ f $\begin{pmatrix} -1 \\ -2 \end{pmatrix} + \begin{pmatrix} 3 \\ 2 \end{pmatrix}$

g $\begin{pmatrix} 3 \\ -7 \end{pmatrix} + \begin{pmatrix} -4 \\ 5 \end{pmatrix}$ h $\begin{pmatrix} -2 \\ 1 \end{pmatrix} + \begin{pmatrix} 1 \\ -3 \end{pmatrix}$ i $\begin{pmatrix} 4 \\ 5 \end{pmatrix} + \begin{pmatrix} -10 \\ -2 \end{pmatrix}$ j $\begin{pmatrix} 2 \\ 0 \end{pmatrix} + \begin{pmatrix} -1 \\ 2 \end{pmatrix} + \begin{pmatrix} 3 \\ 3 \end{pmatrix}$

k $\begin{pmatrix} -6 \\ 3 \end{pmatrix} + \begin{pmatrix} 4 \\ -2 \end{pmatrix} + \begin{pmatrix} 4 \\ -1 \end{pmatrix}$ l $\begin{pmatrix} -1 \\ -2 \end{pmatrix} + \begin{pmatrix} -5 \\ 5 \end{pmatrix} + \begin{pmatrix} 7 \\ -1 \end{pmatrix}$ m $\begin{pmatrix} 1 \\ 2 \end{pmatrix} + \begin{pmatrix} -3 \\ -1 \end{pmatrix} + \begin{pmatrix} 1 \\ -3 \end{pmatrix}$

n $\begin{pmatrix} 3 \\ -7 \end{pmatrix} + \begin{pmatrix} -4 \\ 5 \end{pmatrix} + \begin{pmatrix} -1 \\ 3 \end{pmatrix} + \begin{pmatrix} 3 \\ 1 \end{pmatrix}$ o $\begin{pmatrix} -2 \\ 1 \end{pmatrix} + \begin{pmatrix} 6 \\ 4 \end{pmatrix} + \begin{pmatrix} -3 \\ -3 \end{pmatrix} + \begin{pmatrix} -1 \\ -2 \end{pmatrix}$

p $\begin{pmatrix} -6 \\ 3 \end{pmatrix} + \begin{pmatrix} 10 \\ 2 \end{pmatrix} + \begin{pmatrix} -1 \\ -12 \end{pmatrix} + \begin{pmatrix} -2 \\ 9 \end{pmatrix}$ q $\begin{pmatrix} -1 \\ -2 \end{pmatrix} + \begin{pmatrix} 3 \\ 2 \end{pmatrix} + \begin{pmatrix} -4 \\ 1 \end{pmatrix} + \begin{pmatrix} 2 \\ -1 \end{pmatrix}$

Write the vectors for these routes, all of which start in Brussels.
r   Amsterdam – Bonn – Rome   s   London – Copenhagen – Bonn
t   Paris – Rome – Copenhagen   u   Dublin – Paris – Rome – Bonn
v   Bonn – London – Rome – Brussels
w   Copenhagen – Amsterdam – Rome – Bonn

7   a   Take any point on squared paper. Translate it using these vectors and draw
the route it takes.

$\begin{pmatrix} 2 \\ 0 \end{pmatrix} + \begin{pmatrix} 0 \\ 2 \end{pmatrix} + \begin{pmatrix} -2 \\ 0 \end{pmatrix} + \begin{pmatrix} 0 \\ -2 \end{pmatrix}$ You should have drawn a square.

Take any other starting point and draw each of these routes.

b $\begin{pmatrix} 3 \\ 3 \end{pmatrix} + \begin{pmatrix} 3 \\ -3 \end{pmatrix} + \begin{pmatrix} -3 \\ -3 \end{pmatrix} + \begin{pmatrix} -3 \\ 3 \end{pmatrix}$ c $\begin{pmatrix} 1 \\ -3 \end{pmatrix} + \begin{pmatrix} 3 \\ 1 \end{pmatrix} + \begin{pmatrix} -1 \\ 3 \end{pmatrix} + \begin{pmatrix} -3 \\ -1 \end{pmatrix}$

d $\begin{pmatrix} 1 \\ 2 \end{pmatrix} + \begin{pmatrix} 2 \\ -1 \end{pmatrix} + \begin{pmatrix} -1 \\ -2 \end{pmatrix} + \begin{pmatrix} -2 \\ 1 \end{pmatrix}$ e $\begin{pmatrix} 3 \\ 2 \end{pmatrix} + \begin{pmatrix} -2 \\ 3 \end{pmatrix} + \begin{pmatrix} -3 \\ -2 \end{pmatrix} + \begin{pmatrix} 2 \\ -3 \end{pmatrix}$

Translations

8 Take any point on squared paper and translate it many times using the given vectors. Draw the path which the point takes.

a $\quad \begin{pmatrix} 2 \\ 2 \end{pmatrix} + \begin{pmatrix} -1 \\ 1 \end{pmatrix} + \begin{pmatrix} 3 \\ 0 \end{pmatrix} + \begin{pmatrix} 0 \\ -3 \end{pmatrix} + \begin{pmatrix} -1 \\ 1 \end{pmatrix} + \begin{pmatrix} -2 \\ -2 \end{pmatrix} + \begin{pmatrix} -1 \\ 1 \end{pmatrix}$

b $\quad \begin{pmatrix} 4 \\ 1 \end{pmatrix} + \begin{pmatrix} 0 \\ -1 \end{pmatrix} + \begin{pmatrix} -3 \\ -3 \end{pmatrix} + \begin{pmatrix} 3 \\ 1 \end{pmatrix} + \begin{pmatrix} 0 \\ -1 \end{pmatrix} + \begin{pmatrix} -4 \\ -1 \end{pmatrix} + \begin{pmatrix} 0 \\ 1 \end{pmatrix} + \begin{pmatrix} 3 \\ 3 \end{pmatrix} + \begin{pmatrix} -3 \\ -1 \end{pmatrix} + \begin{pmatrix} 0 \\ 1 \end{pmatrix}$

c $\quad \begin{pmatrix} 4 \\ 2 \end{pmatrix} + \begin{pmatrix} -4 \\ 1 \end{pmatrix} + \begin{pmatrix} 3 \\ -3 \end{pmatrix} + \begin{pmatrix} -1 \\ 4 \end{pmatrix} + \begin{pmatrix} -2 \\ -4 \end{pmatrix}$

d $\quad \begin{pmatrix} 3 \\ 0 \end{pmatrix} + \begin{pmatrix} 1 \\ -2 \end{pmatrix} + \begin{pmatrix} 3 \\ -1 \end{pmatrix} + \begin{pmatrix} 0 \\ -1 \end{pmatrix} + \begin{pmatrix} -3 \\ 0 \end{pmatrix} + \begin{pmatrix} 2 \\ -2 \end{pmatrix} + \begin{pmatrix} -4 \\ 1 \end{pmatrix} + \begin{pmatrix} -3 \\ -3 \end{pmatrix} +$

$\quad\quad \begin{pmatrix} -2 \\ 1 \end{pmatrix} + \begin{pmatrix} 1 \\ 5 \end{pmatrix} + \begin{pmatrix} 2 \\ 2 \end{pmatrix} + \begin{pmatrix} 1 \\ -4 \end{pmatrix} + \begin{pmatrix} 2 \\ 4 \end{pmatrix}$

e $\quad \begin{pmatrix} 0 \\ 1 \end{pmatrix} + \begin{pmatrix} 1 \\ 2 \end{pmatrix} + \begin{pmatrix} 1 \\ 1 \end{pmatrix} + \begin{pmatrix} 2 \\ 1 \end{pmatrix} + \begin{pmatrix} 1 \\ 0 \end{pmatrix} + \begin{pmatrix} 3 \\ -1 \end{pmatrix} + \begin{pmatrix} 3 \\ -2 \end{pmatrix} + \begin{pmatrix} 1 \\ 0 \end{pmatrix} + \begin{pmatrix} 2 \\ 1 \end{pmatrix} + \begin{pmatrix} 0 \\ 3 \end{pmatrix} +$

$\quad\quad \begin{pmatrix} 2 \\ -2 \end{pmatrix} + \begin{pmatrix} 3 \\ 0 \end{pmatrix} + \begin{pmatrix} -3 \\ -2 \end{pmatrix} + \begin{pmatrix} -2 \\ -2 \end{pmatrix} + \begin{pmatrix} -4 \\ -1 \end{pmatrix} + \begin{pmatrix} -6 \\ 0 \end{pmatrix} + \begin{pmatrix} -4 \\ \frac{1}{2} \end{pmatrix} + \begin{pmatrix} 2 \\ \frac{1}{2} \end{pmatrix} + \begin{pmatrix} -2 \\ 0 \end{pmatrix}$

f $\quad \begin{pmatrix} 1 \\ -1 \end{pmatrix} + \begin{pmatrix} 3 \\ -1 \end{pmatrix} + \begin{pmatrix} 2 \\ 0 \end{pmatrix} + \begin{pmatrix} 2 \\ -1 \end{pmatrix} + \begin{pmatrix} 1 \\ -3 \end{pmatrix} + \begin{pmatrix} -1 \\ 1 \end{pmatrix} + \begin{pmatrix} -1 \\ -2 \end{pmatrix} + \begin{pmatrix} 0 \\ -3 \end{pmatrix} + \begin{pmatrix} -1\frac{1}{2} \\ 0 \end{pmatrix} +$

$\quad\quad \begin{pmatrix} 0 \\ 3 \end{pmatrix} + \begin{pmatrix} -2\frac{1}{2} \\ 0 \end{pmatrix} + \begin{pmatrix} -2 \\ -3 \end{pmatrix} + \begin{pmatrix} -2 \\ 0 \end{pmatrix} + \begin{pmatrix} 2 \\ 3 \end{pmatrix} + \begin{pmatrix} -1 \\ 1 \end{pmatrix} + \begin{pmatrix} -1 \\ 2 \end{pmatrix} + \begin{pmatrix} -1 \\ 0 \end{pmatrix} +$

$\quad\quad \begin{pmatrix} -1 \\ 1 \end{pmatrix} + \begin{pmatrix} -1 \\ -1 \end{pmatrix} + \begin{pmatrix} 0 \\ -2 \end{pmatrix} + \begin{pmatrix} 1 \\ -1 \end{pmatrix} + \begin{pmatrix} -1 \\ 0 \end{pmatrix} + \begin{pmatrix} -1 \\ 1 \end{pmatrix} + \begin{pmatrix} 0 \\ 2 \end{pmatrix} +$

$\quad\quad \begin{pmatrix} 1 \\ 4 \end{pmatrix} + \begin{pmatrix} 2 \\ 1 \end{pmatrix} + \begin{pmatrix} 2 \\ 0 \end{pmatrix} + \begin{pmatrix} 0 \\ -3 \end{pmatrix} + \begin{pmatrix} -1 \\ -1 \end{pmatrix} + \begin{pmatrix} -1 \\ 0 \end{pmatrix}$

9 Draw and label both axes from 0 to 10.
Answer the following by drawing on these axes.

a Find the image of the point (1, 10) after being translated by $\begin{pmatrix} 5 \\ -1 \end{pmatrix}$.

b Find the image of the point (7, 8) after being translated by $\begin{pmatrix} 3 \\ 2 \end{pmatrix}$.

c Find the vector which translates the point (1, 4) onto (2, 8).

d Find the vector which translates the point (10, 4) onto (4, 6).

e Find the object point which has the image (4, 3) after a translation of $\begin{pmatrix} 2 \\ 2 \end{pmatrix}$.

f Find the object point which has the image (6, 1) after being translated by $\begin{pmatrix} 5 \\ 1 \end{pmatrix}$.

g Find the object point which has the image (10, 0) after a translation of $\begin{pmatrix} 4 \\ -2 \end{pmatrix}$.

Translations

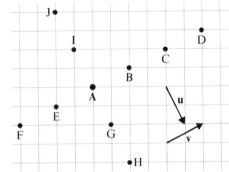

10 Write the image points which point *A*
   maps onto after a translation of
   a **v**   b 3**v**   c −2**v**
   d 2**u**   e −2**u**   f **u**
   g −**v**   h 2**v**   i −**u**.

11

Which image points does *A*
map onto after being
translated by these vectors?
   a **p**   b −**p**   c −**q**
   d 2**p**   e 2**q**   f 3**q**
   g **p** + **q**   h **p** + 3**q**
   i 2**p** + 2**q**   j 3**q** + **p**
   k 2**q** + 2**p**

Part 2 Translating shapes

1 Write the vectors of the
   translations which map
   a A onto B   b A onto C
   c B onto C   d B onto A.

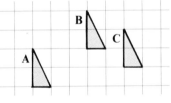

2

Write the vectors of the
translations for which
   a D → E   b D → F
   c G → H   d E → G
   e F → H   f F → G
   g H → D   h F → E
   i G → D   j H → E.

3 a Copy this triangle onto squared paper.
      Translate each corner of it using the vector
      $\begin{pmatrix} 4 \\ 1 \end{pmatrix}$ and so draw the image triangle.

   b   Copy this triangle onto squared paper.
                            Translate each corner using the vector
                            $\begin{pmatrix} 3 \\ -2 \end{pmatrix}$ and so draw the image triangle.

Translations

4 Copy each of the following shapes onto squared paper.
Translate each of them, corner by corner, using the given vector.

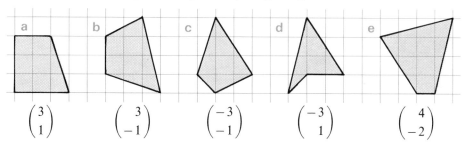

$$\begin{pmatrix} 3 \\ 1 \end{pmatrix} \qquad \begin{pmatrix} 3 \\ -1 \end{pmatrix} \qquad \begin{pmatrix} -3 \\ -1 \end{pmatrix} \qquad \begin{pmatrix} -3 \\ 1 \end{pmatrix} \qquad \begin{pmatrix} 4 \\ -2 \end{pmatrix}$$

5 Draw and label both axes from 0 to 12.
Draw these four object shapes, and use the given vectors to draw their images after a translation.

	Object shape		Vector
a	Triangle	(1, 7), (2, 8), (1, 10)	$\begin{pmatrix} 2 \\ 2 \end{pmatrix}$
b	Quadrilateral	(6, 10), (6, 12), (7, 11), (9,11)	$\begin{pmatrix} 1 \\ -2 \end{pmatrix}$
c	Triangle	(8, 4), (10, 4), (9, 7)	$\begin{pmatrix} -4 \\ -4 \end{pmatrix}$
d	Parallelogram	(2, 1), (2, 4), (4, 5), (4, 2)	$\begin{pmatrix} -1 \\ 2 \end{pmatrix}$

6 Draw and label both axes from 0 to 10.
Draw these object triangles and their images.
Write the vectors which translate the objects onto their images.

	Object triangle	Image triangle
a	(0, 3), (0, 6), (2, 4)	(3, 4), (5, 5), (3, 7)
b	(0, 10), (4, 10), (2, 8)	(3, 8), (7, 8), (5, 6)
c	(8, 6), (10, 6), (10, 4)	(7, 10), (9, 10), (9, 8)
d	(7, 1), (7, 3), (10, 3)	(1, 0), (1, 2), (4, 2)

7 Draw both axes labelled from 0 to 12.
   a Join these points in order to make a capital letter T:
      (2, 7) (3, 7) (3, 9) (4, 9) (4, 10) (1, 10) (1, 9) (2, 9).
      The letter T is translated so that the point (1, 10) moves to (5, 11).
      Draw the image of the letter T after this translation.
   b Join in this order to make a letter L:
      (1, 2) (1, 6) (2, 6) (2, 3) (5, 3) (5, 2).
      This letter L is translated so that the point (2, 3) moves to (4, 1).
      Draw the image of the letter L after this translation.
   c Join in this order to make a letter V:
      (7, 7) (8, 7) (9, 5½) (10, 7) (11, 7) (9, 4).
      The letter V is translated so that the point (8, 7) moves to (6, 6).
      Draw the image of the letter V after this translation.

73

Translations

8 Triangle A maps onto triangle B under a translation given by the vector **v**.
What is the image of A after a translation of
a 2**v**   b 4**v**   c 5**v**?
What is the image of C after a translation of
d 3**v**   e −**v**   f −2**v**?
What is the image of E after a translation of
g **v**   h −3**v**   i −4**v**?

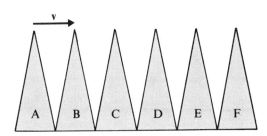

9

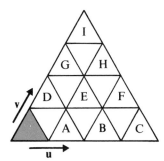

The coloured triangle maps onto triangle A after a translation given by the vector **u**; and it also maps onto triangle D after a translation given by the vector **v**.
What is the image of the coloured triangle after a translation of
a 3**u**   b 2**v**   c 2**u**   d 3**v**
e **u** + **v**   f 2**u** + **v**   g **u** + 2**v**?

T	U	V	W	X
O	P	Q	R	S
K	L		M	N
F	G	H	I	J
A	B	C	D	E

10 The translation given by the vector **a** maps the coloured square onto square Q.
The translation given by the vector **b** maps the coloured square onto square R.
Find the image of the coloured square after a translation of
a 2**a**   b −2**a**   c 2**b**
d −2**b**   e **a** + **b**   f 2**b** − **a**
g 2**b** − 3**a** h **b** − 2**a**   i **a** − **b**
j **a** − 2**b**   k 2**a** − **b**   l −**a** − **b**.

11

100	99	98	97	96	95	94	93	92	91
81	82	83	84	85	86	87	88	89	90
80	79	78	77	76	75	74	73	72	71
61	62	63	64	65	66	67	68	69	70
60	59	58	57	56	55	54	53	52	51
41	42	43	44	45	46	47	48	49	50
40	39	38	37	36	35	34	33	32	31
21	22	23	24	25	26	27	28	29	30
20	19	18	17	16	15	14	13	12	11
1	2	3	4	5	6	7	8	9	10

The snakes and ladders on this board are all based on two vectors **p** and **q**.
The vector **p** translates a player's counter up the ladder from square 3 to square 24.
The vector **q** translates a player's counter down the snake from square 33 to square 9.
Write these translations along the snakes and ladders in terms of **p** and **q**:
a from 74 to 93   b from 41 to 83
c from 22 to 85   d from 26 to 5
e from 89 to 47   f from 80 to 42
g from 97 to 35   h from 31 to 69.

Translations

Part 3   Letters for translations

Exercises **1 – 5** use four translations:

Translation **A** of $\begin{pmatrix} 2 \\ 2 \end{pmatrix}$ Translation **B** of $\begin{pmatrix} 3 \\ -1 \end{pmatrix}$

Translation **C** of $\begin{pmatrix} -2 \\ -1 \end{pmatrix}$ Translation **D** of $\begin{pmatrix} -3 \\ 0 \end{pmatrix}$.

1   Which points on this diagram are
the images under these translations?

a   **A**(G)   b   **B**(G)   c   **C**(G)
d   **A**(K)   e   **B**(K)   f   **C**(K)
g   **D**(J)   h   **C**(M)

2   Which triangles on this diagram are
the images under these translations?

a   **A**(F)   b   **B**(F)   c   **C**(F)
d   **B**(G)   e   **A**(J)   f   **C**(J)
g   **B**(I)   h   **D**(M)

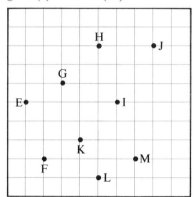

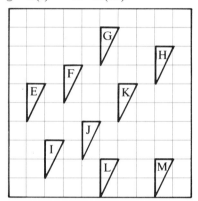

3   Draw and label both axes from 0 to 12.
Draw all of these shapes on one diagram, labelling each one.

a   P is the parallelogram (5, 9), (7, 9), (8, 10), (6, 10).
Draw P, **A**(P), **B**(P) and **C**(P).

b   T is the triangle (3, 5), (5, 5), (5, 6).
Draw T, **A**(T), **B**(T) and **C**(T).

c   K is the kite (8, 1), (9, 3), (8, 4), (7, 3).
Draw K, **A**(K), **B**(K) and **C**(K).

4   Draw and label both axes from 0 to 8. Label each shape which you draw.

a   T is the triangle (1, 5), (1, 6), (3, 5). Draw T, **A**(T), **BA**(T), **CBA**(T).

b   R is the rectangle (5, 3), (5, 4), (7, 4),
(7, 3). Draw R, **D**(R), **CD**(R),
BCD(R) and **ABCD**(R).

5   Which points on the diagram are
the images of these translated points?

a   **A**(E)   b   **BA**(E)   c   **CBA**(E)

d   **A**(F)   e   **BA**(F)   f   **CBA**(F)
g   **BCBA**(F)

h   **A**(L)   i   **BA**(L)   j   **CBA**(L)
k   **DCBA**(L)

l   **D**(P)   m   **CD**(P)   n   **BCD**(P)
o   **ABCD**(P)

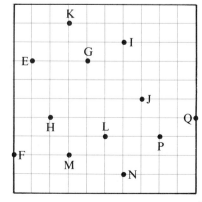

75

Translations

Draw your own diagrams to answer the following problems.

6 T_1 is the translation $\begin{pmatrix} -2 \\ 4 \end{pmatrix}$ and T_2 is the translation $\begin{pmatrix} 4 \\ 1 \end{pmatrix}$.

If P is the point (3, 2), draw a diagram to find the point Q where $Q = T_2T_1(P)$.
What single translation is equivalent to T_2T_1?

7 Y is the translation $\begin{pmatrix} -1 \\ 5 \end{pmatrix}$ and Z is the translation $\begin{pmatrix} 3 \\ -1 \end{pmatrix}$.

If P is the point (2, 1), draw a diagram to find the point Q where $Q = ZY(P)$.
What single translation is equivalent to ZY?

8 T is the triangle (1, 1), (4, 2), (0, 4).

G and H are the translations $\begin{pmatrix} 3 \\ 2 \end{pmatrix}$ and $\begin{pmatrix} -1 \\ 4 \end{pmatrix}$ respectively.

Draw and label the triangles T, G(T) and HG(T).
Write the single translation which is equivalent to HG.

9 U and V are the translations $\begin{pmatrix} 4 \\ -1 \end{pmatrix}$ and $\begin{pmatrix} 1 \\ 2 \end{pmatrix}$ respectively.

The rectangle R has corners (3, 2), (3, 3), (1, 3), (1, 2).
Draw its image R′ where R′ = VU(R).
Write the single translation which is equivalent to VU.

10 P is the point (−2, 1).

T is the translation $\begin{pmatrix} 1 \\ 3 \end{pmatrix}$; U is the translation $\begin{pmatrix} 2 \\ -5 \end{pmatrix}$;

and V is the translation $\begin{pmatrix} 3 \\ -1 \end{pmatrix}$.

On one diagram, find the positions of
a VUT(P)   b TUV(P)   c UTV(P).
Does the order of the three translations affect the position of the final image?

Part 4 Powers and inverses

Exercises 1–5 use the same four translations as part 3:

Translation A of $\begin{pmatrix} 2 \\ 2 \end{pmatrix}$ Translation B of $\begin{pmatrix} 3 \\ -1 \end{pmatrix}$ Translation C of $\begin{pmatrix} -2 \\ -1 \end{pmatrix}$

Translation D of $\begin{pmatrix} -3 \\ 0 \end{pmatrix}$.

1 Find the image points under the
   following translations on the
   diagram.

   a A(M)   b A²(M)
   c B(P)   d B²(P)
   e D(V)   f D²(V)
   g C(S)   h C²(S)   i C³(S)
   j A(L)   k A²(L)   l A³(L)
   m D²(Z)   n D²(Q)   o C²(X)

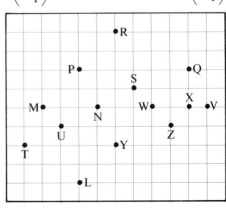

Translations

2   Draw and label both axes from 0 to 14.
   a   L is the triangle (1, 10), (2, 11), (2, 9).
       Draw and label L, **B**(L), **B²**(L), **B³**(L) and **B⁴**(L).
   b   M is the triangle (2, 1), (4, 1), (2, 3).
       Draw and label M, **A**(M), **A²**(M), **A³**(M) and **A⁴**(M).
   c   N is the triangle (13, 2), (13, 4), (12, 4).
       Draw and label N, **D**(N), **D²**(N), **D³**(N) and **D⁴**(N).

3   If the direction of a translation **A** is reversed, then we have the inverse translation **A⁻¹**, as shown in this diagram, which also shows the translations **S**, **T**, **U**, **V** and **W** operating on a set of points.

   By reversing the arrows (but without drawing on this diagram), write the co-ordinates of the images of these inverse translations.

   a   **S⁻¹**(N)   b   **T⁻¹**(Q)
   c   **U⁻¹**(X)   d   **V⁻¹**(R)
   e   **W⁻¹**(Z)

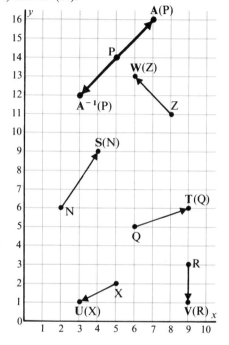

4   Draw and label both axes from 0 to 12.
   a   R is the triangle (7, 8), (7, 11), (8, 10).
       Draw and label R, **B**(R) and **B⁻¹**(R).
   b   S is the square (4, 3), (5, 5), (3, 6), (2, 4).
       Draw and label S, **A**(S) and **A⁻¹**(S).
   c   T is the triangle (8, 0), (9, 2), (7, 2).
       Draw and label T, **D**(T) and **D⁻¹**(T).

5   Draw and label both axes from 0 to 12.
   a   L is the point (8, 4). Plot and label L, **A**(L), **A²**(L), **A⁻¹**(L) and **A⁻²**(L).
   b   M is the point (9, 8). Plot and label M, **B**(M), **B⁻¹**(M), **B⁻²**(M) and **B⁻³**(M).
   c   T is the triangle (4, 4), (4, 5), (6, 5). Draw and label T, **D**(T), **D⁻¹**(T) and **D⁻²**(T).

6   Quadrilateral Q (6, 6), (6, 7), (7, 7), (8, 5) has two images R and S where R = **T²**(Q) and S = **T⁻²**(Q).

   If **T** is the translation $\begin{pmatrix} 2 \\ 1 \end{pmatrix}$, draw Q, R and S on one diagram with both axes labelled from 0 to 12.

7   U is a translation of $\begin{pmatrix} 4 \\ -2 \end{pmatrix}$ and V is a translation of $\begin{pmatrix} -3 \\ 1 \end{pmatrix}$.

   Without drawing any diagrams, write the vectors for these translations:
   a   **U²**   b   **V²**   c   **U⁻¹**   d   **V⁻¹**   e   **U³**
   f   **V³**   g   **U⁻²**   h   **V⁻²**   i   **V⁴**   j   **U⁻³**.

77

Stretches

1   A **stretch** lengthens an object in *one* direction only.
    It alters the shape and the size of the object.
    These diagrams show objects coloured and images outlined black.
    Which of the objects have been *stretched* (in one direction)?

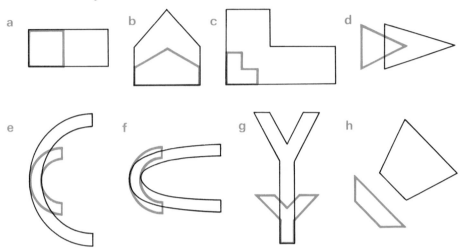

2   A stretch has an **invariant line** and a **scale factor**.
    In this diagram, AB is the invariant line. Find the scale factor for each object
    and image pair.

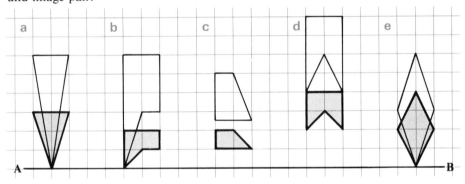

3   Copy these object shapes onto squared paper.
    Take AB as the invariant line and use the given scale factor to draw the image
    of each object.

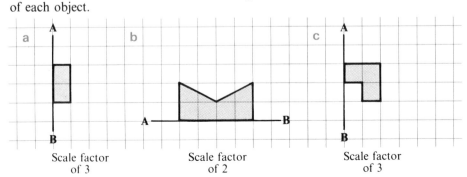

| Scale factor of 3 | Scale factor of 2 | Scale factor of 3 |

78

Stretches

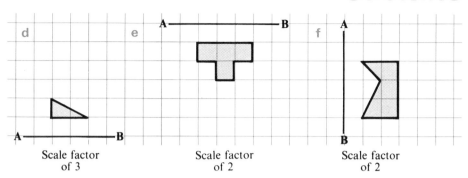

Scale factor
of 3

Scale factor
of 2

Scale factor
of 2

4 Draw and label both axes from 0 to 16.
Draw the three objects given here and stretch each of them parallel to the *x*-axis
with the *y*-axis invariant, using the given scale factors.
a *First object*   (1, 1), (4, 1), (3, 3), (4, 4), (1, 4), (2, 3)   scale factor of 4
b *Second object* (2, 6), (1, 9), (4, 10), (5, 7)   scale factor of 3
c *Third object*   (2, 12), (2, 15), (3, 13), (6, 15), (6, 12)   scale factor of $2\frac{1}{2}$

5 Draw and label both axes from 0 to 16.
Draw the three objects given here and stretch each of them parallel to the *y*-axis
with the *x*-axis invariant, using the given scale factors.
a *First object*   (1, 2), (1, 7), (3, 7), (3, 6), (2, 6), (2, 5),   scale factor of 2
(3, 5), (3, 4), (2, 4), (2, 2)
b *Second object* (5, 4), (5, 5), (8, 5), (8, 4), (7, 1), (6, 1)   scale factor of 3
c *Third object*   (10, 2), (10, 5), (11, 5), (13, 4), (15, 5),   scale factor of $2\frac{1}{2}$
(16, 5), (16, 2), (15, 2), (15, 4), (13, 3),
(11, 4), (11, 2)

6 In these diagrams, the slanting lines *AB* are invariant.
Find the scale factor for each object and image pair.

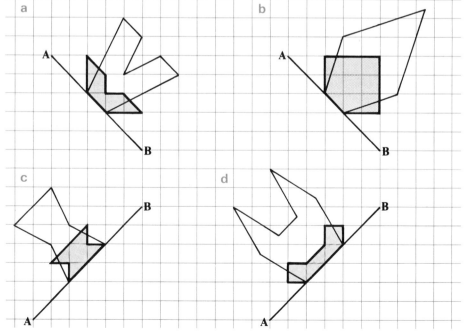

Stretches

7   Copy these object shapes onto squared paper.
Take *AB* as the invariant line and use the given scale factor to draw the image of each object.

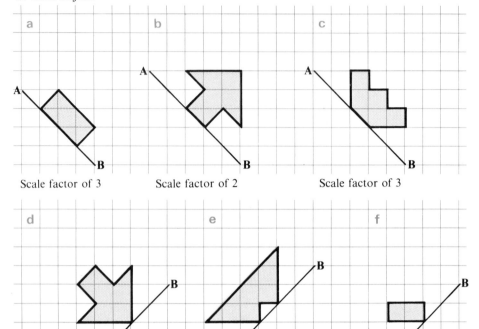

a   Scale factor of 3   b   Scale factor of 2   c   Scale factor of 3

d   Scale factor of 2   e   Scale factor of 2   f   Scale factor of 3

8   Draw and label both axes from 0 to 16.
Join the points (10, 0) and (0, 10) with a straight line and take this line as invariant for the stretches described below.
Draw the four objects given here and stretch each of them using the given scale factor.

a   *First object*   (1, 9), (1, 12), (4, 12), (3, 11), (5, 9),   scale factor of 2
(4, 8), (2, 10)

b   *Second object*   (5, 5), (6, 8), (8, 8), (8, 6)   scale factor of 3

c   *Third object*   (9, 2), (9, 5), (11, 5), (11, 4), (10, 4),   scale factor of 2
(10, 3), (11, 3), (11, 2)

d   *Fourth object*   (3, 6), (6, 3), (5, 2), (4, 3), $(2\frac{1}{2}, 2\frac{1}{2})$,   scale factor of 2
(3, 4), (2, 5)

9   **S** is a stretch of scale factor 4 which keeps the *y*-axis invariant.
T is a stretch of scale factor 2 which keeps the *x*-axis invariant.
The kite **K** has corners (0, 3), (2, 2), (3, 3), (2, 4).
Draw and label both axes from 0 to 12; and on them draw the positions of **K**, **S**(**K**) and **TS**(**K**).

10   **M** is a stretch of scale factor 3 which keeps the *y*-axis invariant.
N is a stretch of scale factor 2 which keeps the *x*-axis invariant.
The hexagon **H** has corners (1, 3), (1, 4), (2, 3), (3, 3), (3, 2), (2, 2).
Draw and label both axes from 0 to 12; and on them draw the positions of **H**, **M**(**H**) and **NM**(**H**).

Stretches

11 U is a stretch of scale factor 3 which keeps the y-axis invariant.
V is a stretch of scale factor 3 which keeps the x-axis invariant.
A shape S has corners (1, 1), (1, 3), (3, 2), (2, 2), (2, 1).
Draw and label both axes from 0 to 12; and on them draw the positions of S,
U(S) and **VU**(S).

12 P is a stretch of scale factor 2 which keeps the line $x + y = 6$ invariant.
Q is a stretch of scale factor 2 which keeps the y-axis invariant.
R is the rectangle (1, 6), (2, 7), (4, 5), (3, 4).
Draw and label both axes from 0 to 12; and on them draw the positions of R,
P(R) and **QP**(R).

13 Label both axes from 0 to 12 and draw the two lines $x + y = 6$ and $y = x - 6$.
A is a stretch of scale factor 4 with the line $x + y = 6$ invariant.
B is a stretch of scale factor 2 with the line $y = x - 6$ invariant.
S is a shape with corners (4, 3), (5, 4), (6, 3), (5, 2), (5, 3).
Draw the positions of S, A(S) and **BA**(S).

14 Draw and label both axes from 0 to 20.
C is a circle of radius 5 units and centre (5, 5).
S_1 and S_2 are both stretches with scale factors of 2. S_1 has the y-axis as its
invariant line; and S_2 has the x-axis invariant.
Draw the positions of C, S_1(C) and $S_2 S_1$(C).
What are the mathematical names of the shapes of S_1(C) and $S_2 S_1$(C)?

Enlargements

Part 1   Scale factors

1   The word **enlargement** is often used in photography when the size of a picture is to be increased.

A transparency or slide can be projected onto a screen by passing light through it.

If the slide is 2 cm tall and the picture on the screen is 50 cm high, what is the *scale factor* for these heights?

2

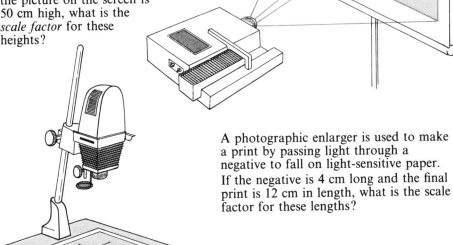

A photographic enlarger is used to make a print by passing light through a negative to fall on light-sensitive paper.

If the negative is 4 cm long and the final print is 12 cm in length, what is the scale factor for these lengths?

3   Each of these diagrams shows an object shape which has been transformed under an enlargement onto its image.

For each answer, find
(i) how many times longer the sides of the image are than the sides of the object
(ii) how many times the object will fit into its image.

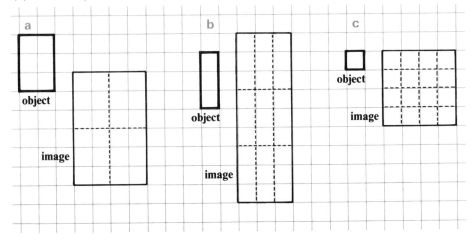

Enlargements

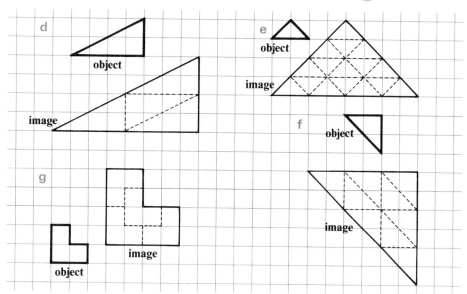

h   You have been finding the length scale factors and the area scale factors of
these enlargements. Copy this table and enter your results. Do you see any
relation between the two sets of scale factors?

	a	b	c	d	e	f	g
Length scale factor							
Area scale factor							

4   In addition to a *scale factor*, a mathematical enlargement must also have a *centre*.
This diagram shows the corners of the object shape $WXYZ$ joined to the corners
of its image with straight lines which intersect each other at the *centre* of the
enlargement C.

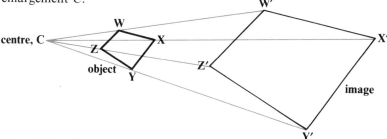

Copy this table and complete it by taking measurements from the diagram with
a ruler.

Object point	Distance of object point from centre	Distance of its image from centre	Length scale factor
W			
X			
Y			
Z			

Check the length scale factor by measuring the sides of the object and image.
The length scale factor can thus be found *either* by measuring distance from the
centre, *or* by measuring the sides of object and image.

83

Enlargements

5   Trace (or perhaps your teacher could supply you with copies of) these object shapes and their images. Construct the centre of each enlargement. Find the length scale factors by measuring the sides of object and image; and check your answers by measuring distances from the centres of the enlargements.

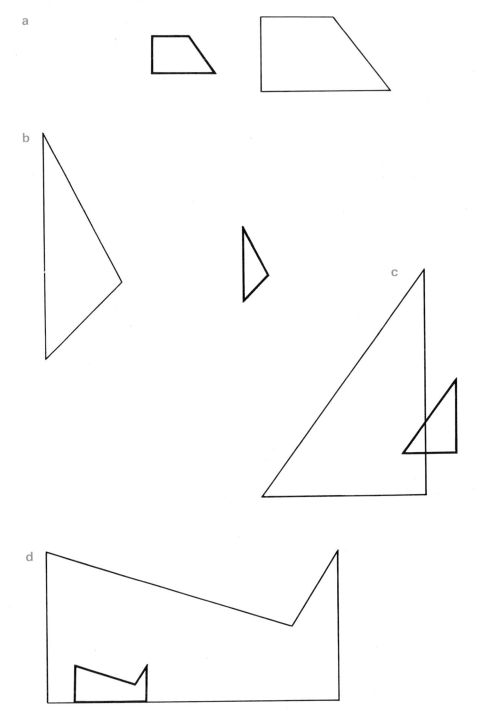

a

b

c

d

Enlargements

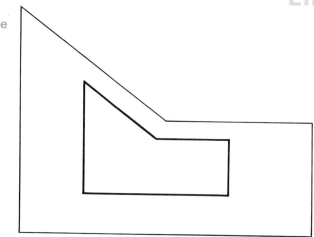

e

6 Draw and label the x-axis from 0 to 20 and the y-axis from 0 to 24.
Draw these four object shapes and their images on the one diagram.
For each pair, find (i) the centre of the enlargement
                    (ii) the length scale factor   (iii) the area scale factor.

a First pair   *Object*   (2, 2), (4, 2), (4, 4)
                   Image   (4, 1), (8, 1), (8, 5)
b Second pair   *Object*   (13, 3), (14, 6), (12, 6)
                   Image   (17, 7), (20, 16), (14, 16)
c Third pair   *Object*   (4, 8), (6, 8), (6, 9), (5, 9), (5, 10), (4, 10)
                   Image   (1, 11), (9, 11), (9, 15), (5, 15), (5, 19), (1, 19)
d Fourth pair   *Object*   (3, 23), (5, 23), (5, 24), (3, 24)
                   Image   (8, 18), (20, 18), (20, 24), (8, 24)

7 When the image is *smaller* than the object, then the length scale factor of the
enlargement is a *fraction*.
Find (i) the length scale factor
      (ii) the area scale factor of these enlargements.

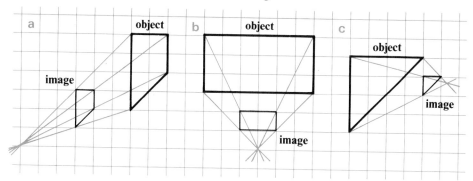

8 Draw and label the x-axis from 0 to 20 and the y-axis from 0 to 24.
Draw these four object shapes and their images on the one diagram.
For each pair, find (i) the centre of the enlargement
                     (ii) the length scale factor
                     (iii) the area scale factor.

a First pair   *Object*   (3, 20), (9, 20), (3, 16)
                   Image   (2, 21), (5, 21), (2, 19)

Enlargements

b Second pair   *Object*   (11, 19), (11, 13), (20, 13), (20, 19), (17, 16)
                   Image   (13, 21), (13, 19), (16, 19), (16, 21), (15, 20)

c Third pair   *Object*   (10, 11), (18, 9), (18, 7), (10, 3)
                   Image   (11, 8), (15, 7), (15, 6), (11, 4)

d Fourth pair   *Object*   (4, 0), (0, 12), (8, 16)
                   Image   (4, 6), (5, 10), (3, 9)

9 When the image is on the *opposite* side of the centre to the object, it appears *upside down*, and the length scale factor of the enlargement is *negative*.
Find (i) the length scale factor
       (ii) the area scale factor of these enlargements.

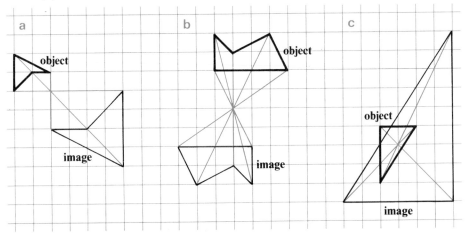

10 This diagram shows the triangle *T* and its five images on a square grid under five enlargements, all having the same point as centre.
Copy and complete this table.

Enlargement	$T \to T_1$	$T \to T_2$	$T \to T_3$	$T \to T_4$	$T \to T_5$
Length scale factor					
Area scale factor					

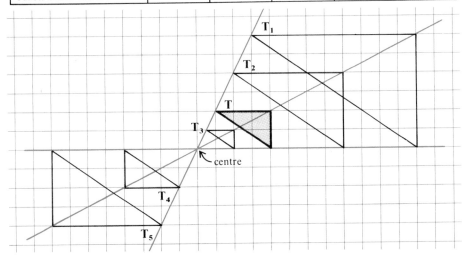

Enlargements

11 Draw and label the *x*-axis from 0 to 20 and the *y*-axis from 0 to 24.
Draw these four object shapes and their images on the one diagram.
For each pair, find (i) the centre of the enlargement
(ii) the length scale factor
(iii) the area scale factor.

a	First pair	*Object*	(7, 4), (8, 5), (8, 2)
		Image	(19, 4), (16, 1), (16, 10)
b	Second pair	*Object*	(1, 1), (4, 1), (4, 2), (2, 2)
		Image	(7, 10), (1, 10), (1, 8), (5, 8)
c	Third pair	*Object*	(14, 16), (14, 19), (15, 17), (19, 16)
		Image	(17, 22), (17, 16), (15, 20), (7, 22)
d	Fourth pair	*Object*	(3, 14), (3, 16), (4, 16), (5, 15)
		Image	(7, 18), (7, 12), (4, 12), (1, 15)

12 This problem has a mixture of the different length scale factors.
Repeat the instructions of **11**.

a	First pair	*Object*	(6, 5), (6, 7), (5, 7), (5, 6)
		Image	(6, 1), (6, 11), (1, 11), (1, 6)
b	Second pair	*Object*	(14, 1), (20, 7), (20, 13), (14, 7), (8, 13), (8, 7)
		Image	(14, 3), (16, 5), (16, 7), (14, 5), (12, 7), (12, 5)
c	Third pair	*Object*	(2, 15), (5, 15), (5, 13)
		Image	(8, 18), (2, 18), (2, 22)
d	Fourth pair	*Object*	(14, 15), (16, 17), (16, 19), (11, 19), (11, 18)
		Image	(14, 24), (10, 20), (10, 16), (20, 16), (20, 18)

13 Repeat the instructions of **11** for these objects and their images.

a	First pair	*Object*	(2, 12), (5, 14), (5, 11), (4, 12)
		Image	(0, 4), (9, 10), (9, 1), (6, 4)
b	Second pair	*Object*	(11, 2), (13, 10), (17, 2), (15, 0)
		Image	(15, 5), (16, 9), (18, 5), (17, 4)
c	Third pair	*Object*	(6, 18), (10, 18), (10, 20), (5, 22)
		Image	(9, 24), (1, 24), (1, 20), (11, 16)
d	Fourth pair	*Object*	(12, 21), (15, 24), (18, 15)
		Image	(20, 21), (19, 20), (18, 23)

Part 2   Finding images

1 Trace each of these shapes and mark the lettered points.
Use the lettered points as the centres of enlargements with the given scale factors
and draw the images of the shapes. (You will need to give the shapes more
space than is used on this page.)

a

b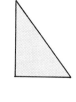

c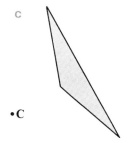

Scale factor of 2   Scale factor of 2   Scale factor of 3

Enlargements

d

•D

Scale factor of 3

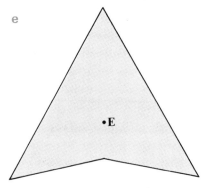

e

•E

Scale factor of $1\frac{1}{2}$

2   For each of the three object shapes given below:
   draw and label the x-axis from 0 to 20 and the y-axis from 0 to 25
   draw and shade the object shape
   take the given point as the centre of enlargement
   enlarge the object shape several times and draw its images using length
   scale factors of
   (i) 3   (ii) 2   (iii) $\frac{1}{2}$ (iv) -2 (v) -1 (vi) $-\frac{1}{2}$.

	Object shape	Centre of enlargement
a	Triangle (8, 13), (10, 15), (14, 13)	(12, 10)
b	Quadrilateral (8, 14), (8, 11), (9, 12), (12, 11)	(12, 14)
c	Quadrilateral (9, 13), (9, 15), (11, 15), (12, 13)	(8, 10)

3   Draw and label the x-axis from 0 to 20 and the y-axis from 0 to 25.
   Draw the three object shapes given below and shade them.
   Take the centre of enlargement and the given length scale factor, and draw the
   image of each object shape.

	Object shape	Centre of enlargement	Length scale factor
a	Rectangle (3, 14), (3, 16), (7, 16), (7, 14)	(5, 8)	2
b	Triangle (20, 3), (19, 3), (19, 5)	(20, 1)	5
c	Rectangle (8, 4), (9, 3), (11, 5), (10, 6)	(9, 4)	3

4   Draw axes as in **3**, and repeat the same instructions for these three object
   shapes.

	Object shape	Centre of enlargement	Length scale factor
a	Triangle (2, 7), (2, 10), (4, 8)	(3, 3)	3
b	Parallelogram (11, 6), (13, 6), (11, 8), (9, 8)	(9, 4)	$2\frac{1}{2}$
c	Pentagon (10, 16), (10, 22), (14, 22), (12, 20), (14, 16)	(4, 24)	$\frac{1}{2}$

Enlargements

5 Draw axes as in **3**, and repeat the same instructions for these four object shapes.

	Object shape	Centre of enlargement	Length scale factor
a	Trapezium (1, 25), (1, 19), (4, 22), (4, 25)	(13, 22)	$\frac{1}{3}$
b	Rectangle (4, 6), (12, 14), (8, 18), (0, 10)	(8, 14)	$\frac{1}{4}$
c	Pentagon (15, 22), (19, 22), (19, 23), (16, 23), (15, 24)	(17, 19)	-2
d	Trapezium (1, 2), (3, 2), (3, 3), (2, 4)	(5, 3)	-3

6

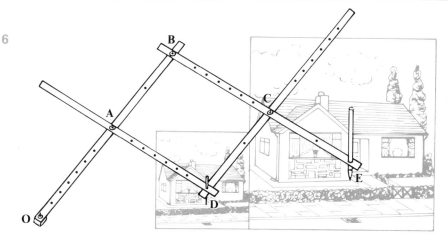

A **pantograph** is an instrument used for making enlargements of a drawing.

Four rods are joined as shown, such that $ABCD$ is a parallelogram with $OA = AD$ and $DC = CE$.

Point O is fixed; at point D there is a metal pointer; and at point E there is a pen or pencil.

As the pointer at D traces over the object shape, the pen at point E draws an enlarged image of length scale factor $\frac{OB}{OA}$.

Interchanging D and E produces an image smaller than the object.

By moving points A and C along the rods, different scale factors can be obtained.

See if you can make a pantograph out of wood or thick card.

Part 3 Problems

1 Square B is an enlargement of square A where a length of 4 cm maps onto a length of 12 cm.
   Find
   a the length scale factor
   b the area scale factor of the enlargement.

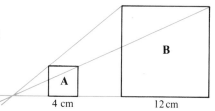

Enlargements

2 Triangle *T* enlarges onto triangle *U*.
Find
a   the length scale factor
b   the area scale factor
c   the value of *x*.

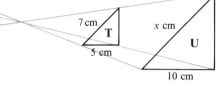

3

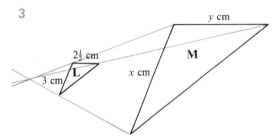

An enlargement of length scale factor 4 maps triangle *L* onto triangle *M*.
Find
a   the length *x*
b   the length *y*
c   the area scale factor
d   the area of triangle *M* if triangle *L* has an area of 2 cm^2.

4 Triangle *PQR* maps onto triangle *PQ'R'* under an enlargement of length scale factor -2.
Find
a   the values of *x*, *y* and *z*
b   the area scale factor of the enlargement
c   the area of triangle *PQ'R'* if the area of triangle *PQR* is 21 cm^2.

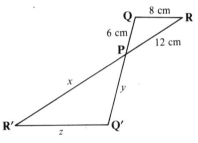

5

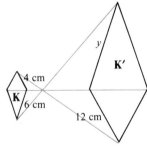

The rectangle *OLMN* maps onto the rectangle *OL'M'N'* under an enlargement with centre *O* and length scale factor 2.
Find
a   the length *ON'*
b   the area scale factor
c   the area of rectangle *OL'M'N'*.

6 The kite *K* maps onto the kite *K'* under an enlargement.
Find
a   the length scale factor
b   the length *y*
c   the area scale factor
d   the area of *K'* if *K* has an area of 16 cm^2.

7

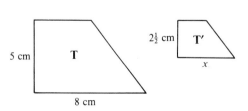

An enlargement maps the trapezium *T* onto its image *T'*.
Find
a   the length scale factor
b   the length *x*
c   the area scale factor
d   the area of *T'* if *T* has an area of 36 cm^2.

Enlargements

8   The rectangle $SQ'R'S'$ is the image of $PQRS$ under an enlargement of length scale factor $\frac{1}{3}$.
Find
a   the length SS'
b   the length $R'S'$
c   the length RQ'
d   the area of rectangle $PQRS$
e   the area scale factor of the enlargement
f   the area of rectangle $SQ'R'S'$.

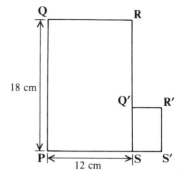

9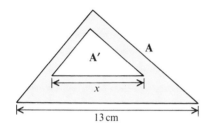

An enlargement of length scale factor $\frac{1}{2}$ maps triangle A onto triangle A'.
Find
a   the length x
b   the area scale factor
c   the area of A' if A has an area of 60 cm^2
d   the area of the shaded region.

10 The line $P'Q'$ is an enlargement of the line PQ, with centre O.
Find
a   the length scale factor
b   the area scale factor
c   the length OP'
d   the length PP'
e   the area of triangle $OP'Q'$ if triangle OPQ has an area of 18 cm^2
f   the area of the trapezium $PP'Q'Q$.

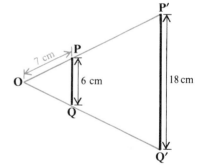

11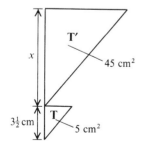

Triangle T' is the image of T under an enlargement, and their areas are 45 cm^2 and 5 cm^2 respectively.
Find
a   the area scale factor
b   the length scale factor
c   the length x.

12 The area of triangle OMN is 4 cm^2 and of trapezium $MM'N'N$ is 96 cm^2.
Find
a   the area of triangle $OM'N'$
b   the area scale factor of the enlargement
c   the length scale factor of the enlargement
d   the length OM'
e   the length MM'.

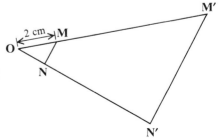

Enlargements

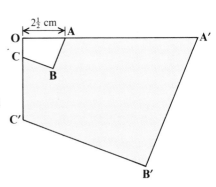

13 The shaded region has an area of 75 cm²
    and the area of quadrilateral $OABC$ is
    5 cm².
    Find
    a   the area of $OA'B'C'$
    b   the area scale factor of the enlargement
    c   its length scale factor
    d   the length OA'
    e   the length AA'.

14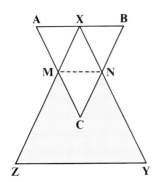

Triangle ABC maps onto triangle XYZ under an
enlargement where M, N and X are the midpoints
of AC, BC and AB.
The areas of the small triangles AMX and BNX
are each 4 cm².
The shaded area is 136 cm².
Find
a   the area of the rhombus $MXNC$
b   the areas of triangle ABC and triangle XYZ
c   the area scale factor of the enlargement
d   the length scale factor of the enlargement.

15 Triangle LMN maps onto triangle
    $L'M'N'$ under an enlargement such
    that the points L, M and N are the
    midpoints of the sides of triangle
    $L'M'N'$.
    Find
    a   the area scale factor
    b   the length scale factor
    c   the length of LM.

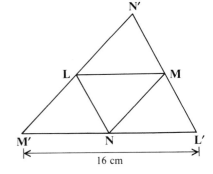

Similarity

Part 1 Similarity and congruence

1 **Similar** figures have the same shape but different sizes.
Congruent figures have the same shape and also the same size.
Decide whether these pairs of figures are *similar*, *congruent* or *neither*.

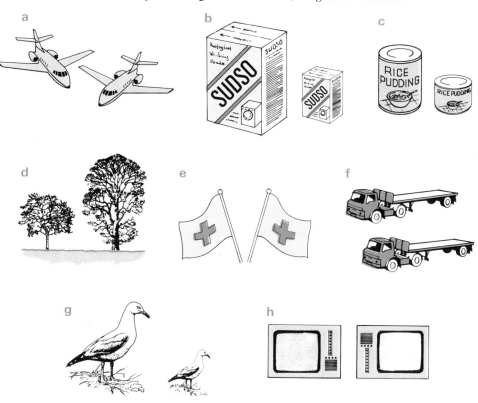

2 The *lengths* of corresponding sides of similar figures are *different*; but
corresponding *angles* will be the *same*.
Compare the shapes of these pairs of drawings, and say which pairs are similar.

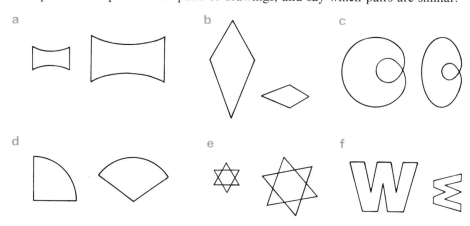

Similarity

3   A more exact test of similarity is to look at the sizes of corresponding angles.
Do these pairs of figures have the same *shape*?
Say whether they are *similar* or not.

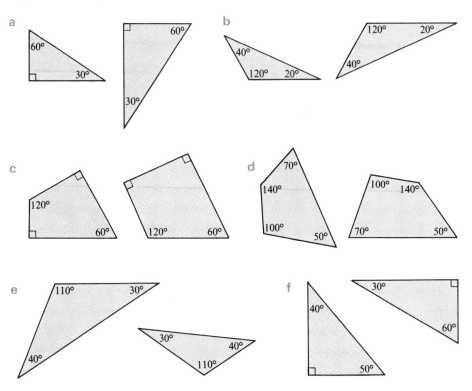

4   Eight triangles are drawn here. Calculate the third angle of each one and so
decide which *pairs* of triangles are *similar*.

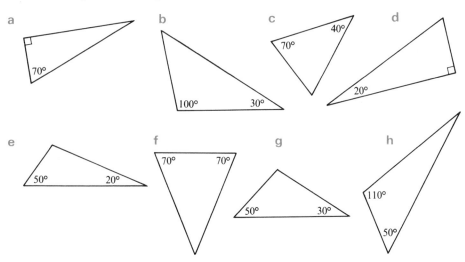

5 *Congruent* figures have the same *shape* and same *size*.
Eight triangles are drawn here. Calculate the third angle of each one and so
decide which pairs of triangles are *congruent*.

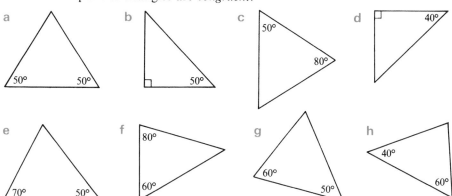

6 Draw each pair of triangles on their own diagrams, with both axes labelled from
0 to 12.
Use a ruler and protractor to measure their sides and angles, and write your
results on the diagrams.
Decide whether the triangles in each pair are *congruent, similar* or *neither*.

	First triangle	Second triangle
a	(1, 1), (7, 1), (7, 8)	(9, 5), (9, 11), (2, 11)
b	(1, 8), (4, 1), (10, 5)	(5, 3), (9, 9), (2, 12)
c	(1, 1), (6, 1), (3, 7)	(12, 1), (12, 11), (0, 5)
d	(1, 4), (10, 2), (8, 12)	(1, 9), (7, 1), (12, 7)
e	(4, 1), (4, 7), (0, 5)	(12, 12), (0, 12), (8, 4)
f	(1, 8), (8, 7), (11, 0)	(4, 1), (12, 11), (5, 8)
g	(3, 1), (5, 10), (12, 10)	(9, 1), (1, 12), (1, 5)

7 For each of these diagrams,
(i) what are the sizes of the angles labelled *w*, *x*, *y* or *z*
(ii) do the triangles *PQR* and *PST* have the same sizes of angles
(iii) are the triangles *PQR* and *PST similar*?

a
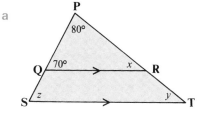

b
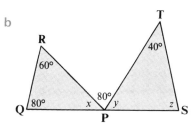

c
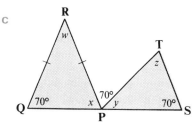

d
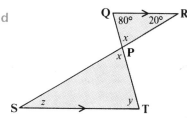

95

Similarity

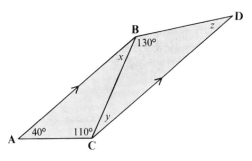

8 a Calculate angles x, y and z.
   b Do the two triangles ABC
      and BCD have the same sizes
      of angles?
   c Are triangles ABC and BCD
      similar?

9

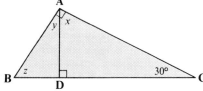

   a Calculate angles x, y and z.
   b Are triangles ABD and ACD
      similar?
   c Are triangles ABC and ACD
      similar?

Part 2   Different scale factors

1 a

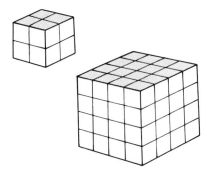

   b

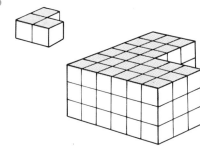

   c

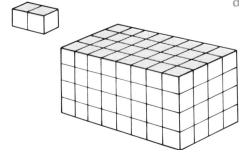

   d

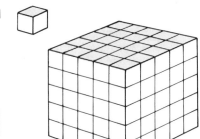

These diagrams show pairs of *similar* solids.
   (i) Count along their edges to find how many times longer the edges of the
       larger solid are than those of the smaller solid. This is called the **length scale
       factor**.
   (ii) Count the number of squares in the shaded faces to find how many times
       bigger the faces of the larger solid are than those of the smaller solid. This
       is called the **area scale factor**.

Similarity

(iii) Count the number of cubes in each solid to find how many times bigger in volume the larger solid is than the smaller solid. This is called the **volume scale factor**.

(iv) Copy this table and enter your results. Follow the pattern which they produce to complete the table.

Length scale factor	2	3	4	5	6	7	8	9	10	m
Area scale factor										
Volume scale factor										

2   A square has sides of 5 cm. It is enlarged so that its sides are 10 cm long.
Find
a   the length scale factor
b   its original area
c   its final area
d   the area scale factor.

5 cm   10 cm

3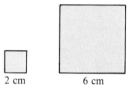

2 cm   6 cm

Another square has sides of 2 cm. It is enlarged so that its sides are 6 cm long.
Find
a   the length scale factor
b   its original area
c   its final area
d   the area scale factor.

4   A square has sides of 2 cm. It is enlarged so that its sides are 10 cm long.
Find
a   the length scale factor   b   its original area
c   its final area   d   the area scale factor.

5   A square of side 5 cm is enlarged so that its sides are 20 cm long.
Find
a   the length scale factor   b   its original area
c   its final area   d   the area scale factor.

6   A cube has edges of 2 cm. It is enlarged so that all its edges are 4 cm long.
Find
a   the length scale factor
b   its original volume
c   its final volume
d   the volume scale factor.

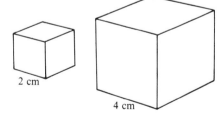

2 cm

4 cm

7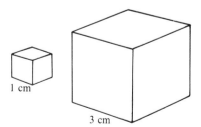

1 cm

3 cm

Another cube has edges of 1 cm. It is enlarged so that all its edges are 3 cm long.
Find
a   the length scale factor
b   its original volume
c   its final volume
d   the volume scale factor.

8   A cube of edge 2 cm is enlarged so that its edges are 10 cm long.
Find
a   the length scale factor   b   its original volume
c   its final volume   d   the volume scale factor.

Similarity

9   Two similar milk bottles have heights of
    25 cm and 50 cm.
    Find
    a   the length scale factor
    b   the volume scale factor
    c   the volume of the larger bottle if the
        smaller one holds 0.2 litres.

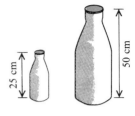

10 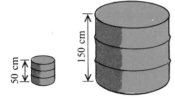   Two similar oil drums have heights of
    50 cm and 150 cm.
    Find
    a   the length scale factor
    b   the volume scale factor
    c   the volume of the large drum if the
        small one holds 30 litres.

11 A chemical is stored in two similar metal canisters 15 cm and 60 cm high. The
    small canister holds $\frac{1}{2}$ litre.
    Find
    a   the length scale factor   b   the volume scale factor
    c   the capacity of the larger canister.

12 A photograph 6 cm long is enlarged so that it is 30 cm long.
    Find
    a   the length scale factor   b   the area scale factor
    c   the area of the enlargement if the original has an area of 20 cm^2.

13 Two maps are made of the same region. One is 40 cm wide and the other is
    120 cm wide.
    Find
    a   the length scale factor   b   the area scale factor
    c   the area of the large map if the small one has an area of $\frac{1}{2}$ m^2.

14 The front and back gardens of a house have lawns of the same shape but
    different sizes. The front lawn is 8 m long and has an area of 40 m^2. The back
    lawn is 32 m long.
    Find
    a   the length scale factor   b   the area scale factor
    c   the area of the back lawn.

15 The labels from two similar tins of soup have areas of 100 cm^2 and 900 cm^2.
    Find
    a   the area scale factor   b   the length scale factor
    c   the radius of the larger tin if that of the smaller one is 4 cm.

16 Two editions of different sizes are made of the same book. The small one has a
    cover of area 50 cm^2. The area of the large cover is 1250 cm^2.
    Find
    a   the area scale factor   b   the length scale factor
    c   the width of the large book if the small one is 6 cm wide.

17 Cooking oil is sold to hotels in two similar sizes of drum which have volumes of
    2 litres and 54 litres.
    Find
    a   the volume scale factor   b   the length scale factor
    c   the height of the larger drum if the smaller one has a height of 25 cm.

18 Two similar tins of motor oil hold $\frac{1}{2}$ litre and 4 litres. The smaller tin has a
    radius of 6 cm.
    Find
    a   the volume scale factor   b   the length scale factor
    c   the radius of the larger tin.

Similarity

19 A house is 15 metres wide, and has a volume of 2000 m³. A scale model is made of the house so that the volume of the model is 2 m³.
Find
a the volume scale factor   b the length scale factor
c the width of the model.

20 Two similar barrels hold 5 litres and 135 litres, and the larger barrel is 90 cm high.
Find
a the volume scale factor   b the length scale factor
c the height of the smaller barrel.

21 Gas is held in two similar containers. The smaller one is 75 cm long and holds enough gas to fill 200 balloons. If the large cylinder will fill 1600 balloons, write down
a the volume scale factor   b the length scale factor
c the length of the larger cylinder.

22 A painting is 96 cm long and a postcard-sized replica is made 12 cm long.
Find
a the length scale factor   b the area scale factor
c the area of the painting if the postcard's area is 85 cm².

23 A baking tin has a base area of 60 cm² and a volume of 300 cm³. A similar tin has a base area of 240 cm².
Find
a the area scale factor   b the length scale factor
c the volume scale factor   d the volume of the larger tin.

24 A car has a windscreen of area 4500 cm² and a boot which holds 2 m³. A model of the car is made so that its windscreen has an area of 45 cm².
Find
a the area scale factor   b the volume scale factor
c the capacity of the boot in the model.

25 Two similar drain-pipes will hold 4 litres and 500 litres of liquid.
Find
a the volume scale factor   b the area scale factor
c the area of cross-section of the smaller pipe, if that of the larger pipe is 75 cm².

26 A shoe box has a volume of 32 000 cm³ and a label of area 120 cm².
A similar shoe box has a volume of 4000 cm³.
Find
a the volume scale factor   b the area scale factor
c the area of the label on the smaller box.

27 A girl makes a doll's dress using a full-sized pattern with all lengths scaled down to a fifth.
a If the full-sized pattern is 150 cm long, how long is the doll's pattern?
b She uses 0.1 m² of material for the doll. What area of material would the full-sized pattern use?

28 A pocket dictionary is 1.2 cm thick with pages of area 40 cm². It is similar to a larger edition but with lengths scaled down to a third.
a How thick is the large edition?
b What is the area of the pages of the large edition?

29 An enlargement is made of a photograph so that it is nine times bigger in area. If the original photograph is 10 cm long and 6 cm wide with a white border of area 8 cm², find
a the length and width of the enlargement
b the area of the white border on the enlargement.

Similarity

30 Two similar metal washers are 2 mm and 6 mm thick. The smaller one has an area of 4 cm^2 and a volume of 0.2 cm^3.
Find
a   the length, area and volume scale factors
b   the area of the larger washer   c   the volume of the larger washer.

31 Two similar water tanks stand 6 m and 9 m high. The smaller one has a base area of 8 m^2 and it will hold 16 000 litres.
Find
a   the length scale factor   b   the base area of the larger tank
c   the capacity of the larger tank.

32 A model is made of a dam using a scale of 1 : 100 for lengths.
The dam wall is 50 metres high and 300 metres long.
The area of the dam wall is 12 000 m^2, and it holds back 2 000 000 m^3 of water in the reservoir.
Find
a   the height and length of the model wall
b   the area of the model wall
c   the volume of water needed in the model reservoir.

Part 3   Similar triangles and similar pyramids

By finding unknown angles, show that the two triangles in each diagram are similar, and find the lettered lengths.

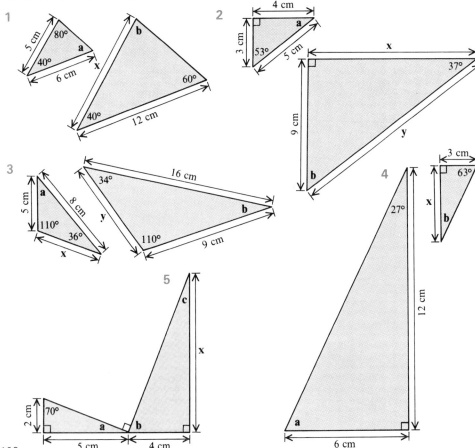

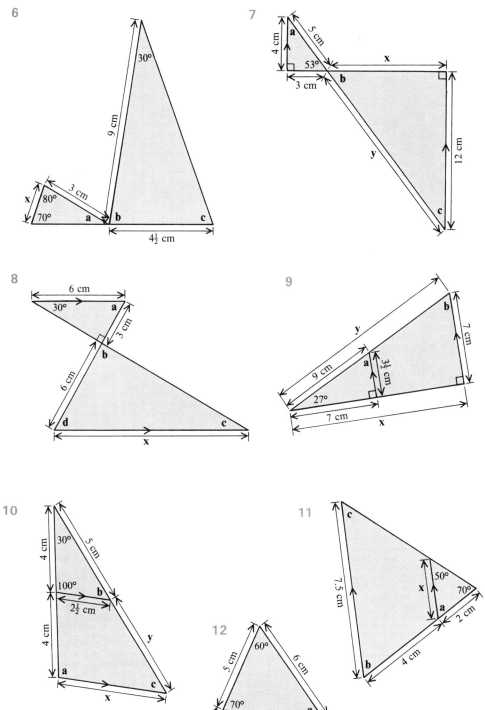

6

30°

9 cm

3 cm

x

80°

70°

a b

c

4½ cm

7

a

4 cm

5 cm

53°

3 cm

b

x

12 cm

y

c

8

6 cm

30°

a

3 cm

b

6 cm

d

c

x

9

y

b

7 cm

9 cm

a

3½ cm

27°

7 cm

x

10

4 cm

30°

5 cm

100°

b

2½ cm

4 cm

a

y

c

x

11

c

7.5 cm

50°

x

70°

a

2 cm

b

4 cm

12

60°

5 cm

6 cm

70°

a

x

3 cm

b

c

101

Similarity

13 In each of these diagrams, triangle ABC is similar to triangle $A'B'C'$, and the area of triangle ABC is given.
   Find   (i) the length and area scale factors   (ii) the lettered lengths
          (iii) the area of triangle $A'B'C'$.

   a   Area of triangle $ABC = 6\frac{1}{2}$ cm²   b   Area of triangle $ABC = 3$ cm²

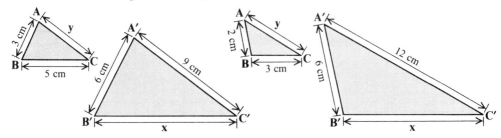

   c   Area of triangle $ABC = 1\frac{1}{2}$ cm²   d   Area of triangle $ABC = 10$ cm²

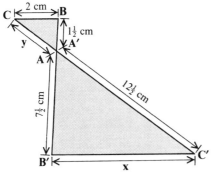

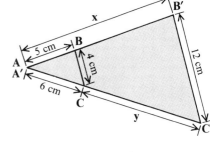

14 Triangle OPQ enlarges onto triangle $OP'Q'$.
   Find
   a   the length PP'
   b   the area of triangle $OP'Q'$ if triangle OPQ has an area of 5 cm²
   c   the area of the trapezium $PP'Q'Q$.

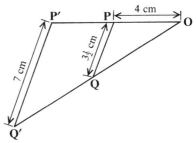

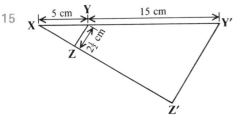

15 Triangle XYZ enlarges onto triangle $XY'Z'$.
   Find
   a   the length $Y'Z'$
   b   the area of triangle $XY'Z'$ if the area of triangle XYZ is 9 cm²
   c   the area of trapezium $YY'Z'Z$.

16 The line LM enlarges to give the line $L'M'$ using the point O as the centre of the enlargement.
   Find
   a   the length $L'M'$
   b   the area of triangle $OL'M'$ given that triangle OLM has an area of 8 cm²
   c   the area of the trapezium $LMM'L'$.

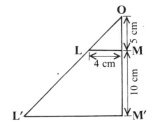

17 Under an enlargement with centre O, the line XY enlarges onto $X'Y'$.
   a Find the length $X'Y'$.
   b If triangle OXY has an area of 10 cm², find the area of triangle $OX'Y'$ and of the trapezium $XYY'X'$.

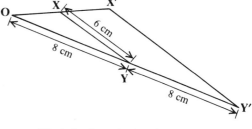

18

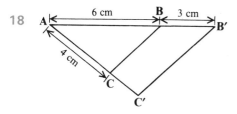

a Find the length CC' in this diagram.
b If the area of triangle ABC is 8 cm², find the area of triangle $AB'C'$ and the trapezium $BB'C'C$.

19 A street light 6 metres tall stands 2 metres from a wall 3 metres high.
   Find the length x of the shadow cast by the wall on the ground.

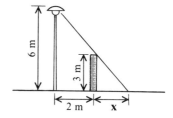

20

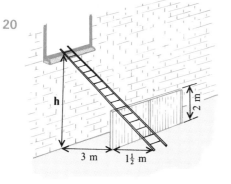

The top of a ladder rests on a window sill, and its foot is $4\frac{1}{2}$ metres from the wall. The ladder just touches the top of a fence which is 2 metres high and 3 metres from the wall.
Find the height h of the window sill above the ground

21 Two ships set sail from port P at the same time, travelling due north at different speeds. Some time later, they both turn simultaneously due east.
Find the distance x from the data on the diagram.

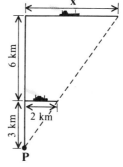

22

A vertical ruler $\frac{1}{4}$ m long, when placed 1 m from your eye, just obscures the view of a hill which is 800 m away from you.
Find the height h of the hill.

Similarity

23 A step-ladder 150 cm long is held open by a string so that its two feet are 90 cm apart. How long is the string if it is fixed 50 cm from the feet of the ladder?

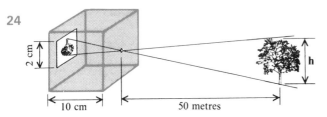

24

A pin-hole camera is used to photograph a tree 50 m away. If the camera is 10 cm across and it produces a photograph of the tree 2 cm high, find the actual height h of the tree.

25 Tree A on one bank of a river is directly opposite tree B on the other bank.
A man, wishing to find the width of the river, positions a post P between B and C as shown. He then walks directly away from tree C until he reaches point Q where A, P and Q are in line.
If he measures CQ as 10 m, calculate the width w of the river for him.

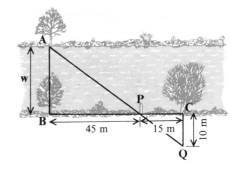

26

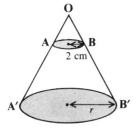

The cone OAB is enlarged with length scale factor of 3 onto the cone $OA'B'$.
Find
a the base radius r
b the volume of cone $OA'B'$ if the small cone OAB has a volume of 12 cm³
c the volume of the frustum which is left when the small cone OAB is removed.

27 The cone OLM of height 5 cm is enlarged to give the cone $OL'M'$ of height 10 cm.
Find
a the base radius r of the cone $OL'M'$
b the volume of the cone $OL'M'$ if the small cone OLM has a volume of 84 cm³
c the volume of the frustum $LMM'L'$.

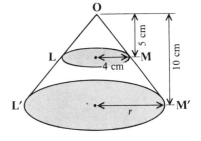

28

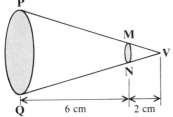

If the volume of the cone VMN is 4 cm³, find the volume of
a the cone VPQ
b the frustum $MNQP$.

29 The large pyramid $VABCD$ has a square base of side 12 cm. The square $PQRS$ (of side 4 cm) cuts the pyramid forming a smaller one of height 6 cm.
Find

a the lengths VE and TE

b the volume scale factor of the enlargement which maps the small pyramid onto the large one

c the volume of the large pyramid if the small one has a volume of 32 cm³

d the volume of the frustum left when the small pyramid is removed.

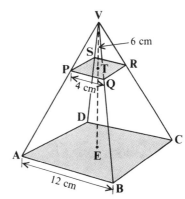

30

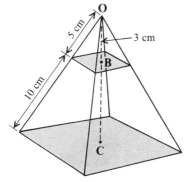

The pyramid shown has an axis OBC.
Calculate

a the height OC

b the distance BC

c the volume of the whole pyramid if the volume of the smaller one is 25 cm³

d the volume of the frustum between the two square planes.

31 A pyramid with a rectangular base of area 54 cm² has its top cut off by a rectangular plane of area 6 cm², which is 2 cm from the vertex V.
Find

a the height h of the pyramid

b the distance x between the two rectangular planes.

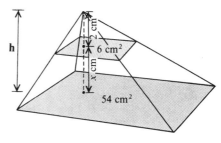

32

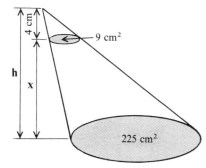

A pyramid has an oval base of area 225 cm². Its area of cross-section is 9 cm² at a distance of 4 cm from its vertex.
Calculate

a the height h of the pyramid

b the distance x between the two ovals

c the volume of the whole pyramid if the volume of the small one is 12 cm³

d the volume of the frustum between the two oval planes.

33 A small light L hangs $\frac{1}{2}$ metre above a table with a top T of area $1\frac{1}{2}$ m².
The shadow on the floor F covers an area of $13\frac{1}{2}$ m².
How high is the table top T above the floor F?

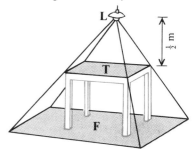

Similarity

34 A waste-paper bin has the shape of a frustum made from a square-based pyramid of side 40 cm with a small square-based pyramid of side 20 cm removed. If the volume removed is 16 litres, find the volume of the waste-paper bin.

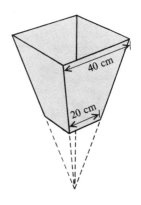

35

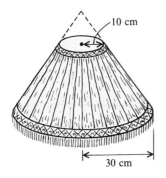

A lampshade is made in the shape of the frustum of a cone having radii of 10 cm and 30 cm. If the volume of the small cone removed is 1500 cm³, find the volume inside the lampshade.

Part 4   Scales, plans and maps

1 These five objects are drawn to a scale of 1 cm = 2 metres. Use a ruler to find their heights in metres.

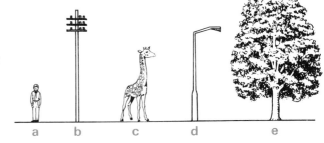

2

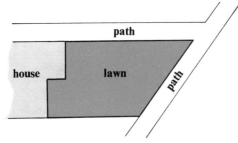

This is a plan of the lawn of a house, drawn to a scale of 1 cm = 6 metres.

Use a ruler to measure the lengths of its six edges and so find its perimeter in metres.

3 This elephant is drawn to a scale of 1 : 100. This means that 1 cm on the diagram represents 100 cm on the actual elephant.

Find its overall height and its length in metres.

106

Similarity

4   A ground plan of a village
    church is drawn here to a scale
    of 1 : 500. This means that 1 cm
    on the plan stands for 500 cm in
    the actual church.

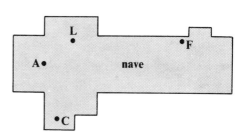

Use a ruler to find in *metres*:
a   the overall length of the
    church
b   the width of its nave

the shortest distance from
c   the altar *A* to the lectern *L*   d   the chapel *C* to the font *F*
e   the lectern *L* to the font *F*   f   the altar *A* to the chapel *C*.

5

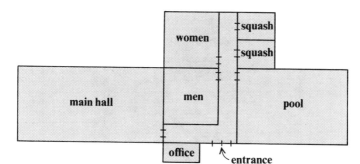

This is the ground plan of a leisure centre drawn to a scale of 1 : 800.
Take measurements to find, in metres,
a   the length and width of the main hall
b   the length and width of the pool
c   the length and width of the office
d   the overall length of the centre
e   its greatest width.

6   A map will use a large scale-factor which geographers call a **representative
    fraction**.
    One *centimetre* on the map can represent several *kilometres* of actual distance.
    Find the distance (in kilometres) which 1 cm stands for on a map with a scale
    factor of
    a   1 : 100 000   b   1 : 200 000   c   1 : 800 000   d   1 : 1 500 000
    e   1 : 50 000   f   1 : 25 000   g   1 : 5 000 000   h   1 : 25 000 000.

7   A map has a scale of 1 : 800 000. Find the actual distance (in kilometres) which
    these lengths on the map represent:
    a   1 cm   b   2 cm   c   5 cm   d   7 cm
    e   1½ cm   f   3½ cm   g   0.4 cm   h   2.3 cm.

8   How many kilometres do these lengths represent on a map which has a scale of
    1 : 250 000 ?
    a   1 cm   b   4 cm   c   5 cm   d   3 cm
    e   3.2 cm   f   12.8 cm   g   1.6 cm   h   0.6 cm

Similarity

9 The scale of a map is 1 : 50 000. What distance in kilometres do these lengths on the map stand for?

| a | 1 cm | b | 2 cm | c | 6 cm | d | 5 cm |
| e | 5.2 cm | f | 6.4 cm | g | 1.8 cm | h | 0.8 cm |

10 This map of southern Italy has a scale of 1 : 10 000 000.
Find the distance in kilometres
a for 1 cm on the map
b from Rome to Reggio
c from Rome to Taranto
d from Naples to Rome
e from Taranto to Palermo
f from Palermo to Rome
g from Reggio to Naples
h from Naples to Taranto.

11

This map of the Irish Sea has a scale of 1 : 4 000 000.
Find the distance in kilometres
a for 1 cm on the map
b from Douglas to Caernarvon
c from Belfast to Carlisle
d from Liverpool to Belfast
e from Carlisle to Liverpool
f from Dublin to Carlisle
g from Caernarvon to Belfast.

12 Copy this table which gives the distances on a map between various cities. The scale of the map is 1 : 22 000 000.
Complete the table by finding the actual distances in kilometres between the cities.

Cities	Distance on map	Actual distance
Edinburgh – Copenhagen	4.3 cm	☐ km
London – Rome	6.4 cm	☐ km
Paris – Oslo	6.1 cm	☐ km
York – Helsinki	7.6 cm	☐ km
Bristol – Venice	5.7 cm	☐ km

13 A map of the British Isles has a scale of 1 : 6 000 000.
Calculate the actual distances between these places in kilometres.
a   Cardiff to Dublin is 4.9 cm on the map.
b   The Isle of Arran to the Aran Isles is 6.6 cm on the map.
c   John o' Groats to Land's End is 16.2 cm on the map.
d   The Shetland Islands to the Channel Islands is 20.5 cm on the map.

14 A map of the USA has a scale of 1 : 12 000 000.
Calculate (to the nearest 10 km) the actual distances between these cities.
a   New York to Washington is 2.7 cm on the map.
b   Chicago to New Orleans is 11.3 cm on the map.
c   Boston to Los Angeles is 35.1 cm on the map.

15 Find the scale of the maps on which:
a   1 cm stands for 3 km   b   1 cm stands for 12 km
c   1 cm stands for 250 km   d   1 cm stands for 3.5 km
e   1 cm stands for 12.5 km   f   1 cm stands for 0.8 km
g   1 cm stands for 440 km   h   1 cm stands for 200 metres
i   1 cm stands for 25 metres   j   1 cm stands for 750 metres.

16 Find the scale of the map on which:
a   2 cm stands for 8 km   b   5 cm stands for 30 km
c   3 cm stands for 36 km   d $\frac{1}{2}$ cm stands for 1 km
e   4 cm stands for 10 km   f   10 cm stands for 45 km
g $1\frac{1}{2}$ cm stands for 15 km   h   6 cm stands for 1.2 km
i   1 mm stands for 2 km   j   2 mm stands for 16 km
k   3 mm stands for 21 km   l   6 mm stands for 1.8 km.

17 On a map of North Wales, Bala and Ffestiniog are 13 cm apart. If the actual distance between them is 26 km, find
a   how many kilometres each centimetre on the map stands for
b   the scale of the map (in the form 1 : n where n is a large number).

18 The capital cities of Czechoslovakia and Austria are Prague and Vienna, and they are 250 km apart. If a map shows them 5 cm apart, what is the scale of the map?

19 This table shows the actual distances between certain places, and also their distance apart on various maps.
Find the scale of each map.

	Places	Distance on map	Actual distance
a	Stockport – Sheffield	3 cm	45 km
b	Londonderry – Belfast	5 cm	100 km
c	Plymouth – Southampton	4 cm	200 km
d	Inverness – Aberdeen	3 cm	120 km
e	Ben Nevis – Snowdon	8 cm	400 km
f	London – Athens	12 cm	2400 km
g	Glasgow – Copenhagen	2 cm	1000 km

20 The Australian cities of Melbourne and Sydney are 700 km apart. If a map shows them $3\frac{1}{2}$ cm apart, what is the scale of the map?

Similarity

Map X	Map Y	Map Z
	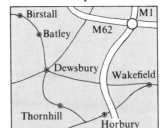	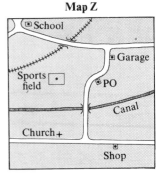

21 Map X shows towns and cities in Yorkshire and Lancashire. Part of this map is enlarged and shown as map Y. The village of Thornhill on map Y is then enlarged and shown as map Z.

a If the actual distance from Blackburn to Skipton is 40 km, use your ruler and calculate the scale of map X in the form $1:n$.

b If the actual distance from Dewsbury to Batley is 2 km, use your ruler and calculate the scale of map Y in the form $1:n$.

c If the actual distance from the school to the shop in Thornhill is 0.8 km, use your ruler and calculate the scale of map Z in the form $1:n$.

Use these answers and take measurements from the maps to find the actual distances in kilometres between

d Thornhill church and the canal bridge

e the sports field and Thornhill church

f Thornhill church and the garage

g the school and post office in Thornhill   h Birstall and Wakefield

i Wakefield and Horbury   j Thornhill and Wakefield

k Birstall and Horbury   l Blackburn and Dewsbury

m Sheffield and Blackburn   n Manchester and Wakefield

o Skipton and Sheffield   p Sheffield and Manchester.

Areas on maps

22 A set of maps has these scales.
Find, for each map,
(i) the distance which 1 cm stands for   (ii) the area which 1 cm^2 stands for.

a $1:400\,000$ b $1:500\,000$ c $1:1\,200\,000$

d $1:1\,000\,000$ e $1:300\,000$ f $1:800\,000$

g $1:900\,000$ h $1:1\,500\,000$ i $1:250\,000$

j $1:120\,000$ k $1:450\,000$ l $1:50\,000$

m $1:60\,000$ n $1:70\,000$ o $1:2\,500\,000$

p $1:1\,600\,000$

23 A map has a scale of $1:300\,000$.

a What distance in km does
(i) 1 cm on the map stand for   (ii) 4 cm on the map stand for?

b What area in km^2 does
(i) 1 cm^2 on the map stand for   (ii) 5 cm^2 on the map stand for?

Similarity

24 The scale of a map is 1 : 600 000.
What area in km^2 does
a 1 cm^2 on the map stand for   b 4 cm^2 on the map stand for
c $\frac{1}{2}$ cm^2 on the map stand for?

25 A map has a scale of 1 : 200 000.
How many square kilometres do these areas on the map represent?
a 1 cm^2 b 4 cm^2 c 5 cm^2 d 2.4 cm^2
e 6.5 cm^2 f 12.5 cm^2

26 On a map with a scale of 1 : 500 000, a city is shown by a shaded area of 4 cm^2.
a How many km^2 does each cm^2 of map represent?
b What is the area of the city in km^2?

27 A lake is represented by a blue area of 3 cm^2 on a map with a scale factor of
1 : 1 200 000.
a How many square kilometres does each square centimetre stand for?
b What is the actual area of the lake in km^2?

28
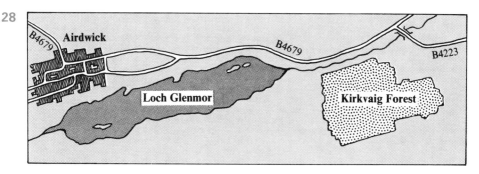

This map shows part of a Scottish glen.
a Draw a grid of square centimetres on a piece of tracing paper, and estimate
the areas in cm^2 on this map of
(i) the town of Airdwick   (ii) Kirkvaig Forest   (iii) Loch Glenmor.
b The map has a scale of 1 : 200 000.
Estimate the actual areas in km^2 of
(i) the town of Airdwick   (ii) Kirkvaig Forest   (iii) Loch Glenmor.

29 A map of England has a scale of 1 : 1 500 000 and one of the counties has an
area of 2.4 cm^2 on this map. Find its actual area in km^2.

30 A forest is shown as a green area of 124 cm^2 on a map whose scale is 1 : 50 000.
What is its actual area in km^2?

31 A farm is shown on a map of scale 1 : 20 000 as an area of 85 cm^2. Find the
actual area of the farm in km^2.

32 A map of Britain has a scale of 1 : 2 000 000. Find the actual areas of these
countries (in km^2) from their areas on the map:
a Wales 51.8 cm^2 b Scotland 196.9 cm^2
c England 325.9 cm^2 d Ireland 209.8 cm^2.

Similarity

33 A map of Europe has a scale of 1 : 6 000 000. Given these areas on the map, find the actual areas of the countries in km^2. Give your answers to three significant figures.

a Belgium 8.4 cm^2 b France 153.0 cm^2

c UK 63.8 cm^2 d Spain 141.5 cm^2

e Finland 93.6 cm^2

34 An area of 63 km^2 is represented on a map as 7 cm^2.

a How many km^2 does each cm^2 represent?

b What distance (in km) will 1 cm stand for?

c Find the scale of the map in the form 1 : n.

35 An island of 100 km^2 is shown on a map by an area of 4 cm^2.

a How many km^2 does 1 cm^2 represent?

b What distance (in km) does 1 cm represent?

c Write down the scale of the map in the form 1 : n.

36 A farm of area 2 km^2 has an area of 8 cm^2 on a map. Find the scale of the map.

37 A river estuary has an area 48 km^2 and on a map it has an area of $\frac{1}{3}$ cm^2. Find the scale of the map.

Combining transformations

One transformation operating on a shape can be followed by a second transformation; and the second can be followed by a third; and so on.

For example, these three diagrams show that the shape of a human skull can be transformed into that of a chimpanzee, and a second transformation changes the shape into that of a baboon's skull.

Notice especially the changes which occur in the size of the jaw and the braincase.

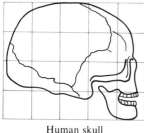

Human skull

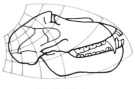

Skull of chimpanzee

Skull of baboon

Another combination of transformations will change a circle into an aerofoil. This is useful in the design of aeroplane wings.

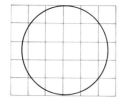 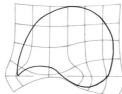 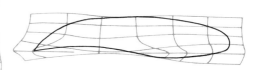

Part 1

Each of these problems will require a diagram with both axes labelled from -8 to 8. The transformations used in these twelve problems are:

X   a reflection in the x-axis   **Y**   a reflection in the y-axis

U   a reflection in the line $y = x$ **W**   a reflection in the line $x = 4$

H   a half-turn rotation about the origin

S   a translation of $\begin{pmatrix} 2 \\ -4 \end{pmatrix}$ **T**   a translation of $\begin{pmatrix} 6 \\ -4 \end{pmatrix}$.

1   An arrowhead shape A has corners $(-4, 0)$, $(-2, 2)$, $(-4, 4)$, $(-3, 2)$ joined in this order.
Draw the positions of a A   b **Y**(A)   c **WY**(A) on one diagram.
What *single* transformation maps A directly onto **WY**(A)?

2   A capital letter F is made from three straight lines by joining $(-5, 1)$ to $(-5, 3)$ to $(-1, 3)$, and then $(-5, 2)$ to $(-1, 2)$.
Draw the positions of a F   b **T**(F)   c **YT**(F) on one diagram.
Give full details of the *single* transformation which maps F directly onto **YT**(F).

3   A triangle T has corners $(0, 0)$, $(1, 4)$, $(6, 4)$.
Draw the positions of a T   b **H**(T)   c **XH**(T) on one diagram.
Give full details of the *single* transformation which maps T directly onto **XH**(T).
Would you say that **XH** = **Y** was a *true* or *false* statement?

113

Combining transformations

4 The points $(-2, 5)$, $(-1, 5)$, $(-1, 3)$ are the corners of triangle A.
   Draw the positions of   a A   b Y(A)   c UY(A) on one diagram.
   Describe fully the transformation which maps A *directly* onto UY(A).

5 The triangle B has corners $(5, 2)$, $(1, 2)$, $(2, 5)$.
   Draw the positions of   a B   b Y(B)   c XY(B) on one diagram.
   Describe the transformation which maps B *directly* onto XY(B).
   Would you say that XY = H was a *true* or *false* statement?

Draw each of these object shapes on its own diagram (with both axes labelled from -8 to 8); and transform each one several times to find the position of its final image.
Describe in detail the *single* transformation which maps each object shape *directly* onto its final image.

	The object shape and its corners		Its final image
6	Quadrilateral Q	$(-2, 6), (-1, 6), (-1, 1), (-2, 4)$	WSY(Q)
7	Triangle C	$(6, 0), (4, 3), (5, 5)$	XYXW(C)
8	Triangle D	$(1, 2), (3, 3), (1, 6)$	YU(D)
9	Quadrilateral E	$(-5, 3), (-5, 2), (-3, 1), (-1, 2)$	WXT(E)
10	Triangle F	$(6, 2), (4, -1), (4, 2)$	YXUW(F)
11	Quadrilateral G	$(1, 1), (1, 5), (3, 4), (2, 4)$	SXU(G)
12	Pentagon P	$(4, -2), (8, -2), (8, -6), (6, -3), (4, -4)$	YTU(P)

Part 2 Particular cases

Each problem **1** to **10** describes an object transformed twice in succession.
In each case,
a draw both axes labelled from -8 to 8
b draw the object and its two images
c describe the *single* transformation which maps the object *directly* onto its final image.

Two reflections

1 The triangle T $(-6, 2)$, $(-6, 8)$, $(-4, 8)$ is reflected in the line $y = 2$ onto triangle T′ which is then reflected in the line $y = x$ onto triangle T″.

2 The triangle S $(-7, 1)$, $(-7, 3)$, $(-3, 3)$ is reflected in the line $y = x + 6$ onto triangle S′ which is then reflected in the line $y = x$ onto triangle S″.

Two rotations

3 The triangle U $(-6, 0)$, $(-6, 2)$, $(-2, 2)$ is rotated clockwise 90° about the point $(-2, -6)$ onto triangle U′ which is then rotated anticlockwise 90° about the point $(2, 0)$ onto triangle U″.

4 The triangle V $(2, 4)$, $(2, 8)$, $(4, 8)$ is rotated anticlockwise 90° about the point $(2, 2)$ onto triangle V′ which is then rotated anticlockwise 90° about the point $(-2, -2)$ onto triangle V″.

Reflection and rotation with translation

5 The triangle W $(2, 6)$, $(6, 6)$, $(6, 8)$ is reflected in the line $y = 5$ onto triangle W′ which is then translated by $\begin{pmatrix} 0 \\ -10 \end{pmatrix}$ onto triangle W″.

6 The triangle X $(-4, -4)$, $(-4, -8)$, $(-2, -8)$ is rotated anticlockwise 90° about the point $(-2, -2)$ onto triangle X′ which is then translated by $\begin{pmatrix} 2 \\ 6 \end{pmatrix}$ onto triangle X″.

Combining transformations

Two shears

7   The rectangle R $(2, 0)$, $(2, 6)$, $(4, 6)$, $(4, 0)$ is sheared onto R′ so that the x-axis is invariant and $(4, 6) \to (-2, 6)$.
R′ is then sheared onto R″ so that the line $y = 6$ is invariant and $(4, 0) \to (-2, 0)$.

Two stretches

8   The square S $(0, 0)$, $(2, 0)$, $(2, 2)$, $(0, 2)$ is stretched by a factor of 3 parallel to the y-axis onto S′ which is then stretched by a factor of 3 parallel to the x-axis.

Two enlargements

9   The triangle T $(1, 2)$, $(1, 4)$, $(0, 4)$ is enlarged onto T′ using the point $(0, 8)$ as centre with a length scale factor of 2.
T′ is then enlarged onto T″ using the point $(6, -1)$ as centre with a length scale factor of 2.

10   The quadrilateral Q $(-6, 3)$, $(-6, 2)$, $(-2, 2)$, $(-4, 3)$ is enlarged onto Q′ using the centre $(-8, 0)$ and a length scale factor of 2.
Q′ is then enlarged using the centre $(8, -8)$ and a length scale factor of $\frac{1}{2}$.

Two mirrors

11   a   A flag F stands 5 cm in front of two parallel mirrors M_1 and M_2 which are 7 cm apart. F′ is the reflection of F in M_1, and F″ is the reflection of F′ in M_2.

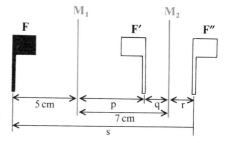

   (i) What type of transformation maps F directly onto F″?
   (ii) Calculate the distances p, q, r and s.

   b

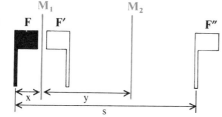

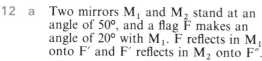

If the flag F stands a distance x in front of M_1 and the two mirrors are a distance y apart, use the same method as in **a** to find the distance s in terms of x and y.

12   a   Two mirrors M_1 and M_2 stand at an angle of 50°, and a flag F makes an angle of 20° with M_1. F reflects in M_1 onto F′ and F′ reflects in M_2 onto F″.

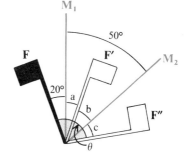

   (i) What type of transformation maps F directly onto F″?
   (ii) Calculate the angles a, b, c and hence the angle of rotation θ.

   b

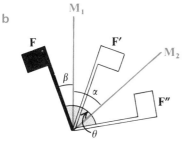

If the flag F makes an angle β with M_1, and the two mirrors are at an angle α apart, use the same method as in **a** to find the angle of rotation θ in terms of α and β.

Combining transformations

13 The flag F can be transformed onto the three
    images of this diagram by rotations and reflections.

    Let **H** stand for a half-turn rotation about the
            origin
        X stand for a reflection in the *x*-axis
        Y stand for a reflection in the *y*-axis
    and **I** stand for the identity transformation
            which maps F onto itself.

    Any two of these transformations, one after the
    other, are equivalent to a *single* transformation.

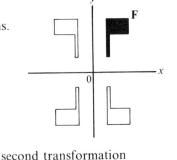

    Copy and complete this table
    to show all possible combinations.

    Use the diagram and your table
    to say whether these statements
    are *true* or *false*.

	second transformation			
first transformation	**X**	**Y**	**H**	**I**
X				
Y				
H				
I				

    a **XY = H**   b **H² = I**   c **X² = I**   d **YX = I**   e **XYX = Y**
    f **YXH = I**   g **Y² = H**   h **H³ = H**   i **XYXY = I**

14 In addition to **X**, **Y**, **H** and **I**,
    let **Q** denote a clockwise $\frac{1}{4}$-turn rotation about the origin
        R denote an anticlockwise $\frac{1}{4}$-turn rotation about the origin
        U denote a reflection in the line $y = x$
    and **V** denote a reflection in the line $y = -x$.
    Copy this table and use the diagram to help you complete it. The results of **13**
    above can be quoted directly.

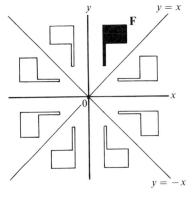

	second transformation							
first transformation	**X**	**Y**	**H**	**I**	**Q**	**R**	**U**	**V**
X								
Y								
H								
I								
Q								
R								
U								
V								

15 a This crossword pattern is incomplete,
       but the quarter shown will either
       reflect or rotate onto any other
       quarter of the crossword. Copy and
       complete the whole pattern.

    b Can you make a crossword of your
       own which will reflect and rotate in
       this way?

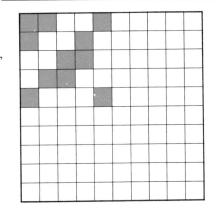

Topology

Topology
Networks
Route matrices

Topology

Topology is the branch of mathematics concerned with shapes which change into other shapes without any cutting or tearing or joining together. A shape can be deformed by bending or stretching as if it were elastic. Indeed, some people call topology "rubber-sheet geometry".

Part 1

Two shapes which can be changed into each other in this way are said to be **topologically equivalent**.

1 Are these pairs of diagrams topologically equivalent? Answer *yes* or *no*.

2 In each group of three shapes, two are topologically equivalent. Find the odd one out.

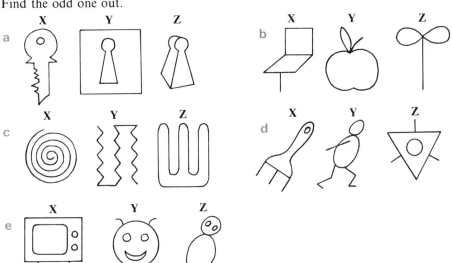

Topology

3 Here are eight drawings labelled *A* to *H*.
They can be arranged into four pairs which are topologically equivalent.
Write the letters of the four pairs.

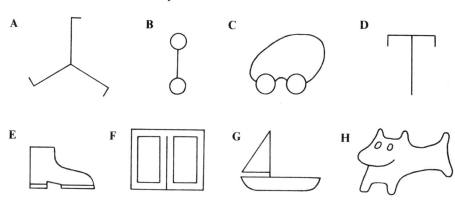

4 Ten numerals are printed here.
Which of them are topologically equivalent to   a   the 1   b   the 6?

0123456789

5 Which letters of the alphabet, as printed here, are topologically equivalent to
a   the C   b   the E   c   the H   d   the A   e   the K?

ABCDEFGHIJKLM
NOPQRSTUVWXYZ

6 This is an electrical circuit using a battery, two lights and a switch.

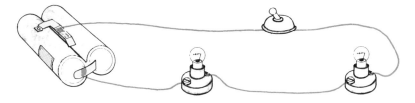

Which one of these three diagrams can represent this circuit?

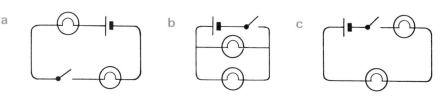

Topology

7 Which two of these three electrical circuits are topologically equivalent, and which is the odd one out?

a 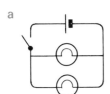   b 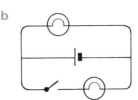   c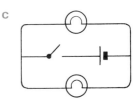

8 Which three of these four electrical circuits are topologically equivalent, and which is the odd one out?

a 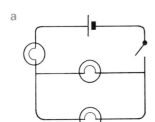   b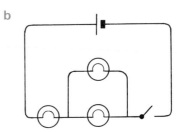

c 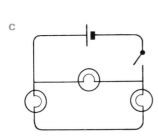   d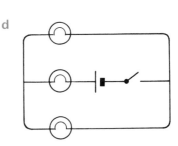

9 These pairs of drawings are topologically equivalent.
The first drawing in each pair has a point labelled *P*.
Copy each of the second drawings and label the point equivalent to *P*.

a 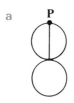   b 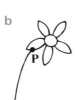   c    d

a   b   c    d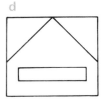

Topology

10   Here is a street map of part of a town centre on which ten important buildings are marked.

Match these buildings with the letters *A* to *J* on the other map which shows the same area of the town.

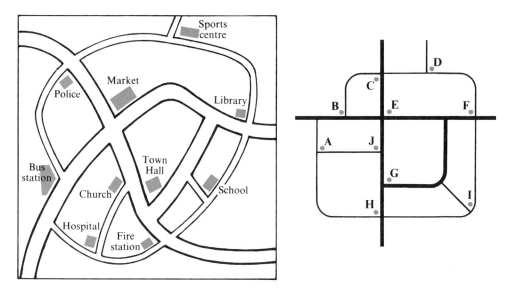

11   Here is another map of a town centre with buildings marked on it.

Copy the second map, which is topologically equivalent, and mark on it the ten buildings. Also draw a line to represent the railway.

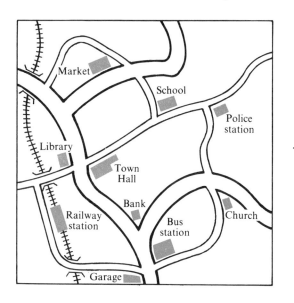
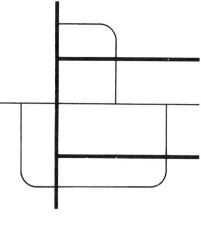

Topology

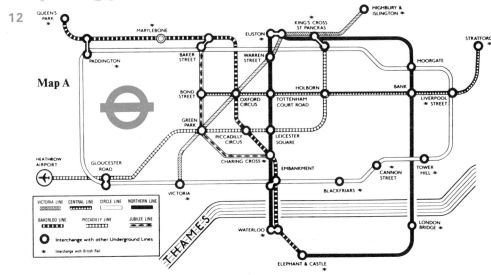

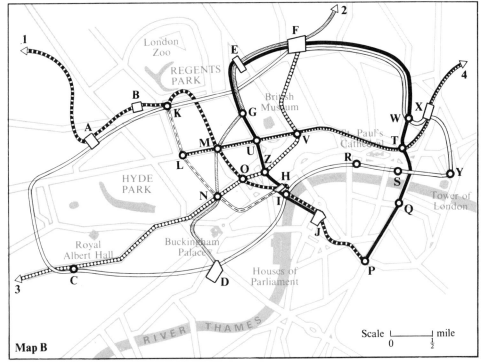

These two maps are topologically equivalent.

Map A shows those lines on the London Underground which link the main-line stations of British Rail.

Map B shows the major roads of central London as well as the same routes of the Underground as map A.

a Match the names of the stations on map A with the letters of the stations on map B. Work alphabetically from *A* to *Z*.

b Four of these lines end off the edge of map B. What are the names of the stations which the numbered arrows *1* to *4* lead to?

Topology

c   Which of these two maps would be the more useful if you wanted to go from Paddington to Victoria
(i) by car   (ii) on the Underground   (iii) on foot?

d   Which of these two maps would be the more useful if you wanted to visit St. Paul's Cathedral after arriving at Euston Station?

e   Map B has been given a scale. Give a reason for map A *not* having a scale.

f   Describe the journey on the Underground if you travel between these stations. Give the lines you travel on and any stations you might change at.
  (i) Euston to Waterloo
  (iii) King's Cross and St. Pancras to Victoria
  (v) Victoria to Bond Street
  (vii) Marylebone to Heathrow Airport
  (ix) Heathrow Airport to Euston
  (ii) Paddington to Victoria
  (iv) Paddington to Oxford Circus
  (vi) Euston to Piccadilly Circus
  (viii) Leicester Square to Paddington
  (x) Charing Cross to Liverpool Street

13   Answer this question *yes* or *no* for each item on the list.
  "Does the item stay unchanged when a shape is transformed topologically?"
  a   the length of a line
  b   the size of an angle
  c   the area of a region
  d   the number of regions
  e   the number of junctions
  f   two parallel lines
  g   the order of points on a line

Part 2   Three dimensions

Solids can also change their shape by stretching and moulding as if they were putty. Care must be taken not to make any extra holes pierce the solid.

1

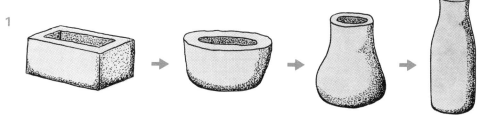

These diagrams show an open box being transformed into a milk bottle.
Which *one* of these objects is *not* topologically equivalent to the box?
  a   a water tank
  b   a waste-paper basket
  c   a button
  d   a plate

2

The doughnut shape is called a **torus**.
A torus can be transformed into a teacup.
Which *one* of these objects is *not* topologically equivalent to a torus?
  a   a wedding-ring
  b   a ruler
  c   a drain-pipe
  d   a metal nut

Topology

3

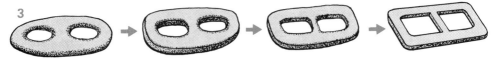

This is a **double-torus** which can be transformed into a buckle.

Which *one* of these objects is *not* topologically equivalent to a double-torus?

a   a pair of trousers   **b**   a door with letter-box and keyhole
c   a button   **d**   a glove

4   Here is a list of objects.
Make three columns labelled *sphere*, *torus* and *double-torus*.
Write each object in the column with which it is topologically equivalent.

a bar of soap   a shirt
a needle   a stone
a pin   a washing-up bowl
a funnel   a pair of shorts
a knife   a life-belt
a brick   a record
a bath without taps   a two-headed ring spanner
a length of wire   a length of hose-pipe
a cricket bat   a log of wood
a Yale key   a loaf of bread
a drinking straw   a milk bottle
a washer   a test tube
a knitting needle   a boot with a hole in it
a wellington boot   a jacket
a glove   a fork
a watering-can   a spectacles frame without lenses
a walking-stick   a pea-shooter

5   Describe how you would make one straight cut through a torus
  a   to leave it in one piece   **b**   to make two separate tori.

6   Which *one* of these objects is topologically equivalent to a three-hole torus?
a   a smoker's pipe   **b**   a balloon
c   a pullover   **d**   a pair of trousers

7   Which *one* of these objects is topologically equivalent to a torus with many holes in it?
a   a comb   **b**   a cog-wheel
c   a hairbrush   **d**   a ladder

8

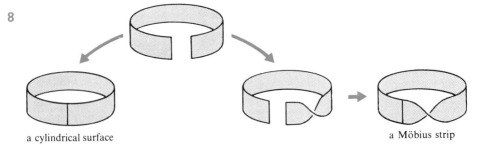

a cylindrical surface   a Möbius strip

Make a cylindrical surface from a strip of paper by joining the two ends together as shown.

Topology

Make a Möbius strip by bringing a strip of paper into a loop, but before joining the ends, put a half-turn twist in the strip. This was invented by August Ferdinand Möbius (1790–1868), a German mathematician and professor of astronomy at Leipzig University.

a   How many edges has the cylindrical surface?

b   How many sides has the cylindrical surface?

c   Mark any point on the edge of your Möbius strip. Start at this point and run your finger along the edge. How many edges has a Möbius strip?

d   Colour the surface of the Möbius strip. How many colours do you need? How many sides has the strip?

e   Copy and complete these two sentences.
     "A cylindrical surface has ... edges and ... sides."
     "A Möbius strip has ... edge and ... side."

9

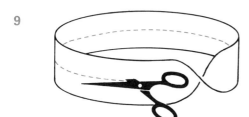 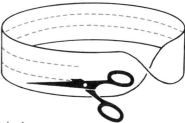

a   Take a Möbius strip with its half-turn twist in it.
     Cut along a line half-way across the strip until you arrive back at where you started. Describe the result.

b   Take another strip. This time, cut along a line one third of the way across, and keep cutting until you arrive back at the start. Describe what happens this time.

10   Repeat problem **9** with a Möbius strip which has *two* half-turn twists in it. Repeat again with one which has *three* half-turn twists in it.

11   Here are two more unusual surfaces. You can make them from pieces of paper stuck together with half-turn twists in some of them as shown.

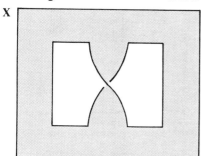 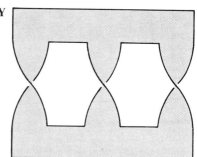

a   How many sides has each surface?

b   How many edges has each surface?

c   How many colours would be needed to shade the whole of each surface if every side has a different colour?

Topology

12 Felix Klein (1849–1925), a German professor of
    mathematics at Leipzig and Göttingen Universities,
    invented a closed surface which has no *inside* or
    outside.

You can make one from a piece of rubber tube
by turning one end *outside in*, passing this end
through a slit in the side of the tube and joining
it to the other end of the tube.

The object is called a **Klein bottle**. Can you
imagine what happens to any water which is
poured into it?

Can you see how to cut a Klein bottle into two
pieces, so that you produce two Möbius strips?

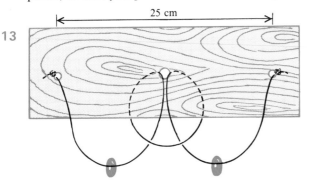

13 A length of string about
    50 cm long, tied at each
    end through holes in a
    piece of wood, passes
    through a small central
    hole, and two beads
    hang on the loops as
    shown.

The object of the puzzle
is to thread one bead
along the string so that
both beads hang together
on the same loop.

You can make the puzzle using an old wooden or plastic ruler with two buttons
or washers – but the central hole must be too small for the buttons to pass
through!

14 If you are wearing a pullover and a jacket, can you take the pullover off *without*
    removing your jacket?

Networks

Part 1 Games and puzzles with networks

Puzzle 1

Copy this network.

Can you write the numbers 1 to 5 in the rings so that no number is joined to one more or one less than itself (e.g. 4 must *not* be joined to 3 or 5)?

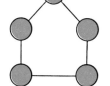

Puzzle 2

Four villages, A, B, C and D are on an island. Three villages X, Y and Z are on a nearby island.

How many telephone lines must there be for all the villages on one island to be directly connected to all the villages on the other island?

How many more lines are needed if a new village W on the second island is introduced?

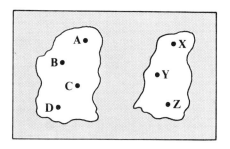

Puzzle 3

This diagram shows three houses which have to be connected to Gas, Water and Electricity supplies.

Copy the diagram and see if it is possible to make the connections so that no connection crosses another. (The three gas pipes have already been drawn for you.)

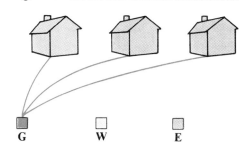

Puzzle 4

You have the Ace, King, Queen, Jack and Ten of Spades. Use a diagram like this one to find how many ways you can choose *two* cards from these five.

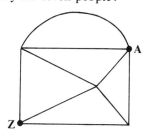

Puzzle 5

Five people meet each other, and everyone shakes hands once with everyone else. Use a diagram like this one to find how many handshakes take place.

How many handshakes take place if six people meet?

How many for seven people?

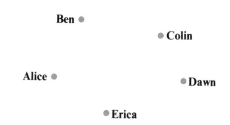

Ben •
• Colin
Alice •
•Dawn
•Erica

Puzzle 6

How many different routes can you take from A to Z if each route must not cross itself or use the same line twice?

Networks

Puzzle 7

Sixteen points arranged in a square are connected by a network of paths.

You always start at point *O* and your route along the paths must *always* take you further and further from *O*. You are not allowed to move nearer to *O*.

Copy the diagram and draw an arrow on each path to show the direction allowed.

How many of these routes are there

a	from *O* to *D*	b from *O* to *B*
c	from *O* to *E*	d from *O* to *H*
e	from *O* to *G*	f from *O* to *K*?

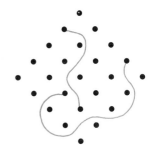

Can you see how your answers for *D*, *B*, *E* and *H* are related?
Can you see how your answers for *G*, *D*, *H* and *K* are related?

How many of these routes are there

g	from *O* to *J*	h from *O* to *M*	i from *O* to *Z*?

Game 1   The Game of Dots

Draw a diamond-shaped pattern of dots of any size.

Two players take it in turn to join two dots without touching any other dot or any line which has already been drawn.

The player who loses is the one who first touches another dot or line whilst trying to join his two dots.

Sharp pencils are needed, and the game is a draw if all the dots are used.

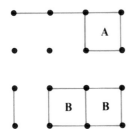

Game 2   The Game of Squares

This popular game needs a grid of dots of any size with each player taking turns to join two adjacent dots. When a player completes a square, he initials the inside and takes an extra turn.

The winner is the player who has initialled most squares.

Game 3   The Game of Tips and Tails

Put nine dots in any position on a piece of paper.

The first player draws an arrow from one dot to another. The second player must draw his arrow from the tip of the first arrow to a third point.

The first player then draws his next arrow from the tip of the previous one; and so on.

No point can be used twice, and no arrow must cross another arrow. The winner is the last player who can draw an arrow.

(In the diagram shown here, the first player is the winner.)

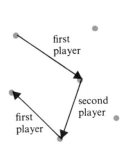

Networks

Game 4 The Game of Fox and Hounds

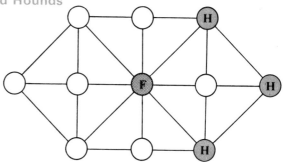

Copy this grid and its rings.

The three hounds are the coloured counters which start in rings *H*.

The counter for the fox starts in ring *F*.

The hounds move from one ring to another along a line, but must *always* move from right to left or up and down. The fox moves in any direction.

The aim is for the fox to break through the line of hounds (or for the same moves to be repeated over and over again); in which case the fox wins.

But the hounds win if they corner the fox so that it cannot move.

The players take turns to move, and the hounds move first.

Game 5 The Game of Sprouts

Draw two dots on paper.

The first player draws a line from one dot either to the other dot or back to the same dot. He then marks a *new* dot on this line.

The second player now draws a line from one dot either to another dot or back to the same one. He also marks a *new* dot on his line.

This continues in turns until the winner is the last player to draw a line.

There are three rules.

1 No line must cross another line.

2 A dot is 'dead' when three lines meet there. Such a dot cannot be used again.

3 A loop line back to the same dot is allowed, provided rule **2** is not broken.

This diagram shows the two starting dots coloured black.

Each player has drawn one line, and two new dots *A* and *B* have appeared.

Dot *A* is 'dead' and cannot be used again.

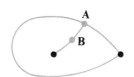

Part 2 Networks

1 A network is **traversable** or **unicursal** if you can draw it in one movement without lifting your pencil or going over the same part twice.
Which of these networks are traversable?

a
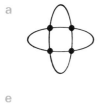

b

c

d

e
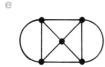

f

g

h

Networks

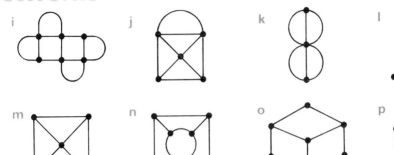

2 The points where the lines of a network meet are called **nodes**.
If an odd number of lines meet there, it is an *odd node*.
If an even number of lines meet there, it is an *even node*.
Copy and complete this table for the networks in **1** above.

Network	Number of		Is the network traversable?
	odd nodes	even nodes	
a			
b			
c			
p			

a There is a pattern in these results which tells you whether a network is traversable. Why is the number of *odd nodes* important?

b Is there a particular node to start at when traversing the network if the network has   (i) only even nodes   (ii) any odd nodes?

3 Each of these next networks is traversable.
Decide which nodes are even and which are odd. At which node must you start to traverse each network?
Now see if you can traverse each one.

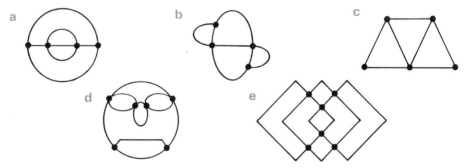

4 Which capital letters of the alphabet are   a traversable   b not traversable?

5 The lines joining the nodes are called **arcs**.
If four arcs meet at a node, it is called a **4-node**.
Can you design your own network so that it has
  a four 4-nodes
  b four 2-nodes
  c two 4-nodes and two 3-nodes
  d one 6-node
  e two 3-nodes
  f four 2-nodes and one 4-node
  g one 6-node and one 4-node
  h one 5-node and five 3-nodes.

6 The arcs of a network divide it into areas called **regions**.
Even the area *outside* a network is counted as a region.
Copy and complete this table for each network in problem **1** above.

Network	Number of nodes N	Number of regions R	Number of arcs A	$N + R - A$
a				
b				
c				
p				

What do you notice about the results in the last column? This is known as **Euler's Network Formula**.

7 Königsberg in 1737 was a city in East Prussia; now it is in the USSR and called Kaliningrad. At that time two islands in the River Pregel were connected by seven bridges.

Leonard Euler, a mathematician born in Basle, Switzerland, was asked if it was possible to take a walk across all the bridges once and only once.

a Draw a network, with nodes A, B, C, D, which is topologically equivalent to this map of the bridges.
Is the network traversable?

b If you were allowed to remove one bridge to make the network traversable, which bridge would you choose, or would any bridge do?

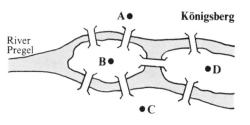

c Today in Kaliningrad, there are two more bridges across the Pregel. Draw a new network for these nine bridges, still using the nodes A, B, C, D.
Is the new network traversable?

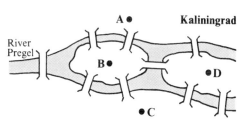

8 This is the plan of the three rooms X, Y, Z of a bungalow. The outside of the bungalow is labelled W.

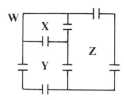
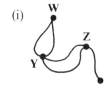
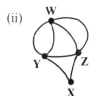
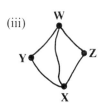

a Which one of these three networks is topologically equivalent to the plan?
b Is the correct network traversable?
c Is it possible to walk through the bungalow and pass through each door only once?

Networks

9   Here are four more plans of bungalows with each room labelled.
Draw a network for each one, and so find out if it is possible to walk through each bungalow passing through each door only once.

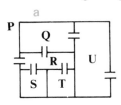 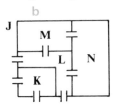 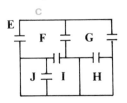 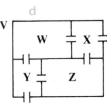

a   b   c   d

10

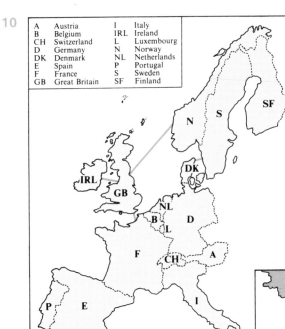

A	Austria	I	Italy
B	Belgium	IRL	Ireland
CH	Switzerland	L	Luxembourg
D	Germany	N	Norway
DK	Denmark	NL	Netherlands
E	Spain	P	Portugal
F	France	S	Sweden
GB	Great Britain	SF	Finland

a   This map shows the countries of Western Europe (except Iceland) with four connecting ferries.
Is it possible to design a holiday tour which visits each country once and only once?
Take care *not* to draw in this book!

b   If part **a** is impossible, can you design a tour where you are allowed to visit just *one* country *twice*? Which country will it be, and where will the tour start and end?

11 The sea areas around the British Isles are shown in this map.
a   Is it possible for a boat to sail so that it visits each area only once?

b   Is it possible to do this, starting and finishing in the same area?

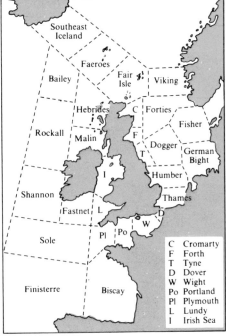

C	Cromarty
F	Forth
T	Tyne
D	Dover
W	Wight
Po	Portland
Pl	Plymouth
L	Lundy
I	Irish Sea

Networks

12 This map shows part of
the British Rail passenger
network in southern England.

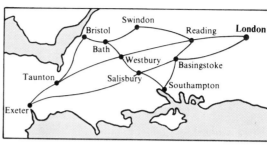

Is it possible for a railway
enthusiast to travel on each
of these lines once and only
once?

If so, where should be the
start and finish?

13

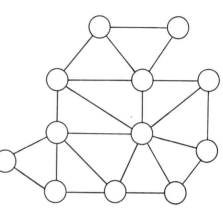

Here is a map of the counties in Northern England.

The network is topologically equivalent to the map with the arcs of the network
joining counties which have a common border.

Copy the network and write the initials of the counties in the correct circles.

Can a tourist organise a route through these counties to visit each just once,
arriving back at the starting point?

What is the least number of county borders that will be crossed?

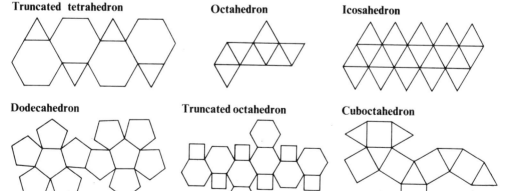

Truncated tetrahedron   **Octahedron**   **Icosahedron**

Dodecahedron   **Truncated octahedron**   **Cuboctahedron**

14 Above are the nets of six polyhedra.

If you copied these onto card, you could make the models.

Which of these nets are traversable and which are not?

Remember first to count the arcs to find the even and odd nodes.

If a net *is* traversable, where do you start to draw it and where do you end?

Networks

15 Can you run your finger along all the edges of these solids without going along any edge twice and without lifting your finger?

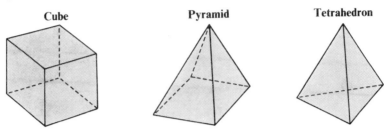

Cube   Pyramid   Tetrahedron

Part 3   Curves and mazes

1 A **simple closed curve** is topologically equivalent to a circle.
Which of these diagrams are simple closed curves?

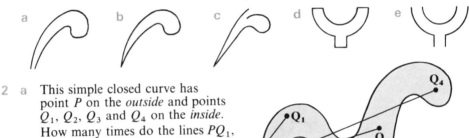

a   b   c   d   e

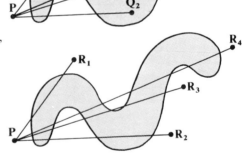

2 a This simple closed curve has point P on the *outside* and points Q_1, Q_2, Q_3 and Q_4 on the *inside*. How many times do the lines PQ_1, PQ_2, PQ_3 and PQ_4 cut the curve?

  b The same curve has points R_1, R_2, R_3 and R_4 on the *outside*. How many times do the lines PR_1, PR_2, PR_3 and PR_4 cut the curve?

  c Can you invent a simple rule to say whether a point is *outside* or *inside* a simple closed curve?

This rule was first discovered by a Frenchman, Camille Jordan (1838–1922) and it is known as **Jordan's Theorem**.

3

Here is a more complicated closed curve. Use the rule to find whether the points W, X, Y, Z are inside or outside the curve. Note that point A is definitely *outside* the curve.

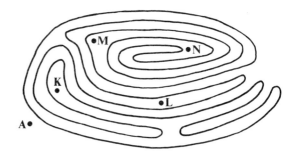

4   Are the points *K, L, M, N*
    inside or outside this closed
    curve?

5   Copy the diagrams in problems **3** and **4**, and shade the inside of the curves.

6   Some mazes are based on a simple closed curve which is
    given one entrance.
    Mazes like this can be solved by keeping one hand in
    touch with the side as you walk through the maze.

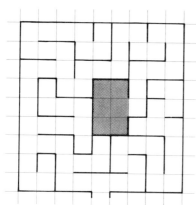

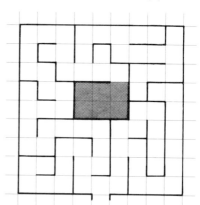

Copy these two mazes on squared paper (starting with a 9 × 9 square).
Use three different colours to draw the paths you take if you
a   keep your left hand running along the sides
b   keep your right hand running along the sides
c   go the shortest way.

7   Other mazes can be based
    on two loops, one inside
    the other. There are now
    two ways of finding the
    centre.

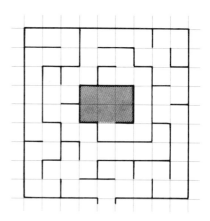

    a   Copy this maze on squared paper
        (starting with a 9 × 9 square). Can
        you draw two different paths to the
        centre?
    b   What happens if you keep your left
        hand to the wall as you walk?
    c   What happens if your right hand
        always touches the wall as you walk?

135

Networks

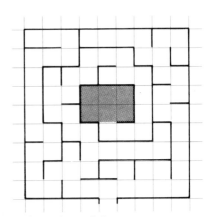

8 This maze *looks* exactly the same as that in problem **7** above. In fact there is one small difference in the top row.

   a   Which of the two types of maze is this?

   b   Is it an easier maze than that in problem **7**?

   c   Will the 'hand-on-the-wall' method work here? Try it with the right hand.

9

This is a plan of the maze at Hampton Court near London which was acquired by King Henry VIII in 1526. The maze itself was not built until the 1690s in'the reign of William III.
Is there more than one way of finding the centre?

10 Make up some mazes of your own on squared paper.

Part 4 Colouring networks

1 These traversable networks have only even nodes.
Copy them and colour their regions using only *two* colours, so that no regions next to each other are in the same colour.
Remember that the *outside* region must also be coloured.

  a   b   c    d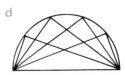

2 These traversable networks have two nodes which are odd.
Copy them and colour their regions using *three* colours, again with no adjacent regions the same colour.

  a   b   c   d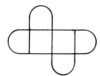

3 These networks are *not* traversable. Copy and colour them using as *few* colours as possible. (Number the regions first in pencil before you colour – you might want to change your mind!)

  a    b   c   d

136

Networks

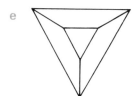
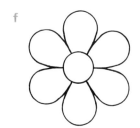
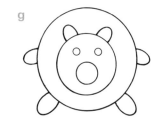

4   So far only four colours at most have been used.
No one has ever drawn a network that needs five colours.
It was proved many years ago that *five* colours will always be enough, but although the problem was first posed in the 1850s, it was not proved that *four* colours is always enough until 1976.
In that year, a proof was discovered by mathematicians at the University of Illinois in America, who extended a British method dating from 1879. The proof required several hundred pages of explanation and used over 1000 hours of computer time for the calculations.
Turn to the pages specified, copy the maps and colour them using no more than four colours.
a   page 132 for the map of Western Europe
b   page 132 for the map of the sea areas around the British Isles
c   page 133 for the map of Northern England

5   From an atlas, trace a map of the continents of   a   South America   b   Africa
and colour them using no more than 4 colours. Remember to include the sea as a region.

6   What is the least number of colours needed for the faces of these solids, so that no two faces sharing the same edge have the same colour?

a   b 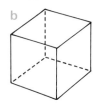   c 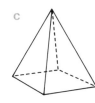   d 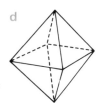   e

7   This large cube is made from small cubes with three small cubes in each row and each column.
All the faces of the large cube are now painted brown.
How many of the small cubes
a   are there altogether   b   have no brown faces
c   have just one brown face
d   have exactly two brown faces
e   have exactly three brown faces
f   have more than three brown faces?

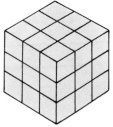

8   A larger cube is made with four small cubes in each row and each column.
The faces of this large cube are also painted brown.
Answer the same questions for this cube as you did in problem **7**.

137

Route matrices

Part 1 By sea, land and air

1 These three maps show boat services between Britain and Europe.
Copy and complete the tables to give the number of direct routes.

a

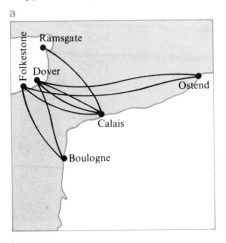

		Boulogne	Calais	Ostend
			to	
from	Dover			
	Folkestone			
	Ramsgate			

b

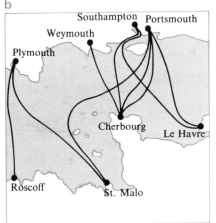

		Roscoff	St. Malo	Cherbourg	Le Havre
				to	
	Plymouth				
from	Weymouth				
	Southampton				
	Portsmouth				

c

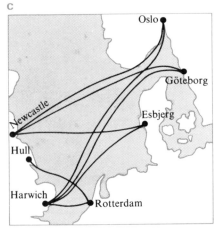

		Rotterdam	Esbjerg	Oslo	Göteborg
				to	
	Newcastle				
from	Hull				
	Harwich				

Route matrices

2 The main roads between several towns and cities are shown on these sketch maps. Copy and complete each matrix to give the number of *direct* routes.

a

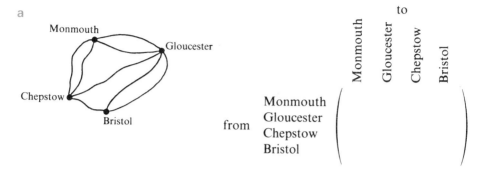

b

c

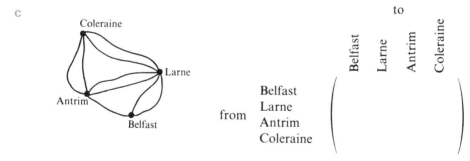

3 Several airlines have flights connecting these cities. Copy and complete the route matrices.

a

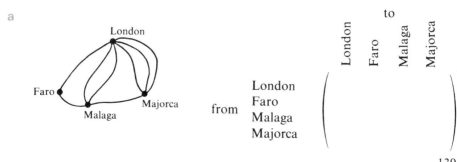

Route matrices

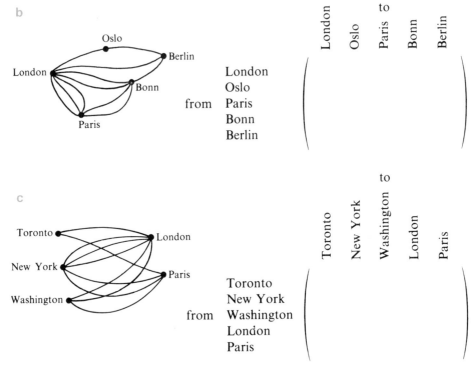

4 a The diagonal which runs from top-left to bottom-right is called the **leading diagonal**. What do you notice about the leading diagonals in the route matrices of questions **2** and **3**?

   b If you place a mirror on each leading diagonal, what happens to each half of the matrix?

   c Copy and complete this sentence with the missing word:
      'In each of these route matrices, the leading diagonal is a line of s.......'

5 These networks have loops, around which you can go in either direction. Each loop thus gives you *two* routes.
   Copy and complete each route matrix.

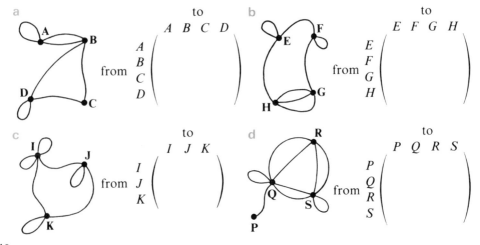

Route matrices

6 The main roads between Stoke-on-Trent, Derby and Wolverhampton are shown in this route matrix.
Copy the positions of the three points S, D and W; then draw a network to show the roads between them.

$$
\begin{array}{c}
\text{to} \\
\begin{array}{ccc}
S & D & W
\end{array}
\end{array}
$$

$$
\text{from} \quad
\begin{array}{c}
S \\ D \\ W
\end{array}
\left(
\begin{array}{ccc}
0 & 2 & 2 \\
2 & 0 & 1 \\
2 & 1 & 0
\end{array}
\right)
$$

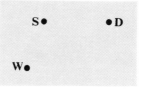

7 The three centres of Leeds, Huddersfield and Sheffield are connected by the main roads given in this matrix.
Copy the positions of these three points L, H and S; and draw a network to show the roads between them.

$$
\begin{array}{c}
\text{to} \\
\begin{array}{ccc}
H & L & S
\end{array}
\end{array}
$$

$$
\text{from} \quad
\begin{array}{c}
H \\ L \\ S
\end{array}
\left(
\begin{array}{ccc}
0 & 3 & 1 \\
3 & 0 & 2 \\
1 & 2 & 0
\end{array}
\right)
$$

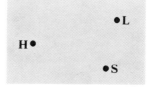

8 This route matrix gives the main roads between the Scottish cities of Glasgow, Edinburgh, Stirling and Perth.
Copy the positions of the points G, E, S and P; then draw a network to show the roads between them.

$$
\begin{array}{c}
\text{to} \\
\begin{array}{cccc}
G & E & S & P
\end{array}
\end{array}
$$

$$
\text{from} \quad
\begin{array}{c}
G \\ E \\ S \\ P
\end{array}
\left(
\begin{array}{cccc}
0 & 3 & 2 & 1 \\
3 & 0 & 2 & 2 \\
2 & 2 & 0 & 2 \\
1 & 2 & 2 & 0
\end{array}
\right)
$$

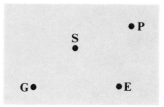

9 For each matrix, position points as you think suitable and draw the network of routes between them as given in the matrix.
Remember that loops are shown on the leading diagonal.

a

$$
\begin{array}{c}
\text{to} \\
\begin{array}{ccc}
P & Q & R
\end{array}
\end{array}
$$

$$
\text{from} \quad
\begin{array}{c}
P \\ Q \\ R
\end{array}
\left(
\begin{array}{ccc}
0 & 2 & 2 \\
2 & 0 & 1 \\
2 & 1 & 0
\end{array}
\right)
$$

b

$$
\begin{array}{c}
\text{to} \\
\begin{array}{ccc}
K & L & M
\end{array}
\end{array}
$$

$$
\text{from} \quad
\begin{array}{c}
K \\ L \\ M
\end{array}
\left(
\begin{array}{ccc}
0 & 1 & 2 \\
1 & 0 & 1 \\
2 & 1 & 2
\end{array}
\right)
$$

c

$$
\begin{array}{c}
\text{to} \\
\begin{array}{cccc}
W & X & Y & Z
\end{array}
\end{array}
$$

$$
\text{from} \quad
\begin{array}{c}
W \\ X \\ Y \\ Z
\end{array}
\left(
\begin{array}{cccc}
0 & 2 & 0 & 1 \\
2 & 0 & 3 & 1 \\
0 & 3 & 0 & 0 \\
1 & 1 & 0 & 2
\end{array}
\right)
$$

d

$$
\begin{array}{c}
\text{to} \\
\begin{array}{cccc}
K & L & M & N
\end{array}
\end{array}
$$

$$
\text{from} \quad
\begin{array}{c}
K \\ L \\ M \\ N
\end{array}
\left(
\begin{array}{cccc}
0 & 2 & 1 & 1 \\
2 & 0 & 1 & 0 \\
1 & 1 & 2 & 3 \\
1 & 0 & 3 & 0
\end{array}
\right)
$$

Route matrices

e

		to			
		A	B	C	D
	A	2	1	0	1
	B	1	0	2	2
from	C	0	2	0	0
	D	1	2	0	2

f

		to		
		R	S	T
	R	2	1	1
from	S	1	2	1
	T	1	1	4

g

		to			
		W	X	Y	Z
	W	0	1	2	0
	X	1	0	1	1
from	Y	2	1	4	0
	Z	0	1	0	2

10 This sketch map shows North Sea crossings from Harwich with some main roads in England and in Europe.

Construct a route matrix for the six places on the map, and explain the zeros which you write in the matrix.

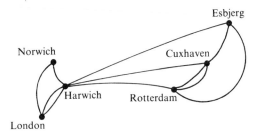

Part 2 One-way streets

A one-way street is shown on a network by an arrow which gives the direction of travel. A route with no arrow means you can travel in either direction.

1 The centre of a town has three one-way streets as shown on this map.

A network is also shown for the roads between four important buildings.

a Copy and complete the route matrix.

b Is the matrix symmetrical about the leading diagonal?

c What is there in the network which destroys the symmetry?

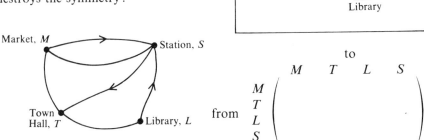

		to			
		M	T	L	S
	M				
from	T				
	L				
	S				

Route matrices

2 Copy and complete the route matrices for these three networks.

a

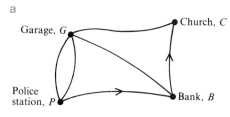

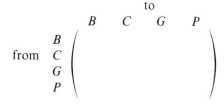

b

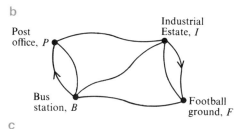

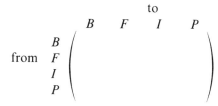

c

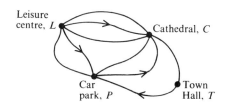

3 Construct your own route matrices for the two networks shown here.
Remember that you can go round a loop in either direction, unless of course
it is a one-way street.

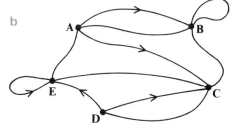

4 Four parts of a town are joined by a road network as shown in the first diagram.
The council then introduce the one-way system given in the second diagram.
Construct two route matrices to give the roads before and after the introduction
of the one-way system.

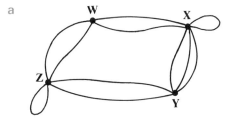

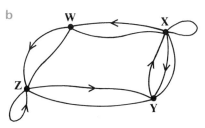

Route matrices

5 Draw the networks described by these three matrices.
Label the points of the networks in a clockwise direction.

a

	to		
from	P	Q	R
P	2	2	1
Q	1	0	1
R	1	0	0

b

	to			
from	A	B	C	D
A	0	3	0	1
B	1	0	1	1
C	0	1	2	1
D	2	1	1	1

c

	to				
from	J	K	L	M	N
J	2	1	0	0	0
K	1	0	2	1	0
L	0	1	0	2	0
M	0	2	1	0	1
N	0	0	0	2	3

Answer the remaining questions *without* drawing any networks.
Use only the matrices given here to find the answers.

6 a How many routes lead from A to B?
   b How many routes lead from B to A?
   c How many one-way routes are there from A to B?
   d How many routes lead from B to C?
   e How many routes lead from C to B?
   f How many one-way routes are there from B to C?

	to		
from	A	B	C
A	0	4	1
B	2	0	4
C	1	1	0

7 a How many routes lead from L to M?
   b How many routes lead from M to L?
   c How many one-way routes lead from L to M?
   d How many routes lead from L to N?
   e How many routes lead from N to L?
   f How many one-way routes lead from L to N?
   g Use the same method to find how many one-way routes there are between M and N.

	to		
from	L	M	N
L	0	3	4
M	1	0	2
N	3	0	0

8 Are these journeys possible or not?
   a from R to S, then from S to T
   b from T to R, then from R to U
   c from T to S, then from S to U
   d from U to R, then from R to T
   e from T to U, then from U to S
   f from S to T, then on to R, then back to S

	to			
from	R	S	T	U
R	0	2	0	1
S	2	0	1	0
T	1	1	0	0
U	1	0	0	0

Route matrices

Part 3 Two-stage journeys

1

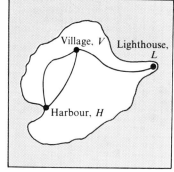

The small island of Stackholm has three roads as shown on this map. Visitors to it who want to use the bus service can buy two kinds of ticket.

The first is a *one-stage* ticket for a journey on any arc of the road network; the second is a *two-stage* ticket for one journey along two arcs of the network.

a Copy the *one-stage* matrix, *M*, and complete it by asking where you can get to and in how many ways, from each of the three places on the island, using a one-stage ticket.

one-stage matrix, *M*

to

$$\text{from} \quad \begin{array}{c} H \\ L \\ V \end{array} \left(\begin{array}{ccc} H & L & V \\ & & \\ & & \\ & & \end{array} \right)$$

b How many different ways can you use a *two-stage* ticket? For example, starting from *H*, there are six possibilities. Find out where they finish, and enter your answers in the first row of the two-stage matrix, *N*.

Complete the other two rows for journeys starting from *L* and from *V*.

two-stage matrix, *N*

to

$$\text{from} \quad \begin{array}{c} H \\ L \\ V \end{array} \left(\begin{array}{ccc} H & L & V \\ & & \\ & & \\ & & \end{array} \right)$$

c Take the one-stage matrix, *M*, and multiply it by itself (by combining rows with columns).

Is it true that $N = M \times M$?

This gives an alternative way of finding a two-stage matrix.

2

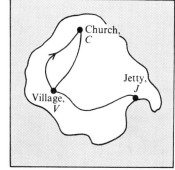

This map shows the road network on the neighbouring island of Glaspay. One road is so narrow that it has been made one-way.

a Construct a one-stage matrix, *M*, for journeys which use just one arc of the network.

b Construct a two-stage matrix, *N*, for journeys which use two arcs, one after the other.

c Multiply matrix *M* by itself and show that $N = M \times M$.

145

Route matrices

3   For each of these networks, construct a one-stage route matrix, M, and a two-stage route matrix, N. Show in each case that $N = M \times M$.

a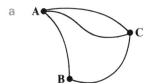

b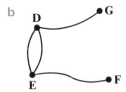

c

d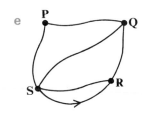

e

f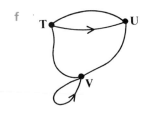

4   a   Write the one-stage route matrix, M, for this network of roads across Yorkshire.

b   Calculate the two-stage route matrix, N, by using $N = M \times M$.

c   How many two-stage routes are there
    (i) from Halifax to York
    (ii) from Leeds to Scarborough?

d   Calculate the three-stage route matrix, P, using $P = M \times M \times M$.

e   How many three-stage routes are there from Leeds to Scarborough? Write the order of the towns you pass through for each of these routes.

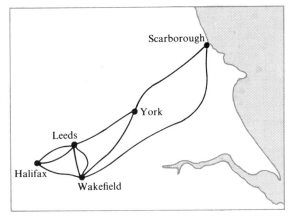

Matrices

Tabulation of information

Introduction

Information, especially numerical information, is often written in rows and columns; i.e. it is **tabulated**.

Most typewriters have special keys which make it easy to tabulate information. Computers can be programmed to print information in the form of tables.

1 Mr Gilbert received this bill from his garage.

   a How much did part no. 140062 cost?

   b What was the charge for labour?

   c How much VAT (Value Added Tax) was paid?

   d How many spark plugs were fitted and how much did each one cost?

   e How many washers were used and what was the total cost of them all?

Customer:	Mr. Gilbert 42 Bridge St. Hawksworth	**BLUNDELLS** of **HAWKSWORTH** CENTRAL GARAGE	
Telephone: 97-2743			
Make: Humdinger GLX		Reg. No: PZX 421Y	
Mileage: 57460		Date: 21/2/84	

PARTS Description	Number	Qty.	Unit cost	Cost
Hose	3A6442	1	1·42	1·42
Points	140062	1	1·75	1·75
Joints	7B2237	2	0·42	0·84
Washers	240165	5	0·12	0·60
Spark plugs	173012	4	0·44	1·76
Oil filter	2A4691	1	2·64	2·64
TOTAL PARTS				9·01
LABOUR				24·63
VAT			15%	5·05
TOTAL AMOUNT DUE			£	38·69

2 Your bank sends you a statement of your account.

   a What was the balance in your account on 10th May?

   b On what day was your salary paid into your account, and how much was it?

   c How much was paid out on 5th May and what was it paid to?

   d On what day was £24·60 paid out, and why was it paid?

   e On what day was there a balance of £262·30?

National Bank

Statement of account with National Bank PLC

MR. M. HARRIS
174 LEES ROAD
BRIESTLY

Description of entries
BGC Bank Giro Credit
D/D Direct Debit
S/O Standing Order

All entries to 18 MAY inclusive are complete.

Account number
0123456

Date	Particulars		Payments		Receipts		Balance When overdrawn marked OD	
1984	Opening Balance						15	84
2 MAY	SALARY	BGC			412	63	428	47
5 MAY	HOMELY BUILDING SOCIETY	S/O	114	72			313	75
10 MAY	CHEQUE	144602	21	24			292	51
11 MAY	CHEQUE	144603	30	21			262	30
14 MAY	INSURANCE	D/D	24	60			237	70
18 MAY	CREDIT BY POST				61	42	299	12

Tabulation of information

3 Mondays to Fridays

Cheltenham Spa	Gloucester	Stonehouse	Stroud	Kemble	Swindon	Reading	Paddington
← departures →					← arrivals →		
06 17	06 30	06 42	06 47	07 03	07 20	08 03	08 34
07 40	07 53	08 06	08 11	08 26	08 42	09 13	09 42
08 50	09 03	→	09 18	09 33	09 47	10 15	10 44
09 37	09 50	10 02	10 07	10 23	10 41	11 40	11 36
10 37	10 50	11 02	11 07	11 23	11 40	12 40	13 13
11 37	11 50	12 02	12 07	12 23	12 40	13 40	13 36
12 37	12 50	13 02	13 07	13 23	13 40	14 40	15 13

Each row of this British Rail timetable shows the times of a morning train from Cheltenham to London Paddington.

a At what time does the first train from Cheltenham arrive in Paddington?
b At what time does the 09.50 from Gloucester arrive in Paddington?
c At what time does the 13.36 into Paddington leave Cheltenham?
d At which station does the 10.44 into Paddington *not* stop?
e At what time should you leave Stroud if you want to arrive in Reading just before midday?

4

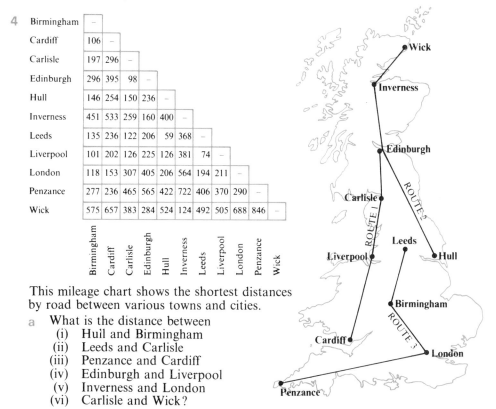

Birmingham	–										
Cardiff	106	–									
Carlisle	197	296	–								
Edinburgh	296	395	98	–							
Hull	146	254	150	236	–						
Inverness	451	533	259	160	400	–					
Leeds	135	236	122	206	59	368	–				
Liverpool	101	202	126	225	126	381	74	–			
London	118	153	307	405	206	564	194	211	–		
Penzance	277	236	465	565	422	722	406	370	290	–	
Wick	575	657	383	284	524	124	492	505	688	846	–
	Birmingham	Cardiff	Carlisle	Edinburgh	Hull	Inverness	Leeds	Liverpool	London	Penzance	Wick

This mileage chart shows the shortest distances by road between various towns and cities.

a What is the distance between
   (i) Hull and Birmingham
   (ii) Leeds and Carlisle
   (iii) Penzance and Cardiff
   (iv) Edinburgh and Liverpool
   (v) Inverness and London
   (vi) Carlisle and Wick?

b Which two places in this table are the furthest apart, and what is the distance between them?

c Which two places are nearest together, and what is the distance between them?

Tabulation of information

d You travel from London to Hull and then continue your journey to Leeds. How long is the journey?

e You leave your home in Cardiff and travel to Birmingham. You then continue your journey by going on to Liverpool before returning directly to home. How far have you travelled altogether?

f The map shows three routes. Find the length of
(i) route 1 from Cardiff to Edinburgh
(ii) route 2 from Wick to Hull
(iii) route 3 from Penzance to Leeds.

5 A holiday brochure advertises the hotel 'Costa del Oro' on Majorca and includes this table of prices in £s.

Costa del Oro Board arrangement: HB Holiday No: TH15

Departure Airport	Gatwick		Luton		Birmingham		Manchester		Newcastle		Add Week	% Child discount
No. of Nights	7	14	7	14	7	14	7	14	7	14		
Departures on or before: 22 Oct – 6 Nov	**165**	**227**	**167**	**229**	–	–	**175**	**237**	**189**	**247**	**62**	**10**
7 Nov – 20 Nov	**152**	**216**	**154**	**218**	–	–	**162**	**226**	**176**	**240**	**64**	**20**
21 Nov – 11 Dec	**138**	**179**	–	–	–	–	**148**	**189**	**162**	**203**	**103**	**40**
12 Dec – 18 Dec	**123**	**235**	–	–	–	–	**133**	**245**	**147**	**264**	**112**	**10**
19 Dec – 24 Dec	**195**	**263**	–	–	–	–	**205**	**273**	**223**	**289**	**68**	**10**
26 Dec – 31 Dec	**176**	**232**	–	–	–	–	**186**	**242**	**200**	**262**	**56**	**10**
1 Jan – 22 Jan	**129**	**187**	–	–	–	–	**139**	**197**	**153**	**211**	**58**	**50**
23 Jan – 12 Feb	**143**	**204**	–	–	–	–	**153**	**214**	**167**	**228**	**61**	**30**
13 Feb – 26 Feb	**152**	**216**	–	–	**159**	**223**	**162**	**226**	**175**	**239**	**64**	**20**
27 Feb – 18 Mar	**163**	**226**	–	–	**170**	**233**	**173**	**236**	**187**	**250**	**63**	**20**
19 Mar – 1 Apr	**168**	**232**	**170**	**234**	**175**	**239**	**178**	**242**	**192**	**256**	**64**	**20**
2 Apr – 14 Apr	**176**	**240**	**178**	**242**	**183**	**247**	**186**	**250**	**200**	**264**	**64**	**20**
Day/Flight code	Saturday SGB10		Saturday SLB10		Saturday NBB10		Saturday NMB10		Saturday NNB10			

Note – Three and four week holiday. The price for an extra week's holiday can be found by adding the two week price to the price of the 'Add Week' in the same season band.

a How much would a 7-night holiday cost which departs from Gatwick on 7th November?

b How much would a 14-night holiday cost which departs from Manchester on 8th January?

c If I paid £159 for a holiday, leaving Birmingham on 20th February, how many nights did I go for?

d How much more expensive is any holiday starting from Luton rather than Gatwick?

e What percentage discount does a child get on a holiday starting on 28th November?

f Between which two dates is the child's discount greatest?

g On what date does the first flight leave Birmingham?

h I leave Newcastle on 20th February for a *three-week* holiday. How much do the first two weeks cost, how much extra is the third week, and what is the total cost of the three weeks?

Tabulation of information

Part 1 Completing a table

Each situation below involves numerical information.
Copy the tables provided and complete them using the information.

1 The sales room of a large garage exports 52 tractors and 87 cars in the same week that it sells 34 tractors and 103 cars on the home market.

	Tractors	Cars
For export		
For home		

2 A garden nursery stocks 6 different winter-flowering trees and 8 different winter-flowering shrubs. It also stocks 14 types of trees and 23 types of shrubs which flower in summer.

	Winter	Summer
Trees		
Shrubs		

3 In a class at a school, 5 boys and 4 girls own some kind of pet, but 11 boys and 9 girls own no pets.

	Pet	No pet
Girls		
Boys		

4 Bruddersfax Symphony Orchestra has 62 string players, 7 woodwind players, 8 brass players and 2 percussionists. Their smaller Chamber Orchestra has 16 strings, 4 woodwind, 2 brass and one percussionist.

	Strings	Woodwind	Brass	Percussion	Total
Symphony Orchestra					
Chamber Orchestra					

5 The PE teacher was annoyed when 4 boys and 5 girls turned up for a lesson without any kit, in a class of 16 boys and 12 girls.

	With kit	Without kit	Total
Boys			
Girls			

6 A survey was made of 100 men and 100 women to find if they watched any television on one particular evening. Of the men, 30 watched BBC, 25 watched ITV, and the rest saw no television at all. Of the women, 32 watched BBC, 41 watched ITV, and the others saw none.

	BBC	ITV	None	Total
Men				
Women				

7 On Friday afternoon in a certain school, only 85% of the boys and 92% of the girls were present.

%	Present	Absent
Boys		
Girls		

Tabulation of information

8 In England, 35% of people live in cities, 53% in towns, and the rest in rural areas. In France, 22% live in cities, 45% in towns, and the others in rural areas.

%	Cities	Towns	Rural areas	Total
England				
France				

9 In 1880 in the village of Elthorpe, there lived 150 people, of whom 44 were men, 46 were women, and the others were children. By 1980 the population of the village had doubled exactly; and there were now 104 men and 125 women, the others being children.

	Men	Women	Children	Total
1880				
1980				

10 This chart shows the number of pupils entering a primary school between 1979 and 1983. Each column of the chart is divided into boys and girls.
Copy the table and use the chart to complete it.

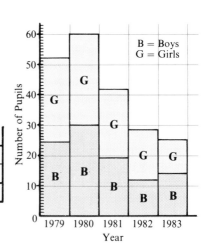

	1979	1980	1981	1982	1983
Boys					
Girls					
Total					

11

Over a six-year period, a manufacturing firm sells its products at home and abroad. Each column of this chart is divided into home and export sales.
Copy the table, and use the chart to complete it.

£ millions	1978	1979	1980	1981	1982	1983
Export sales						
Home sales						
Total sales						

Tabulation of information

12 The populations of two countries *A* and *B* live in cities, towns and villages as shown by the pie charts.

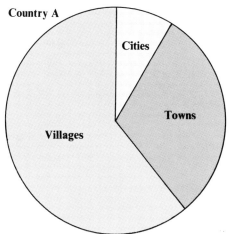

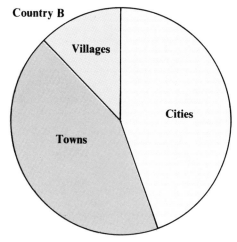

Copy the table and complete it by using a protractor to measure the angles on the pie charts.

Angles	Cities	Towns	Villages	Total
Country *A*				
Country *B*				

Which of these two countries do you think is

a an industrial Western nation

b a developing Third World nation?

Give your reasons.

13 This map has a scale of 1 cm = 20 km (or 1 mm = 2 km).

Use your ruler to find the shortest distances in km between the places shown.

Copy this table and enter your results.

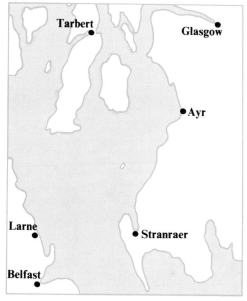

	Ayr	Belfast	Larne	Glasgow	Tarbert	Stranraer
Ayr	–					
Belfast		–				
Glasgow			–			
Larne				–		
Tarbert					–	
Stranraer						–

Tabulation of information

Part 2 Constructing a table

In these problems, no tables are provided. Design your own tables to display the information given, and label the rows and columns.

1 A pet shop sells dogs, cats and rabbits. Last month, it sold 6 male pups and 4 female pups, 8 male cats and 3 female cats, 12 male rabbits and 15 female rabbits.

2 The cafeteria of a ship on the 3-hour crossing of the English Channel sold 120 cups of tea, 95 coffees and 87 fruit juices in the first hour; 75 teas, 62 coffees and 108 fruit juices in the second hour; and 82 teas, 112 coffees and 66 fruit juices in the third hour of the journey.

3 Three sisters went to a summer fair. Angela spent 35 pence on ice cream, 60 pence on chocolate and 54 pence on drinks; Belinda spent 46 pence on ice cream, 15 pence on chocolate and 38 pence on drinks; and Christine spent 15 pence on ice cream, 40 pence on chocolate and 84 pence on drinks.

4 A travel agent sold 127 package holidays abroad and 46 within Britain for the month of June. For July he sold 212 holidays abroad and 106 within Britain; for August he sold 241 holidays abroad and 205 within Britain; and for September he sold 78 for abroad and 82 within Britain.

5 A garage specialises in the MOT testing of cars.
In the first week of last month, it failed 16 cars on their brakes, 12 on their lights, 4 on their steering, and 2 on their tyres. In the second week of the month, it failed 13 on brakes, 14 on lights, 8 on steering and 3 on tyres. In the third week of the month, it failed 8 on brakes, none on lights, 2 on steering and one on tyres. In the last week of the month, it failed 12 on brakes, 5 on lights, 4 on steering and 3 on tyres.
In your table, include extra entries for the *total* number of failures for each item.

6 In the exams at the end of the year, Peter got 64% in English, 72% in Maths, 53% in French, 47% in Science and 81% in History. His sister Amanda got 75% in English, 56% in Maths, 66% in French, 59% in Science and 63% in History. Their brother Simon got 70% in English, 51% in Maths, 61% in French, 53% in Science and 65% in History.

7 Mr Owens earns £642 per month of which £112 goes on his mortgage, £34 on life insurance and £27 on rates. His neighbour Mr Jones earns £583 per month, of which £87 is spent on his mortgage, £28 on life insurance and £25 on rates. His other neighbour, Miss Williams, earns £694 per month and she spends £124 on her mortgage, £18 on life insurance and £32 on rates.

8 Ian Banks is thinking of buying a second-hand car. He has seen a 3-year-old Aurora for £2650 with an engine capacity of 1.3 litres and 42 600 miles on the clock. There is also a 2-year-old 1.6 litre Vespera for £3250 which has done 31 500 miles; and at the same garage a 4-year-old 2.8 litre Noctral costing £2480 with 51 400 miles on the clock. Another garage has a 1.5 litre Meridino for £2990 which has travelled 29 700 miles in its two years.

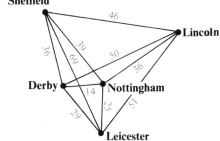

9 This map is *not* drawn to scale and the distances between the cities are given in miles.
Construct a mileage chart (like the one on page 149) for the five places shown.

Tabulation of information

10

This map is drawn to a scale of 1 cm = 100 km (or 1 mm = 10 km).

Use a ruler to find the shortest distances in km between the places shown, and construct a distance chart.

Multiplication by a number

Part 1

Answer each of these problems by writing a matrix with its brackets, but without labelling the rows and columns with words.

1   Mrs Jones buys these amounts of bread *every week.*
    Write a matrix to show how much she buys in a four-week month.

	Large white	Small white	Brown	Rolls
Number of loaves	3	2	3	10

2   Miss Openshaw decides to buy some plants as shown in this matrix, for *each square metre* of flower-bed.
    If her flower-bed has an area of 8 m², write a matrix to show how many plants she bought.

	Geraniums	Aubrietia	Asters	Pansies
Number of plants	3	4	5	6

3   A man has his bank pay four bills *every month* with the amounts shown in this matrix.
    Write a matrix to show how much is paid over a period of six months.

	Insurance	Mortgage	Fuel	Car Loan
Amount paid £	30	100	20	25

4   *Every month* a delivery van supplies a shop with these boxes of dog food.
    Write a matrix which gives the number of boxes delivered in one year.

	Large Wuf	Small Wuf	Snaps	Yelpy	Fidem
Number of boxes	8	10	6	5	7

5   A newspaper boy delivers these papers to two streets *every morning.*
    Write a matrix to show the numbers of papers he delivers in a six-day week.

	Times	Express	Guardian	Mirror	Sun
Larch Avenue	2	5	8	6	2
Mill Lane	3	9	7	7	5

6   A traffic census takes place in a narrow city street for a three-hour period on *one* morning. The results are shown in this matrix.
    Write a matrix which shows the total figures which might be expected for the *five* mornings of a working week.

	Lorries	Buses	Cars	Bicycles
7 a.m. – 8 a.m.	12	10	84	12
8 a.m. – 9 a.m.	6	12	102	10
9 a.m. –10 a.m.	4	8	90	4

7 A youth club raised £500 for an extension and £100 for equipment in several ways as shown in this matrix.
The following year they decided to try and raise *three times* as much for a further extension and more equipment.
Write a matrix to show where they might expect the money to come from.

	Sponsored events	Raffle	Fair	Grants	Total
For the extension	145	45	110	200	500
For equipment	60	15	25	0	100

8 In three supermarkets, various items of food have the prices (in pence) shown in this matrix.
Over several months, all the prices rise by exactly one half.
Write a matrix to show all the new prices after this increase.

	Sugar	Tea	Rice	Salt
Funfood Ltd	40	40	50	14
Greatgrub Stores	44	42	44	18
Nicenosh Market	38	48	46	16

9 Air fares on two airlines between Britain and North America are shown in this matrix in pounds (£).
Taking £1 = $1\frac{1}{2}$ US dollars, write a matrix to show these fares in dollars.

	Transat Air	Euroam Jetways
London – New York	120	140
Manchester – Toronto	140	150
London – Washington	200	220
Manchester – Boston	150	180

10 Three travel agents offer holidays to Germany at prices in pounds (£) as in this matrix.
If £1 = 4 Deutschmarks, make a matrix to show the prices in Deutschmarks.

	7 days	10 days	14 days
Deutschtours	120	145	180
Teuton Holidays	135	150	180
Allemania Air	112	140	185

11 The makers of two brands of soap powder sell them to shops in four different sizes at the prices (in pence) in this matrix.
The shops then add on 10% ($\frac{1}{10}$th) to these prices before selling to their customers.
Make a matrix to show the prices that the customers are charged.

	Standard	Large	Jumbo	Giant
Whito	40	60	130	240
Sparkle	50	70	150	230

157

Multiplication by a number

12 Miles $\rightarrow$ | Divide by 5 | $\rightarrow$ | Multiply by 8 | $\rightarrow$ Kilometres

This flow diagram will convert distance in miles into distance in kilometres. The matrix gives distances in *miles* between three towns. Construct a matrix which gives these distances in *kilometres*.

$$\begin{array}{c} \\ \text{Aston} \\ \text{Bacester} \\ \text{Cambury} \end{array} \begin{array}{ccc} \text{Aston} & \text{Bacester} & \text{Cambury} \\ \left(\begin{array}{ccc} - & 30 & 15 \\ 30 & - & 25 \\ 15 & 25 & - \end{array} \right) \end{array}$$

13 kg $\rightarrow$ | Divide by 5 | $\rightarrow$ | Multiply by 11 | $\rightarrow$ lb

A fruiterer imports two types of French apples which are divided into three grades: I, II and III. This matrix gives the mass (in kg) of each box.

Use the flow diagram to write a matrix with these masses in pounds (lb).

$$\begin{array}{c} \\ \text{Pomme verte} \\ \text{Fruit d'Or} \end{array} \begin{array}{ccc} \text{Grade I} & \text{Grade II} & \text{Grade III} \\ \left(\begin{array}{ccc} 30 & 20 & 20 \\ 25 & 25 & 15 \end{array} \right) \end{array}$$

14 km/litre $\rightarrow$ | Divide by 4 | $\rightarrow$ | Multiply by 11 | $\rightarrow$ mpg

The two best-selling ranges of car at a garage are the Vitette and the Mirella. The advertisements give their fuel consumptions in kilometres per litre in this matrix.

Use the flow diagram to convert this matrix to one which gives the fuel consumptions in miles per gallon (mpg).

$$\begin{array}{c} \\ \text{Vitette} \\ \text{Mirella} \end{array} \begin{array}{ccc} \text{Saloon} & \text{G.T.} & \text{Estate} \\ \left(\begin{array}{ccc} 20 & 12 & 16 \\ 12 & 8 & 10 \end{array} \right) \end{array}$$

15 The maximum temperatures in degrees Fahrenheit (°F) which are recorded one year at three West Coast resorts are shown here.

$$\begin{array}{c} \\ \text{Morecambe} \\ \text{Blackpool} \\ \text{Southport} \end{array} \begin{array}{ccc} \text{June} & \text{July} & \text{August} \\ \left(\begin{array}{ccc} 68 & 68 & 77 \\ 59 & 68 & 86 \\ 59 & 77 & 95 \end{array} \right) \end{array}$$

Use the flow diagram to construct a matrix showing these temperatures in degrees Celsius (°C).

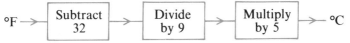

°F $\rightarrow$ | Subtract 32 | $\rightarrow$ | Divide by 9 | $\rightarrow$ | Multiply by 5 | $\rightarrow$ °C

Multiplication by a number

16 How much the three salespersons of a firm earn depends on how much they sell each month.
This matrix gives the total sales in £ of each of them for March and April.

	March	April
Mr White	2500	3800
Miss Tripps	4200	3200
Mr Gaunt	3600	3500

This flow diagram shows how their monthly salary is calculated. Construct a matrix to show their earnings for these two months.

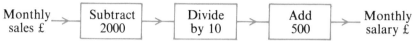

Monthly sales £ → | Subtract 2000 | → | Divide by 10 | → | Add 500 | → Monthly salary £

Part 2

1 Multiply these matrices and write the answers.

a $3\begin{pmatrix} 2 & 4 & 6 \\ 3 & 2 & 1 \end{pmatrix}$

b $4\begin{pmatrix} 1 & 3 \\ 2 & 0 \\ 4 & 2 \end{pmatrix}$

c $5\begin{pmatrix} 3 & 4 \\ 5 & 6 \end{pmatrix}$

d $2\begin{pmatrix} 0 & 1 & 2 \\ 3 & 4 & 5 \\ 6 & 7 & 8 \end{pmatrix}$

e $\frac{1}{2}\begin{pmatrix} 4 \\ 10 \\ 16 \end{pmatrix}$

f $\frac{1}{3}\begin{pmatrix} 0 & 6 & 15 \\ 9 & 0 & 3 \end{pmatrix}$

g $6\begin{pmatrix} 0 & 1 & 2 \\ -2 & 0 & 4 \\ 1 & 3 & -3 \end{pmatrix}$

h $4\begin{pmatrix} -2 & 1 \\ 0 & -5 \\ 3 & 0 \\ -3 & -2 \end{pmatrix}$

i $\frac{1}{2}\begin{pmatrix} 0 & -6 \\ 6 & -10 \end{pmatrix}$

j $3\begin{pmatrix} 1 & 0 & 0 \\ 0 & 1 & 0 \\ 0 & 0 & 1 \end{pmatrix}$

k $8\begin{pmatrix} -2 & 0 & 3\frac{1}{2} & -4 \\ 0 & -4\frac{1}{2} & 6 & -7 \end{pmatrix}$

l $6\begin{pmatrix} 1\frac{1}{2} & -5 & 0 \\ -3\frac{1}{2} & 4 & 2\frac{1}{2} \end{pmatrix}$

2 Find the value of each letter in these matrices.

a $2\begin{pmatrix} 3 & 4 \\ 1 & 5 \end{pmatrix} = \begin{pmatrix} a & 8 \\ 2 & b \end{pmatrix}$

b $4\begin{pmatrix} 3 \\ 0 \\ 5 \end{pmatrix} = \begin{pmatrix} c \\ d \\ 20 \end{pmatrix}$

c $6\begin{pmatrix} 2 & 3 & \frac{1}{2} \\ 4 & 0 & g \end{pmatrix} = \begin{pmatrix} 12 & 18 & h \\ e & f & 42 \end{pmatrix}$

d $5\begin{pmatrix} 3 \\ 7 \end{pmatrix} = \begin{pmatrix} i \\ j \end{pmatrix}$

e $\frac{1}{2}\begin{pmatrix} 8 & 1 \\ 6 & 4 \end{pmatrix} = \begin{pmatrix} 4 & l \\ k & 2 \end{pmatrix}$

f $\frac{1}{4}\begin{pmatrix} 12 & 8 & 10 \end{pmatrix} = \begin{pmatrix} m & 2 & n \end{pmatrix}$

Multiplication by a number

g $\quad 3\begin{pmatrix} p & 4 \\ q & 2 \end{pmatrix} = \begin{pmatrix} 15 & 12 \\ 18 & 6 \end{pmatrix}$

h $\quad 7\begin{pmatrix} r \\ 3 \\ s \end{pmatrix} = \begin{pmatrix} 14 \\ 21 \\ 35 \end{pmatrix}$

i $\quad 2\begin{pmatrix} t \\ 7 \end{pmatrix} = \begin{pmatrix} 8 \\ u \end{pmatrix}$

j $\quad 4\begin{pmatrix} 0 & v & \frac{1}{2} \\ 2 & 5 & w \end{pmatrix} = \begin{pmatrix} 0 & 12 & 2 \\ 8 & x & 28 \end{pmatrix}$

k $\quad \frac{1}{2}\begin{pmatrix} y & 9 \\ 6 & 2 \\ 0 & 7 \end{pmatrix} = \begin{pmatrix} 5 & 4\frac{1}{2} \\ 3 & 1 \\ 0 & z \end{pmatrix}$

3 Find the value of each letter in these harder problems.

a $\quad a\begin{pmatrix} a \\ 5 \end{pmatrix} = \begin{pmatrix} 16 \\ b \end{pmatrix}$

b $\quad c\begin{pmatrix} 0 & d \\ c & 2 \end{pmatrix} = \begin{pmatrix} 0 & 12 \\ 9 & e \end{pmatrix}$

c $\quad 4\begin{pmatrix} 2 & -3 \\ f & g \end{pmatrix} = \begin{pmatrix} 8 & -12 \\ g & 32 \end{pmatrix}$

d $\quad 3\begin{pmatrix} 8 & h & i \end{pmatrix} = \begin{pmatrix} 24 & h^2 & -6 \end{pmatrix}$

e $\quad 5\begin{pmatrix} 3 & k \\ 2 & 4 \end{pmatrix} = \begin{pmatrix} j & m \\ 10 & k \end{pmatrix}$

f $\quad 6\begin{pmatrix} 10 & n & p \end{pmatrix} = 5\begin{pmatrix} q & 6 & 3 \end{pmatrix}$

g $\quad 2\begin{pmatrix} r & s \\ 6 & -9 \end{pmatrix} = 3\begin{pmatrix} r & t \\ t & u \end{pmatrix}$

h $\quad 8\begin{pmatrix} \frac{1}{4} & a \\ c & b \end{pmatrix} = \begin{pmatrix} b & c \\ 32 & d \end{pmatrix}$

i $\quad 4\begin{pmatrix} e & 4\frac{1}{2} \\ f & e \end{pmatrix} = 3\begin{pmatrix} 8 & e \\ g & f \end{pmatrix}$

j $\quad 2\begin{pmatrix} w & x \\ y & z \end{pmatrix} = \begin{pmatrix} w+x & x+y \\ y+z & 1 \end{pmatrix}$

Addition and subtraction

Part 1

1 A cricket team plays 12 matches in the first half of the season and 8 matches in the second half, with the results below.

First half

$$\begin{array}{cccc} \text{Played} & \text{Won} & \text{Lost} & \text{Drawn} \end{array}$$
$$\begin{pmatrix} 12 & 4 & 3 & 5 \end{pmatrix}$$

Second half

$$\begin{array}{cccc} \text{Played} & \text{Won} & \text{Lost} & \text{Drawn} \end{array}$$
$$\begin{pmatrix} 8 & 4 & 2 & 2 \end{pmatrix}$$

Write a matrix to show the results for the 20 matches of the whole season.

2 In a junior school the number of boys in each year is given in the first matrix and the number of girls in the second matrix.

Boys

$$\begin{array}{cccc} \text{1st year} & \text{2nd year} & \text{3rd year} & \text{4th year} \end{array}$$
$$\begin{pmatrix} 23 & 18 & 20 & 15 \end{pmatrix}$$

Girls

$$\begin{array}{cccc} \text{1st year} & \text{2nd year} & \text{3rd year} & \text{4th year} \end{array}$$
$$\begin{pmatrix} 16 & 19 & 24 & 21 \end{pmatrix}$$

Write a matrix to show the total number of children in each year.

3 The following matrices show the results of a traffic census of vehicles using a city road during a particular morning and afternoon.

Morning

$$\begin{array}{cccc} \text{Cars} & \text{Lorries} & \text{Buses} & \text{Others} \end{array}$$
$$\begin{pmatrix} 567 & 312 & 76 & 14 \end{pmatrix}$$

Afternoon

$$\begin{array}{cccc} \text{Cars} & \text{Lorries} & \text{Buses} & \text{Others} \end{array}$$
$$\begin{pmatrix} 363 & 104 & 36 & 75 \end{pmatrix}$$

Write a matrix to show the different vehicles which passed during the whole of this day.

4 At the end of a week, the cleaners in a school find the following articles in the boys' and girls' cloakrooms.

Boys

$$\begin{array}{cccc} \text{Bags} & \text{Books} & \text{Coats} & \text{Scarfs} \end{array}$$
$$\begin{pmatrix} 8 & 15 & 3 & 5 \end{pmatrix}$$

Girls

$$\begin{array}{cccc} \text{Bags} & \text{Books} & \text{Coats} & \text{Scarfs} \end{array}$$
$$\begin{pmatrix} 7 & 12 & 5 & 8 \end{pmatrix}$$

If all these are placed in 'Lost Property', write a matrix to show all the different articles waiting to be collected.

5 A builder is constructing houses and bungalows on two sites, A and B. The numbers of windows and doors he needs for each site are shown here.

Site A

$$\begin{array}{l} \\ \text{Houses} \\ \text{Bungalows} \end{array} \begin{array}{c} \begin{array}{cc} \text{Windows} & \text{Doors} \end{array} \\ \begin{pmatrix} 324 & 126 \\ 116 & 78 \end{pmatrix} \end{array}$$

Site B

$$\begin{array}{l} \\ \text{Houses} \\ \text{Bungalows} \end{array} \begin{array}{c} \begin{array}{cc} \text{Windows} & \text{Doors} \end{array} \\ \begin{pmatrix} 278 & 104 \\ 195 & 83 \end{pmatrix} \end{array}$$

Write a matrix showing the requirements for *both* sites together.

Addition and subtraction

6 Muchrun Harriers is an athletics club which entered a three-day competition with events for men and women. The members of the club had the following successes.

		1st places	2nd places	3rd places
Friday	Men	6	4	2
	Women	4	5	3
Saturday	Men	3	0	4
	Women	1	6	2
Sunday	Men	4	6	0
	Women	5	1	4

Write a matrix to show the men's and women's placings for the whole competition.

7 At the beginning of January, a supermarket has goods for sale in various sizes as shown in the first matrix.

At the end of the month, the manager checks to see how much is still there as given by the second matrix.

1st January	Large	Standard	Small
Boxes of soap powder	250	200	120
Cartons of beans	55	40	32
Cartons of rice	18	24	12

31st January	Large	Standard	Small
Boxes of soap powder	60	45	65
Cartons of beans	12	18	21
Cartons of rice	4	6	6

Write a matrix to show the quantities which have been sold during the month.

8 A school has three fifth-form classes, labelled A, B and C. The number of boys and girls in these groups is given in the first matrix.

The second matrix gives the numbers from each class which enter the sixth form at the end of the year.

Fifth form	A	B	C
Boys	15	12	14
Girls	13	16	12

Sixth form	A	B	C
Boys	8	6	7
Girls	9	8	4

Construct a matrix which shows how many boys and girls left each fifth-form group at the end of the year.

9 This table is a record of the matches played by three football teams during the season. The *home* and *away* matches are shown separately.

Team	Home				Away			
	P	W	L	D	P	W	L	D
United	12	8	3	1	8	3	2	3
City	10	4	5	1	10	3	5	2
Rovers	12	5	2	5	9	4	5	0

Answer these questions:
What was the *total* number of games which United
a played   b won   c lost   d drew?
Write a matrix for these three teams to show the *combined* results for the *home* and *away* matches.

Addition and subtraction

10 A factory has several lorries, vans and cars which at times need spare parts. At the start of the month, the storekeeper notes the number of spares, and he counts them again at the end of the month to see how many are left.

Start of month

	Tyres	Bulbs	Fan belts
Lorries	32	40	12
Vans	26	35	8
Cars	22	28	6

End of month

	Tyres	Bulbs	Fan belts
Lorries	18	21	7
Vans	8	30	4
Cars	12	18	3

Answer these questions:
a How many tyres did the lorries use?
b How many tyres did the vans use?
c How many bulbs did the cars use?

Write a matrix which shows the number of spare parts used on these vehicles during the month.

11 Two schools have a swimming competition during the morning and afternoon of the same day.
These two matrices show the morning's and afternoon's results separately.

Morning — Number of placings

	1st	2nd	3rd	4th
School A	6	2	7	6
School B	4	8	3	4

Afternoon — Number of placings

	1st	2nd	3rd	4th
School A	5	8	6	3
School B	7	4	6	9

Answer these questions:
a How many first places did school A have during the whole day?
b How many second places did school B have during the whole day?
c How many events took place during the morning session?
d How many events took place during the afternoon session?

Write a matrix to show the placings for both schools for the whole day (morning and afternoon together).

12 A record shop has two branches, one in the High Street and one in the Arcade. The two shops have the following records in stock.

High Street

	LPs	EPs +12" Discs	Singles
Popular	80	140	210
Classical	65	12	0
Folk	30	48	36
Light	70	24	6
Jazz	32	16	10

The Arcade

	LPs	EPs +12" Discs	Singles
Popular	30	20	50
Classical	85	40	0
Folk	15	12	14
Light	24	16	0
Jazz	35	21	0

Answer these questions:
a Which shop gives you the better choice of popular music?
b Which shop gives you the better choice of classical music?
c How many folk records does the High Street shop have altogether?
d How many more jazz LPs does the Arcade shop have than the High Street one?
e If the two shops merge and move into larger premises, and their stocks are combined, make a matrix to show the total choice now available.

163

Addition and subtraction

Part 2

1 Add or subtract these matrices. If any are impossible, then say so.

a $\begin{pmatrix} 2 & 3 & 4 \\ 8 & 9 & 6 \end{pmatrix} + \begin{pmatrix} 3 & 1 & 7 \\ 0 & 6 & 4 \end{pmatrix}$
b $\begin{pmatrix} 6 & 9 \\ 2 & 0 \\ 8 & 3 \end{pmatrix} - \begin{pmatrix} 5 & 7 \\ 2 & 0 \\ 7 & 3 \end{pmatrix}$

c $\begin{pmatrix} 6 & 10 \\ 9 & 11 \end{pmatrix} + \begin{pmatrix} 4 & 3 \\ 12 & 14 \end{pmatrix}$
d $\begin{pmatrix} 9 \\ 8 \\ 7 \end{pmatrix} + \begin{pmatrix} 2 \\ 0 \\ 4 \end{pmatrix} + \begin{pmatrix} 6 \\ 3 \\ 2 \end{pmatrix}$

e $\begin{pmatrix} 2 & 7 \\ 8 & 5 \end{pmatrix} - \begin{pmatrix} 3 \\ 4 \end{pmatrix}$
f $\begin{pmatrix} 3 & 9 \\ 8 & 4 \end{pmatrix} - \begin{pmatrix} 2 & 8 \\ 7 & 3 \end{pmatrix}$
g $\begin{pmatrix} 4 \\ 2 \end{pmatrix} + \begin{pmatrix} 6 \\ 3 \\ 1 \end{pmatrix}$

h $\begin{pmatrix} 7 & 7 \\ 9 & 3 \end{pmatrix} - \begin{pmatrix} 6 & 7 \\ 9 & 2 \end{pmatrix}$
i $\begin{pmatrix} 8 & 3 \\ 5 & 2 \\ 7 & 0 \end{pmatrix} - \begin{pmatrix} 6 & 0 \\ 1 & 1 \\ 0 & 0 \end{pmatrix}$

j $\begin{pmatrix} 2 & 1 & 4 \\ 0 & 2 & 0 \\ 6 & 0 & 2 \end{pmatrix} + \begin{pmatrix} 4 & 6 & 4 \\ 1 & 0 & 3 \\ 0 & 7 & 6 \end{pmatrix} - \begin{pmatrix} 3 & 1 & 0 \\ 1 & 1 & 2 \\ 5 & 4 & 6 \end{pmatrix}$

2 Use a number ladder to add or subtract these matrices. If any are impossible to calculate, then say so.

a $\begin{pmatrix} 3 & -1 \\ 0 & -2 \end{pmatrix} + \begin{pmatrix} 2 & 4 \\ 6 & 2 \end{pmatrix}$
b $\begin{pmatrix} 4 \\ -3 \\ -1 \end{pmatrix} + \begin{pmatrix} 2 \\ 5 \\ 3 \end{pmatrix}$

c $\begin{pmatrix} 3 & 7 \\ -1 & 0 \\ 5 & -6 \end{pmatrix} + \begin{pmatrix} 2 & 0 \\ 5 & 2 \\ 1 & 6 \end{pmatrix}$
d $\begin{pmatrix} 3 & 8 & -4 \\ -5 & 0 & -7 \end{pmatrix} + \begin{pmatrix} 1 & 1 & 4 \\ 4 & 3 & 5 \end{pmatrix}$

e $\begin{pmatrix} -8 & 2 \\ 0 & -4 \end{pmatrix} + \begin{pmatrix} 6 & 4 \\ 3 & 1 \end{pmatrix}$
f $\begin{pmatrix} -3 \\ 2 \\ -5 \end{pmatrix} + \begin{pmatrix} 6 \\ 4 \\ 2 \end{pmatrix}$

g $\begin{pmatrix} 2 & 0 \\ 4 & -3 \end{pmatrix} + \begin{pmatrix} 1 & 4 & 6 \\ -2 & 0 & 5 \end{pmatrix}$
h $\begin{pmatrix} -3 & 0 \\ -5 & -6 \end{pmatrix} + \begin{pmatrix} 8 & 4 \\ 9 & 6 \end{pmatrix}$

i $\begin{pmatrix} 7 \\ -3 \end{pmatrix} - \begin{pmatrix} 8 \\ 6 \\ 0 \end{pmatrix}$
j $\begin{pmatrix} -5 & -3 & 2 \\ -9 & 0 & -2 \end{pmatrix} + \begin{pmatrix} 5 & 1 & 6 \\ 2 & 5 & 3 \end{pmatrix}$

Addition and subtraction

k $\begin{pmatrix} 6 & 4 \\ 0 & 0 \\ 2 & -3 \end{pmatrix} - \begin{pmatrix} 3 & 6 \\ 2 & 7 \\ 5 & 2 \end{pmatrix}$ l $\begin{pmatrix} 8 & 4 \\ 0 & -3 \end{pmatrix} - \begin{pmatrix} 3 & 6 \\ 2 & 4 \end{pmatrix}$

m $\begin{pmatrix} 5 \\ 2 \end{pmatrix} + \begin{pmatrix} 3 \\ 6 \end{pmatrix} - \begin{pmatrix} 9 \\ 1 \end{pmatrix}$ n $\begin{pmatrix} 0 \\ 9 \end{pmatrix} + \begin{pmatrix} 3 \\ 1 \end{pmatrix} - \begin{pmatrix} 9 \\ 11 \end{pmatrix}$

3   Find the value of each letter in these matrices.

a $\begin{pmatrix} 3 \\ b \end{pmatrix} + \begin{pmatrix} a \\ 7 \end{pmatrix} = \begin{pmatrix} 5 \\ 8 \end{pmatrix}$ b $\begin{pmatrix} 3 & c \\ d & 2 \end{pmatrix} + \begin{pmatrix} e & 3 \\ 1 & f \end{pmatrix} = \begin{pmatrix} 8 & 7 \\ 3 & 9 \end{pmatrix}$

c $\begin{pmatrix} g \\ 6 \end{pmatrix} - \begin{pmatrix} 2 \\ h \end{pmatrix} = \begin{pmatrix} 3 \\ 5 \end{pmatrix}$ d $\begin{pmatrix} 8 & 7 \\ i & 6 \\ 4 & k \end{pmatrix} - \begin{pmatrix} 4 & 3 \\ 2 & j \\ 1 & 3 \end{pmatrix} = \begin{pmatrix} 4 & 4 \\ 8 & 2 \\ l & 0 \end{pmatrix}$

e $\begin{pmatrix} 6 & x \\ 9 & 4 \end{pmatrix} - \begin{pmatrix} y & 3 \\ 2 & 1 \end{pmatrix} = \begin{pmatrix} 0 & 7 \\ 7 & z \end{pmatrix}$ f $\begin{pmatrix} p \\ 4 \end{pmatrix} + \begin{pmatrix} 3 \\ q \end{pmatrix} + \begin{pmatrix} 2 \\ 6 \end{pmatrix} = \begin{pmatrix} 9 \\ 13 \end{pmatrix}$

g $\begin{pmatrix} 3 & e \\ 5 & 6 \end{pmatrix} + \begin{pmatrix} 6 & 3 \\ f & 4 \end{pmatrix} - \begin{pmatrix} g & 1 \\ 4 & 3 \end{pmatrix} = \begin{pmatrix} 8 & 6 \\ 2 & 7 \end{pmatrix}$

h $\begin{pmatrix} r & 4 & 6 \\ 0 & 8 & u \end{pmatrix} + \begin{pmatrix} 3 & s & 7 \\ 2 & v & 6 \end{pmatrix} = \begin{pmatrix} 12 & 5 & t \\ w & 8 & 9 \end{pmatrix}$

i $\begin{pmatrix} 9 & x \\ 8 & 7 \end{pmatrix} - \begin{pmatrix} 4 & 3 \\ 2 & 5 \end{pmatrix} - \begin{pmatrix} 1 & 4 \\ y & z \end{pmatrix} = \begin{pmatrix} 4 & 2 \\ 1 & 0 \end{pmatrix}$

4   Find the value of each letter in these matrices. You will find a number ladder useful for the negative numbers.

a $\begin{pmatrix} -6 \\ -3 \end{pmatrix} + \begin{pmatrix} a \\ b \end{pmatrix} = \begin{pmatrix} 0 \\ 1 \end{pmatrix}$ b $\begin{pmatrix} -4 \\ -1 \end{pmatrix} + \begin{pmatrix} c \\ 5 \end{pmatrix} = \begin{pmatrix} 2 \\ d \end{pmatrix}$

c $\begin{pmatrix} -5 & -5 \\ -3 & -1 \end{pmatrix} + \begin{pmatrix} e & f \\ 2 & 4 \end{pmatrix} = \begin{pmatrix} 0 & 1 \\ g & h \end{pmatrix}$ d $\begin{pmatrix} 4 \\ 4 \end{pmatrix} - \begin{pmatrix} i \\ j \end{pmatrix} = \begin{pmatrix} 0 \\ -1 \end{pmatrix}$

e $\begin{pmatrix} 2 \\ 0 \end{pmatrix} - \begin{pmatrix} k \\ l \end{pmatrix} = \begin{pmatrix} -3 \\ -5 \end{pmatrix}$ f $\begin{pmatrix} 6 & 0 \\ 1 & 4 \end{pmatrix} - \begin{pmatrix} m & n \\ p & q \end{pmatrix} = \begin{pmatrix} -1 & -3 \\ -2 & -4 \end{pmatrix}$

g $\begin{pmatrix} -8 & -6 & -7 \\ u & v & w \end{pmatrix} + \begin{pmatrix} r & s & t \\ 2 & 1 & 3 \end{pmatrix} = \begin{pmatrix} 0 & -1 & -4 \\ 0 & -5 & -1 \end{pmatrix}$

h $\begin{pmatrix} x \\ -3 \\ z \end{pmatrix} + \begin{pmatrix} 2 \\ y \\ 1 \end{pmatrix} = \begin{pmatrix} 0 \\ -1 \\ -4 \end{pmatrix}$

165

MATRICES

Addition and subtraction

5 Add or subtract these matrices, as required. They are more difficult and you will need to take care with the negative signs.

a $\begin{pmatrix} 6 \\ 4 \end{pmatrix} - \begin{pmatrix} -2 \\ -3 \end{pmatrix}$

b $\begin{pmatrix} 8 & -2 \\ 3 & 0 \end{pmatrix} - \begin{pmatrix} -6 & 4 \\ 5 & -2 \end{pmatrix}$

c $\begin{pmatrix} 5 \\ 0 \\ -3 \end{pmatrix} - \begin{pmatrix} 8 \\ -3 \\ 2 \end{pmatrix}$

d $\begin{pmatrix} 6 & 4 & -1 \end{pmatrix} + \begin{pmatrix} -2 & -1 & 5 \end{pmatrix}$

e $\begin{pmatrix} 6 & 0 \\ 1 & -4 \\ -2 & 7 \end{pmatrix} + \begin{pmatrix} 1 & 7 \\ 3 & 8 \\ -2 & -3 \end{pmatrix}$

f $\begin{pmatrix} 7 \\ 7 \\ 6 \end{pmatrix} + \begin{pmatrix} -5 \\ -8 \\ -9 \end{pmatrix}$

g $\begin{pmatrix} -2 & -3 \\ 0 & 2 \end{pmatrix} + \begin{pmatrix} 6 & 9 \\ -3 & -7 \end{pmatrix}$

h $\begin{pmatrix} 5 & 1 \\ 3 & 9 \\ -2 & -7 \end{pmatrix} + \begin{pmatrix} -4 & -4 \\ -7 & -6 \\ 5 & 3 \end{pmatrix}$

i $\begin{pmatrix} 6 & 2 \end{pmatrix} - \begin{pmatrix} -5 & 7 \end{pmatrix}$

j $\begin{pmatrix} -2 & -7 \end{pmatrix} - \begin{pmatrix} -8 & -3 \end{pmatrix}$

k $\begin{pmatrix} -1 \\ -6 \end{pmatrix} - \begin{pmatrix} -9 \\ -1 \end{pmatrix}$

l $\begin{pmatrix} 8 & 7 \\ -1 & -1 \end{pmatrix} + \begin{pmatrix} -2 & 4 \\ 6 & -1 \end{pmatrix}$

6 Find the value of each letter in these matrices.

a $\begin{pmatrix} 4 \\ a \end{pmatrix} + \begin{pmatrix} a \\ b \end{pmatrix} = \begin{pmatrix} 9 \\ 6 \end{pmatrix}$

b $\begin{pmatrix} c \\ d \end{pmatrix} - \begin{pmatrix} 5 \\ c \end{pmatrix} = \begin{pmatrix} 2 \\ 3 \end{pmatrix}$

c $\begin{pmatrix} e \\ f \\ 1 \end{pmatrix} + \begin{pmatrix} 8 \\ e \\ g \end{pmatrix} = \begin{pmatrix} 12 \\ 10 \\ f \end{pmatrix}$

d $\begin{pmatrix} h & i \\ 3 & 0 \end{pmatrix} + \begin{pmatrix} 4 & 5 \\ j & 3 \end{pmatrix} = \begin{pmatrix} 6 & 9 \\ i & k \end{pmatrix}$

e $\begin{pmatrix} 6 & 8 \end{pmatrix} - \begin{pmatrix} l & m \end{pmatrix} = \begin{pmatrix} 6 & l \end{pmatrix}$

f $\begin{pmatrix} n & 2 \\ p & r \end{pmatrix} - \begin{pmatrix} 4 & n \\ 1 & 8 \end{pmatrix} = \begin{pmatrix} 2 & p \\ q & -2 \end{pmatrix}$

g $\begin{pmatrix} s & t \\ 4 & s \end{pmatrix} + \begin{pmatrix} 1 & 0 \\ 0 & 1 \end{pmatrix} = \begin{pmatrix} t & t \\ 4 & 7 \end{pmatrix}$

h $\begin{pmatrix} -4 \\ u \\ 8 \end{pmatrix} - \begin{pmatrix} u \\ v \\ w \end{pmatrix} = \begin{pmatrix} -6 \\ 0 \\ v \end{pmatrix}$

i $\begin{pmatrix} x \\ y \end{pmatrix} + \begin{pmatrix} 6 \\ 2 \end{pmatrix} = \begin{pmatrix} y+1 \\ 9 \end{pmatrix}$

j $\begin{pmatrix} -6 & z \end{pmatrix} + \begin{pmatrix} z & 4 \end{pmatrix} = \begin{pmatrix} 1 & a+2 \end{pmatrix}$

166

Letters for matrices

Part 1

Rather than write a matrix several times, it is quicker and easier to label it with a letter and write the letter instead.

1 $G = \begin{pmatrix} 2 & 3 \\ 1 & 0 \end{pmatrix}$ $H = \begin{pmatrix} 5 & 0 \\ 2 & 1 \end{pmatrix}$ Write the matrix
a $2G$ b $3H$
c $2G + 3H$.

2 $P = \begin{pmatrix} 1 \\ 4 \\ 3 \end{pmatrix}$ $Q = \begin{pmatrix} 2 \\ 1 \\ 5 \end{pmatrix}$ Write the matrix
a $3P$ b $4Q$
c $3P + 4Q$.

3 $A = \begin{pmatrix} 1 & 2 \\ 0 & 2 \\ 4 & 5 \end{pmatrix}$ $B = \begin{pmatrix} 3 & 0 \\ 3 & 5 \\ 2 & 1 \end{pmatrix}$ Write the matrix
a $5A$ b $2B$
c $5A + 2B$.

4 $Y = \begin{pmatrix} 3 & 2 \\ 6 & 4 \end{pmatrix}$ $Z = \begin{pmatrix} 2 & 7 \\ 0 & 3 \end{pmatrix}$ Write the matrix
a $6Y$ b $3Z$
c $6Y + 3Z$.

5 $E = \begin{pmatrix} 3 & 4 & 2 \\ 5 & 6 & 3 \end{pmatrix}$ $F = \begin{pmatrix} 2 & 3 & 2 \\ 4 & 5 & 1 \end{pmatrix}$ Write the matrix
a $3E$ b $2F$
c $3E - 2F$.

6 $S = \begin{pmatrix} 4 \\ 5 \\ 7 \end{pmatrix}$ $T = \begin{pmatrix} 3 \\ 2 \\ 6 \end{pmatrix}$ Write the matrix
a $4S$ b $3T$
c $4S - 3T$.

7 $I = \begin{pmatrix} 2 & 1 & 4 \\ 4 & 6 & 2 \\ 1 & 7 & 3 \end{pmatrix}$ $J = \begin{pmatrix} 3 & 2 & 2 \\ 4 & 1 & 3 \end{pmatrix}$ $K = \begin{pmatrix} 5 & 3 & 0 \\ 0 & 1 & 2 \end{pmatrix}$

$L = \begin{pmatrix} 0 & 1 & 2 \\ 2 & 3 & 0 \\ 1 & 0 & 1 \end{pmatrix}$ $M = \begin{pmatrix} 1 & 1 \\ 0 & 1 \\ 0 & 1 \end{pmatrix}$ $N = \begin{pmatrix} 4 & 5 \\ 2 & 1 \\ 0 & 2 \end{pmatrix}$

Use the lettered matrices above to perform these calculations.
If any are impossible, then say so.

a $I - L$ b $J + K$ c $N - M$
d $3J$ e $2K$ f $3J + 2K$
g $4M$ h $2N$ i $4M + 2N$
j $2I$ k $5M$ l $2I - 5M$
m $4J - K$ n $2I - L$ o $3K + 2N$

167

Letters for matrices

8 $A = \begin{pmatrix} -2 & 4 \\ 3 & -6 \end{pmatrix}$ $B = \begin{pmatrix} 3 & 4 \\ 5 & 0 \end{pmatrix}$ $C = \begin{pmatrix} 0 & -5 \\ 4 & -2 \end{pmatrix}$ $D = \begin{pmatrix} 8 & 1 \\ 2 & 5 \end{pmatrix}$

Do these additions and subtractions using the lettered matrices above.
You will find a number ladder useful for the negative numbers.

a	$B + D$	b	$A + B$	c	$C + D$
d	$C + B$	e	$B - D$	f	$C - D$
g	$A - B$	h	$A - D$	i	$2A + B$
j	$A + 2B$	k	$C + 2D$	l	$2C - B$
m	$A + B + D$	n	$A - B + D$	o	$C + D - B$

9 Use the lettered matrices of questions **7** and **8** to solve each of these equations
for the matrix X.

a	$X + M = N$	b	$X + L = I$
c	$X + K = 2J$	d	$X - 2M = N$
e	$X - 2B = 3D$	f	$3X + B = 2X + D$
g	$4X + K = 3X + J$	h	$2X - 2D = X + B$
i	$2X = A + 2B$	j	$2X - C = D$

10 $R = \begin{pmatrix} 5 \\ -3 \\ 1 \end{pmatrix}$ $S = \begin{pmatrix} -2 \\ 4 \\ -5 \end{pmatrix}$ $T = \begin{pmatrix} 3 \\ 6 \\ -2 \end{pmatrix}$

Do these additions and subtractions.
Take particular care with the negative signs.

a	$R - S$	b	$R - T$	c	$S + T$
d	$R + S$	e	$R + T$	f	$2R - S$
g	$3T - S$	h	$4S + R$	i	$3S + 2T$
j	$2R + 3S$	k	$R + S + T$	l	$R - S - T$

Part 2

1 Two firms start the year owning the vehicles shown in matrix A.
During the year they buy the extra vehicles in matrix B.

$$A = \begin{matrix} & \text{Lorries} & \text{Vans} & \text{Cars} \\ & \begin{pmatrix} 2 & 3 & 6 \\ 1 & 4 & 8 \end{pmatrix} & & \end{matrix} \begin{matrix} \text{Spaco Ltd.} \\ \text{Dalton Co.} \end{matrix}$$

$$B = \begin{matrix} & \text{Lorries} & \text{Vans} & \text{Cars} \\ & \begin{pmatrix} 0 & 2 & 3 \\ 1 & 1 & 2 \end{pmatrix} & & \end{matrix} \begin{matrix} \text{Spaco Ltd.} \\ \text{Dalton Co.} \end{matrix}$$

Write the matrix $A + B$.
Say, in words, what information $A + B$ gives you.

2 A school's two hockey teams have the results shown in these two matrices,
where matrix B gives the boys' results and G the girls' results.

$$B = \begin{matrix} \text{Played} & \text{Won} & \text{Drawn} & \text{Lost} \\ \begin{pmatrix} 12 & 5 & 3 & 4 \end{pmatrix} \end{matrix}$$ $$G = \begin{matrix} \text{Played} & \text{Won} & \text{Drawn} & \text{Lost} \\ \begin{pmatrix} 15 & 7 & 2 & 6 \end{pmatrix} \end{matrix}$$

Write the matrix $B + G$.
Say, in words, what information $B + G$ gives you.

Letters for matrices

3 A milkman delivers milk, cream and eggs to the houses in a street.
Matrix P gives the orders (for the weekend) to the odd-numbered side of the street and matrix Q to the even-numbered side.

$$P = \begin{pmatrix} \text{Milk} & \text{Cream} & \text{Eggs} \\ 64 & 18 & 9 \\ 120 & 30 & 10 \end{pmatrix} \begin{matrix} \\ \text{Friday} \\ \text{Saturday} \end{matrix} \qquad Q = \begin{pmatrix} \text{Milk} & \text{Cream} & \text{Eggs} \\ 62 & 10 & 4 \\ 105 & 24 & 5 \end{pmatrix} \begin{matrix} \\ \text{Friday} \\ \text{Saturday} \end{matrix}$$

Write the matrix $P + Q$.
Say, in words, what information $P + Q$ gives you.

4 At the start of the year, three primary schools have pupils and staff as given in matrix S.
At the end of the year, the numbers are as given in matrix T.

$$S = \begin{pmatrix} \text{Boys} & \text{Girls} & \text{Staff} \\ 87 & 81 & 5 \\ 110 & 112 & 7 \\ 52 & 55 & 4 \end{pmatrix} \begin{matrix} \\ \text{Littledean} \\ \text{Overton} \\ \text{Highbeck} \end{matrix} \qquad T = \begin{pmatrix} \text{Boys} & \text{Girls} & \text{Staff} \\ 82 & 70 & 5 \\ 95 & 99 & 6 \\ 50 & 51 & 4 \end{pmatrix} \begin{matrix} \\ \text{Littledean} \\ \text{Overton} \\ \text{Highbeck} \end{matrix}$$

Write the matrix $S - T$.
Say, in words, what information $S - T$ gives you.

5 A bookshop has two branches.
Matrix K shows the stocks on 1st August of the book of the latest TV serial.
Matrix L shows the stocks on 31st August.

$$K = \begin{pmatrix} \text{Hardback} & \text{Paperback} \\ 60 & 250 \\ 50 & 220 \end{pmatrix} \begin{matrix} \\ \text{High Street} \\ \text{King's Square} \end{matrix} \qquad L = \begin{pmatrix} \text{Hardback} & \text{Paperback} \\ 24 & 42 \\ 14 & 15 \end{pmatrix} \begin{matrix} \\ \text{High Street} \\ \text{King's Square} \end{matrix}$$

Write the matrix $K - L$.
Say, in words, what information $K - L$ gives you.

6 The amount of vegetables which one lorry can hold is given in matrix L.
Matrix V gives the amount which a van can hold.
A shop has a delivery from two lorries and three vans.

$$L = \begin{pmatrix} \text{Sacks} & \text{Boxes} \\ 25 & 4 \\ 15 & 10 \\ 0 & 20 \\ 30 & 0 \end{pmatrix} \begin{matrix} \\ \text{Potatoes} \\ \text{Carrots} \\ \text{Beans} \\ \text{Onions} \end{matrix} \qquad V = \begin{pmatrix} \text{Sacks} & \text{Boxes} \\ 4 & 5 \\ 3 & 5 \\ 0 & 3 \\ 0 & 4 \end{pmatrix} \begin{matrix} \\ \text{Potatoes} \\ \text{Carrots} \\ \text{Beans} \\ \text{Onions} \end{matrix}$$

Write the matrix $2L + 3V$.
Say, in words, what information $2L + 3V$ gives you.

Letters for matrices

7 The number of aeroplanes landing at an airport every weekday from Monday to Friday is given in matrix M. The number landing on Saturday and on Sunday is given in matrix N.

$$M = \begin{pmatrix} 2 & 12 \\ 10 & 0 \end{pmatrix} \begin{matrix} \text{Runway 1} \\ \text{Runway 2} \end{matrix} \qquad N = \begin{pmatrix} 0 & 20 \\ 4 & 15 \end{pmatrix} \begin{matrix} \text{Runway 1} \\ \text{Runway 2} \end{matrix}$$

with columns headed Cargo planes and Passenger planes.

Write the matrix $5M + 2N$.

Say, in words, what information this matrix gives you.

8 Mr and Mrs Risby have three children.

Four times during their week's holiday, they give their children the pocket-money shown in matrix Y. Matrix Z shows how much was left at the end of the holiday.

$$Y = \begin{pmatrix} 2\cdot50 \\ 2\cdot50 \\ 1\cdot50 \end{pmatrix} \begin{matrix} \text{Karen} \\ \text{Linda} \\ \text{Malcolm} \end{matrix} \qquad Z = \begin{pmatrix} 1\cdot50 \\ 0\cdot75 \\ 0\cdot20 \end{pmatrix} \begin{matrix} \text{Karen} \\ \text{Linda} \\ \text{Malcolm} \end{matrix}$$

(both in £)

Write down the matrix $4Y - Z$.

Say, in words, what information this matrix gives you.

Combining rows and columns

Part 1

1   A postman delivers 10 letters and 4 parcels. Their masses are given in the second matrix.
Find the total mass which he carries.

	Letters	Parcels		Mass in grams	
Number delivered	(10	4)	(	20	) each Letter
				200	each Parcel

2   A housewife buys the food shown in the first matrix. The prices are given in the second matrix.
Find the total cost of the food.

	Tins	Loaves	Oranges		Price in pence	
Number bought	(4	2	5)	(	40	) each Tin
					45	each Loaf
					10	each Orange

3   At Christmas a boy buys the boxes of chocolates given in the first matrix. The second matrix gives the number of chocolates in each box.
Find how many chocolates he buys.

	Dairy Maid	White Magic		Number of chocolates	
Number of boxes	(2	3)	(	15	) in each box of Dairy Maid
				20	in each box of White Magic

4   An estate has three types of house as in the first matrix. The second matrix gives the number of windows in each type.
What was the total number of windows that the builder needed?

	Semis	Terraced	Bungalows		Number of windows	
Number of houses	(10	6	8)	(	9	) in each Semi
					8	in each Terraced
					10	in each Bungalow

5   A secretary buys the materials of the first matrix at prices given in the second matrix.
How much did she spend altogether?

	Pens	Biros	Pencils		Price in pence	
Number bought	(6	4	3)	(	50	) each Pen
					10	each Biro
					20	each Pencil

6   Coffee is kept in three types of container with masses given in the second matrix. If I have the containers shown in the first matrix, how much coffee have I altogether?

	Jars	Packets	Tins		Mass in grams	
Number kept	(3	2	1)	(	100	) each Jar
					50	each Packet
					250	each Tin

171

Combining rows and columns

7   A man decorates a room of his house.
    The first table gives the materials he used. The second table gives their cost.
    Find the total cost of all the materials.

	Tins of paint	Brushes	Rolls of paper	Packets of paste		Cost £	
Amount used	3	2	8	2		4·00	each Tin of paint
						1·50	each Brush
						4·00	each Roll of paper
						0·75	each Packet of paste

8   A gardener plants flowers to make a display.
    The first table gives the number of each kind he used; and the second table gives
    the price of each bulb.
    Find the total cost of his display, giving your answer in £.

	Daffodils	Tulips	Crocuses	Snowdrops	Irises		Price in pence	
Number planted	20	10	30	100	10		10	each Daffodil bulb
							20	each Tulip bulb
							5	each Crocus bulb
							5	each Snowdrop bulb
							40	each Iris bulb

9   A firm owns its own transport as shown in the first table. The second table gives
    the masses of the different vehicles.
    Find the total mass of all these vehicles.

	Cars	Lorries	Trucks	Vans		Mass in tonnes	
Number of vehicles	15	12	20	8		1	each Car
						6	each Lorry
						3	each Truck
						2	each Van

10 A chemistry teacher keeps a certain liquid in different types of container.
    The first table tells you how many containers she has; and the second tells you
    how much each type contains.
    Find the total volume of this liquid.

	Jars	Tins	Drums	Bowls		Volume in litres	
Number of containers	12	16	2	14		2	in each Jar
						$2\frac{1}{2}$	in each Tin
						15	in each Drum
						$\frac{1}{2}$	in each Bowl

11 A rugby team plays thirty matches and their results are shown in the first
    matrix. The second matrix shows the points awarded for each result.
    Find the total points they were awarded in the season.

	Wins	Draws	Losses	Abandoned		Points	
Number of matches	12	6	10	2		4	each Win
						2	each Draw
						0	each Loss
						1	each Abandoned

Combining rows and columns

12 A bookshop orders copies of five books.
The number of copies is given in the first matrix, and the cost of each book in the second matrix.
Find the total cost of the order.

	Book A	Book B	Book C	Book D	Book E	Cost £	
Number of copies	20	15	6	8	30	1·00	each Book A
						2·00	each Book B
						1·50	each Book C
						6·00	each Book D
						4·00	each Book E

13 An office-block orders light bulbs of different wattages as in the first matrix. The cost of each is given in the second matrix.
Find the total cost of the order.

	150W	100W	60W	40W	Cost in pence	
Number of bulbs	20	25	12	6	60	each 150W bulb
					50	each 100W bulb
					40	each 60W bulb
					40	each 40W bulb

14 An aeroplane is loaded with goods packed in four different sizes of crates, as given in the first matrix. The mass of each is given in the second matrix.
Find the total mass of the whole load.

	Giant	Large	Medium	Small	Mass in kg	
Number of crates	3	10	24	18	300	each Giant crate
					250	each Large crate
					200	each Medium crate
					50	each Small crate

15 A greengrocer fills his van with boxes of fruit as in the first matrix. The second matrix gives the mass of each type of box.
Find the total mass of fruit carried by his van.

	Apples	Oranges	Bananas	Grapefruit	Pears	Mass per box in kg	
Number of boxes	10	12	8	6	5	18	Apples
						20	Oranges
						25	Bananas
						15	Grapefruit
						15	Pears

Combining rows and columns

16 Combine these rows and columns giving just one number as your answer.

a $\begin{pmatrix} 2 & 8 & 4 \end{pmatrix} \begin{pmatrix} 6 \\ 2 \\ 5 \end{pmatrix}$

b $\begin{pmatrix} 9 & 0 & 4 & 5 \end{pmatrix} \begin{pmatrix} 4 \\ 6 \\ 1 \\ 3 \end{pmatrix}$

c $\begin{pmatrix} 5 & 6 & 0 & 7 \end{pmatrix} \begin{pmatrix} 4 \\ 3 \\ 7 \\ 5 \end{pmatrix}$

d $\begin{pmatrix} 8 & 7 & 6 & 9 \end{pmatrix} \begin{pmatrix} 10 \\ 2 \\ 0 \\ 3 \end{pmatrix}$

e $\begin{pmatrix} 2 & 12 & 10 \end{pmatrix} \begin{pmatrix} 8 \\ 2 \\ 6 \end{pmatrix}$

f $\begin{pmatrix} 2 & 3 & 4 \end{pmatrix} \begin{pmatrix} 14 \\ 20 \\ 25 \end{pmatrix}$

g $\begin{pmatrix} 5\frac{1}{2} & 3 \end{pmatrix} \begin{pmatrix} 2 \\ 7 \end{pmatrix}$

h $\begin{pmatrix} 4 & 1\frac{1}{2} & 1 \end{pmatrix} \begin{pmatrix} 2\frac{1}{2} \\ 2 \\ 7\frac{1}{2} \end{pmatrix}$

i $\begin{pmatrix} 2 & 4 & 1\frac{1}{2} & 2 \end{pmatrix} \begin{pmatrix} 10 \\ 25 \\ 20 \\ 55 \end{pmatrix}$

j $\begin{pmatrix} 4 & 1 & \frac{1}{2} \end{pmatrix} \begin{pmatrix} 2\frac{1}{2} \\ 5 \\ 6 \end{pmatrix}$

17 Combine these rows and columns, taking care with the negative signs.

a $\begin{pmatrix} 4 & -3 & 0 \end{pmatrix} \begin{pmatrix} 2 \\ -3 \\ 5 \end{pmatrix}$

b $\begin{pmatrix} 6 & -2 & -1 \end{pmatrix} \begin{pmatrix} 2 \\ -4 \\ -5 \end{pmatrix}$

c $\begin{pmatrix} -2 & 3 \end{pmatrix} \begin{pmatrix} 4 \\ 3 \end{pmatrix}$

d $\begin{pmatrix} -5 & 2 \end{pmatrix} \begin{pmatrix} 3 \\ 9 \end{pmatrix}$

e $\begin{pmatrix} 3 & 2 \end{pmatrix} \begin{pmatrix} -6 \\ 4 \end{pmatrix}$

f $\begin{pmatrix} -9 & 1 & 5 \end{pmatrix} \begin{pmatrix} 3 \\ 7 \\ 4 \end{pmatrix}$

g $\begin{pmatrix} 6 & 2 & 3 \end{pmatrix} \begin{pmatrix} -3 \\ 2 \\ 2 \end{pmatrix}$

h $\begin{pmatrix} -7 & -3 & 1 & -2 \end{pmatrix} \begin{pmatrix} 4 \\ -3 \\ 7 \\ -5 \end{pmatrix}$

Combining rows and columns

i $\begin{pmatrix} 6 & -3 \end{pmatrix} \begin{pmatrix} 2 \\ 4 \end{pmatrix}$

j $\begin{pmatrix} 8 & -4 \end{pmatrix} \begin{pmatrix} 3 \\ 6 \end{pmatrix}$

k $\begin{pmatrix} 3 & -5 & 7 & 2 \end{pmatrix} \begin{pmatrix} 10 \\ 6 \\ 4 \\ -5 \end{pmatrix}$

l $\begin{pmatrix} -3 & -8 \end{pmatrix} \begin{pmatrix} 5 \\ -2 \end{pmatrix}$

18 Find the value of each letter in these equations.

a $\begin{pmatrix} 3 & 2 \end{pmatrix} \begin{pmatrix} a \\ 5 \end{pmatrix} = \begin{pmatrix} 16 \end{pmatrix}$

b $\begin{pmatrix} 5 & 3 \end{pmatrix} \begin{pmatrix} b \\ 2 \end{pmatrix} = \begin{pmatrix} 26 \end{pmatrix}$

c $\begin{pmatrix} 4 & -2 \end{pmatrix} \begin{pmatrix} c \\ 3 \end{pmatrix} = \begin{pmatrix} 10 \end{pmatrix}$

d $\begin{pmatrix} 2 & -6 \end{pmatrix} \begin{pmatrix} d \\ 3 \end{pmatrix} = \begin{pmatrix} 4 \end{pmatrix}$

e $\begin{pmatrix} 1 & -3 \end{pmatrix} \begin{pmatrix} x \\ 7 \end{pmatrix} = \begin{pmatrix} 5 \end{pmatrix}$

f $\begin{pmatrix} 3 & 5 \end{pmatrix} \begin{pmatrix} 2 \\ y \end{pmatrix} = \begin{pmatrix} 16 \end{pmatrix}$

g $\begin{pmatrix} 2 & 3 & 4 \end{pmatrix} \begin{pmatrix} 5 \\ 2 \\ z \end{pmatrix} = \begin{pmatrix} 24 \end{pmatrix}$

h $\begin{pmatrix} 6 & -2 & s \end{pmatrix} \begin{pmatrix} 4 \\ 10 \\ 3 \end{pmatrix} = \begin{pmatrix} 19 \end{pmatrix}$

i $\begin{pmatrix} 7 & -9 & t \end{pmatrix} \begin{pmatrix} 7 \\ 5 \\ 2 \end{pmatrix} = \begin{pmatrix} 8 \end{pmatrix}$

j $\begin{pmatrix} 8 & 3 & 4 \end{pmatrix} \begin{pmatrix} 2 \\ -4 \\ j \end{pmatrix} = \begin{pmatrix} 12 \end{pmatrix}$

k $\begin{pmatrix} 3 & -1 & 3 \end{pmatrix} \begin{pmatrix} 5 \\ 9 \\ k \end{pmatrix} = \begin{pmatrix} 15 \end{pmatrix}$

l $\begin{pmatrix} w & -2 \end{pmatrix} \begin{pmatrix} 3 \\ 4 \end{pmatrix} = \begin{pmatrix} -5 \end{pmatrix}$

m $\begin{pmatrix} 6 & -4 \end{pmatrix} \begin{pmatrix} m \\ 5 \end{pmatrix} = \begin{pmatrix} -17 \end{pmatrix}$

n $\begin{pmatrix} 5 & -3 & 2 \end{pmatrix} \begin{pmatrix} 3 \\ 6 \\ n \end{pmatrix} = \begin{pmatrix} 7 \end{pmatrix}$

o $\begin{pmatrix} 3 & 6 & -5 \end{pmatrix} \begin{pmatrix} 3 \\ p \\ 4 \end{pmatrix} = \begin{pmatrix} -8 \end{pmatrix}$

p $\begin{pmatrix} 5 & q & 7 \end{pmatrix} \begin{pmatrix} 4 \\ 3 \\ -3 \end{pmatrix} = \begin{pmatrix} 17 \end{pmatrix}$

175

Combining rows and columns

19 Find the value of x in each of these harder equations.

a $\begin{pmatrix} 3 & -4 \end{pmatrix} \begin{pmatrix} x \\ -5 \end{pmatrix} = \begin{pmatrix} 26 \end{pmatrix}$

b $\begin{pmatrix} 2x & -1 \end{pmatrix} \begin{pmatrix} 3 \\ -4 \end{pmatrix} = \begin{pmatrix} 16 \end{pmatrix}$

c $\begin{pmatrix} 5x & 2x \end{pmatrix} \begin{pmatrix} 1 \\ 2 \end{pmatrix} = \begin{pmatrix} 27 \end{pmatrix}$

d $\begin{pmatrix} 6x & 4 \end{pmatrix} \begin{pmatrix} 2 \\ 2x \end{pmatrix} = \begin{pmatrix} 60 \end{pmatrix}$

e $\begin{pmatrix} x & 2x & 4 \end{pmatrix} \begin{pmatrix} 4 \\ 2 \\ x \end{pmatrix} = \begin{pmatrix} 48 \end{pmatrix}$

f $\begin{pmatrix} 6x & 4 & 2x \end{pmatrix} \begin{pmatrix} 3 \\ 5 \\ -4 \end{pmatrix} = \begin{pmatrix} 100 \end{pmatrix}$

g $\begin{pmatrix} 5x & 3 & -6 \end{pmatrix} \begin{pmatrix} 4 \\ -4x \\ 1 \end{pmatrix} = \begin{pmatrix} 34 \end{pmatrix}$

h $\begin{pmatrix} 7x & -5 & -3 \end{pmatrix} \begin{pmatrix} 2 \\ 2x \\ 4 \end{pmatrix} = \begin{pmatrix} 0 \end{pmatrix}$

i $\begin{pmatrix} 3x & -5 & -1 \end{pmatrix} \begin{pmatrix} 2 \\ -4 \\ 2x \end{pmatrix} = \begin{pmatrix} 22 \end{pmatrix}$

j $\begin{pmatrix} x & -6 \end{pmatrix} \begin{pmatrix} x \\ 1 \end{pmatrix} = \begin{pmatrix} 19 \end{pmatrix}$

k $\begin{pmatrix} x & 3 \end{pmatrix} \begin{pmatrix} x \\ 2 \end{pmatrix} = \begin{pmatrix} 22 \end{pmatrix}$

l $\begin{pmatrix} 5 & -3 & 4x \end{pmatrix} \begin{pmatrix} 2 \\ 3 \\ 2x \end{pmatrix} = \begin{pmatrix} 3 \end{pmatrix}$

20 Write each of these matrix equations as a quadratic equation and hence find the values of x.

a $\begin{pmatrix} x & 6 \end{pmatrix} \begin{pmatrix} x \\ x \end{pmatrix} = \begin{pmatrix} -5 \end{pmatrix}$

b $\begin{pmatrix} x & x \end{pmatrix} \begin{pmatrix} x \\ 7 \end{pmatrix} = \begin{pmatrix} -10 \end{pmatrix}$

c $\begin{pmatrix} x & 2 \end{pmatrix} \begin{pmatrix} x \\ x \end{pmatrix} = \begin{pmatrix} 15 \end{pmatrix}$

d $\begin{pmatrix} x & 3 \end{pmatrix} \begin{pmatrix} x \\ x \end{pmatrix} = \begin{pmatrix} 18 \end{pmatrix}$

e $\begin{pmatrix} x & 4 \end{pmatrix} \begin{pmatrix} x \\ 3 \end{pmatrix} = \begin{pmatrix} 8x \end{pmatrix}$

f $\begin{pmatrix} x & 6 \end{pmatrix} \begin{pmatrix} x \\ 4 \end{pmatrix} = \begin{pmatrix} 11x \end{pmatrix}$

Part 2

Without writing any words, copy each pair of matrices and calculate the totals required.

1 A cricket club plays several games with the results shown in the first matrix. The points gained are shown in the second matrix.
Find the team's total points.

	Won	Drawn	Lost		Points			Total points
Number of games	$\begin{pmatrix} 2$	4	$1 \end{pmatrix}$		$\begin{pmatrix} 10 \\ 2 \\ 0 \end{pmatrix}$	each Win each Draw each Loss	$=$	$\begin{pmatrix} \cdots \end{pmatrix}$

Combining rows and columns

2   Two women buy vegetables as in the first matrix. The cost per kg is given in the second matrix.
Find how much each woman spends.

$$
\begin{array}{c}
\textit{Amount bought, kg} \\
\text{Swedes \quad Peas \quad Beans}
\end{array}
\qquad
\begin{array}{c}
\text{Cost, pence} \\
\text{per kg}
\end{array}
\qquad
\begin{array}{c}
\text{Money} \\
\text{spent} \\
\text{in pence}
\end{array}
$$

$$
\begin{array}{c}
\text{Mrs Jones} \\
\text{Mrs Black}
\end{array}
\begin{pmatrix} 2 & 2 & 1 \\ 3 & 1 & 2 \end{pmatrix}
\qquad
\begin{pmatrix} 30 \\ 50 \\ 60 \end{pmatrix}
\begin{array}{l} \text{Swedes} \\ \text{Peas} \\ \text{Beans} \end{array}
=
\begin{pmatrix} \ldots \\ \ldots \end{pmatrix}
\begin{array}{l} \text{Mrs Jones} \\ \text{Mrs Black} \end{array}
$$

3   Two football teams each play nine games.
The second matrix shows the points gained.
Find their total points.

$$
\begin{array}{c}
\text{Home \quad Away} \\
\text{wins \quad wins \quad Draws \quad Losses}
\end{array}
\qquad
\begin{array}{c}
\text{Points} \\
\text{gained}
\end{array}
$$

$$
\begin{array}{c}
\text{Albion} \\
\text{Rangers}
\end{array}
\begin{pmatrix} 4 & 2 & 2 & 1 \\ 3 & 5 & 0 & 1 \end{pmatrix}
\qquad
\begin{pmatrix} 2 \\ 3 \\ 1 \\ 0 \end{pmatrix}
\begin{array}{l}
\text{each} \\ \text{Home win} \\
\text{each} \\ \text{Away win} \\
\text{each Draw} \\
\text{each Loss}
\end{array}
=
\begin{pmatrix} \ldots \\ \ldots \end{pmatrix}
\begin{array}{l}
\text{Total} \\ \text{points} \\[4pt]
\text{Albion} \\ \text{Rangers}
\end{array}
$$

4   Two trains pull waggons with solid and liquid goods in them, as given by the first matrix. The second matrix gives the mass of each type of waggon.
Find the total mass of each train.

$$
\begin{array}{c}
\textit{Number of waggons} \\
\text{Solid \qquad Liquid} \\
\text{goods \qquad goods}
\end{array}
\qquad
\begin{array}{c}
\text{Mass of} \\
\text{each waggon} \\
\text{in tonnes}
\end{array}
\qquad
\begin{array}{c}
\text{Total mass} \\
\text{of train} \\
\text{in tonnes}
\end{array}
$$

$$
\begin{array}{c}
\text{Slow train} \\
\text{Fast train}
\end{array}
\begin{pmatrix} 10 & 2 \\ 5 & 5 \end{pmatrix}
\qquad
\begin{pmatrix} 10 \\ 8 \end{pmatrix}
\begin{array}{l} \text{Solid} \\ \text{goods} \\ \text{Liquid} \\ \text{goods} \end{array}
=
\begin{pmatrix} \ldots \\ \ldots \end{pmatrix}
\begin{array}{l} \text{Slow} \\ \text{Fast} \end{array}
$$

5   Before going fishing, three boys buy the equipment given in the first matrix. The second matrix gives the cost of each article.
Find how much each boy spends.

$$
\begin{array}{c}
\text{Hook \quad Line \quad Sinker \quad Net}
\end{array}
\qquad
\begin{array}{c}
\text{Cost} \\
\text{in pence}
\end{array}
\qquad
\begin{array}{c}
\text{Total cost} \\
\text{in pence}
\end{array}
$$

$$
\begin{array}{c}
\text{Jim} \\
\text{Jack} \\
\text{John}
\end{array}
\begin{pmatrix} 6 & 1 & 1 & 0 \\ 4 & 2 & 0 & 1 \\ 5 & 2 & 1 & 1 \end{pmatrix}
\quad
\begin{pmatrix} 20 \\ 60 \\ 20 \\ 100 \end{pmatrix}
\begin{array}{l} \text{each Hook} \\ \text{each Line} \\ \text{each Sinker} \\ \text{each Net} \end{array}
=
\begin{pmatrix} \ldots \\ \ldots \\ \ldots \end{pmatrix}
\begin{array}{l} \text{Jim} \\ \text{Jack} \\ \text{John} \end{array}
$$

6   A factory has a workshop and offices.
They need three types of light bulb (50 watt, 100 watt and 150 watt) as shown in the first matrix. The price of each type is given in the second matrix.
Find the cost of bulbs for the workshop and for the offices.

$$
\begin{array}{c}
\text{50W \quad 100W \quad 150W}
\end{array}
\qquad
\begin{array}{c}
\text{Cost} \\
\text{in pence}
\end{array}
\qquad
\begin{array}{c}
\text{Total cost} \\
\text{in pence}
\end{array}
$$

$$
\begin{array}{c}
\text{Workshop} \\
\text{Offices}
\end{array}
\begin{pmatrix} 10 & 50 & 20 \\ 2 & 25 & 4 \end{pmatrix}
\quad
\begin{pmatrix} 10 \\ 20 \\ 20 \end{pmatrix}
\begin{array}{l} \text{each 50W} \\ \text{each 100W} \\ \text{each 150W} \end{array}
=
\begin{pmatrix} \ldots \\ \ldots \end{pmatrix}
\begin{array}{l} \text{Workshop} \\ \text{Offices} \end{array}
$$

Combining rows and columns

7   Three firms own both vans and lorries.
Each vehicle can carry only a certain amount as shown in the second matrix.
Find how much each firm can take in its vehicles.

	Vans	Lorries
Firm X	2	3
Firm Y	1	2
Firm Z	3	5

$$\begin{pmatrix} 3 \\ 12 \end{pmatrix} \begin{matrix} \text{each Van} \\ \text{each Lorry} \end{matrix} = \begin{pmatrix} \ldots \\ \ldots \\ \ldots \end{pmatrix} \begin{matrix} \text{Firm } X \\ \text{Firm } Y \\ \text{Firm } Z \end{matrix}$$

(Tonnes carried / Maximum tonnage)

8   A man redecorates a house and a cottage using the materials of the first matrix.
Find how much he spends on each building.

	Rolls of paper	Tins of paint	Packets of paste	Brushes
House	10	3	4	4
Cottage	6	1	2	2

$$\begin{pmatrix} 4 \cdot 00 \\ 5 \cdot 00 \\ 0 \cdot 50 \\ 1 \cdot 50 \end{pmatrix} \begin{matrix} \text{Roll} \\ \text{Tin} \\ \text{Packet} \\ \text{Brush} \end{matrix} = \begin{pmatrix} \ldots \\ \ldots \end{pmatrix} \begin{matrix} \text{House} \\ \text{Cottage} \end{matrix}$$

(Cost each £ / Total cost £)

9   Three men work the weekly hours shown in the first matrix. The second matrix shows the rates of pay per hour.
Find the total wage for each man.

	Ordinary time	Overtime	Saturday time
Mr Alton	40	8	2
Mr Dolby	30	4	0
Mr Black	35	10	4

$$\begin{pmatrix} 2 \cdot 00 \\ 3 \cdot 00 \\ 3 \cdot 50 \end{pmatrix} \begin{matrix} \text{Ordinary time} \\ \text{Overtime} \\ \text{Saturday time} \end{matrix} = \begin{pmatrix} \ldots \\ \ldots \\ \ldots \end{pmatrix} \begin{matrix} \text{Mr Alton} \\ \text{Mr Dolby} \\ \text{Mr Black} \end{matrix}$$

(Earnings per hour £ / Total earnings £)

10   During a week, the milkman delivers three different kinds of milk to three families, as shown in the first matrix. The cost of each bottle is given in the second matrix.
Find the weekly milk bill for each family.

	Gold Top	Silver Top	Green Top
Williams	20	10	0
Evans	10	20	4
Jones	0	15	10

$$\begin{pmatrix} 25 \\ 22 \\ 20 \end{pmatrix} \begin{matrix} \text{Gold top} \\ \text{Silver top} \\ \text{Green top} \end{matrix} = \begin{pmatrix} \ldots \\ \ldots \\ \ldots \end{pmatrix} \begin{matrix} \text{Williams} \\ \text{Evans} \\ \text{Jones} \end{matrix}$$

(Cost (p) per bottle / Milk bill £)

11   Two families, the Richards and the Samsons, make out their weekly vegetable orders as in the first matrix. The High Street has two vegetable shops which charge prices given in the second matrix.
Calculate how much the orders would cost at the two shops.

Quantity of vegetables, kg

	Carrots	Beans	Peas	Sprouts
Richards	2	1	1	4
Samsons	4	2	1	2

Cost per kg

	Shop A	Shop B	
	25	30	Carrots
	40	30	Beans
	30	40	Peas
	40	35	Sprouts

$$= \begin{pmatrix} \ldots & \ldots \\ \ldots & \ldots \end{pmatrix} \begin{matrix} \text{Richards} \\ \text{Samsons} \end{matrix}$$

Total bill, £
Shop A   Shop B

Combining rows and columns

12 A party of children from two high schools go on a joint holiday.
The numbers of pupils are given in the first matrix, and the second matrix gives the amount of luggage they are allowed.
Find the total amount of luggage taken by each school.

	Girls	Boys			Number of suitcases	Number of shoulder-bags			Total of suitcases	Total of shoulder-bags	
Abergwy	12	10			3	1	each Girl	=	...	...	Abergwy
Wyemouth	15	14			2	1	each Boy		...	...	Wyemouth

13 The first matrix gives the number of houses and bungalows being built on two sites, *A* and *B*. The second matrix gives the number of windows and doors each building needs.
Find how many windows and doors are needed on each site.

	Houses	Bungalows			Windows	Doors			Total of windows	Total of doors	
Site *A*	3	2			8	6	each House	=	...	...	Site *A*
Site *B*	4	1			6	5	each Bungalow		...	...	Site *B*

14 The number of Packair and Flident aircraft landing at four airports in one morning is given in the first matrix. The second matrix shows the maximum number of passengers and the maximum cargo tonnage each aircraft can carry.
Find the maximum loads that could arrive at each airport that morning.

	Number of aircraft			*Capacity*				*Maximum capacity*		
	Packair	Flident		Passengers	Tonnage			Passengers	Tonnage	
Ringway	5	7						...	...	Ringway
Heathrow	8	10		100	20	each Packair	=	...	...	Heathrow
Prestwick	5	5		120	10	each Flident		...	...	Prestwick
Midlands	1	2						...	...	Midlands

15 The first matrix shows how many animals there are at four zoos. The amount of food and drink required daily by each animal is given in the second matrix.
Find the total quantities of food and drink needed by each zoo in one day.

	Number of animals				Food kg	Water litres			*Total amounts* Food kg	Water litres	
	Deer	Bears	Apes	Gnus							
Zoo *A*	12	6	10	5	3	5	each Deer		...	...	Zoo *A*
Zoo *B*	40	12	25	30	4	3	each Bear	=	...	...	Zoo *B*
Zoo *C*	8	4	10	6	1	2	each Ape		...	...	Zoo *C*
Zoo *D*	12	0	6	20	3	6	each Gnu		...	...	Zoo *D*

Combining rows and columns

16 A school has four houses, North, South, East and West, with the numbers of boys and girls shown in the first matrix. The second matrix shows the equipment issued to each boy and girl.

Find how much equipment is required by each house.

	Boys	Girls
North	40	35
South	28	42
East	32	34
West	36	30

Equipment issued per child

	Rulers	Pens	Pencils	Rubbers	
	1	1	2	1	each Boy
	1	2	1	1	each Girl

=

Total numbers

	Rulers	Pens	Pencils	Rubbers	
...	...	...	...	North
...	...	...	...	South
...	...	...	...	East
...	...	...	...	West

17 The Maths, Science and Geography departments in a school order different kinds of exercise books as in the first matrix. The second matrix gives the cost and mass of each type of book.

Find the total cost and total mass of the orders for Maths, Science and Geography.

	Narrow lines	Broad lines	Squared	Plain
Maths	200	0	300	50
Science	100	200	100	50
Geography	100	0	0	200

	Cost/book pence	Mass/book grams	
	10	50	Narrow lines
	10	50	Broad lines
	15	20	Squared
	12	30	Plain

=

	Total cost, pence	Total mass, grams	
...	...	Maths
...	...	Science
...	...	Geography

18 In a certain school pupils can study up to three foreign languages.

The numbers taking these subjects in the 4th and 5th years are given in the first matrix. The second matrix gives the different books required for each subject.

Find the total numbers of the different books required in each year.

Number of pupils

	French	German	Latin
4th year	30	20	10
5th year	35	22	12

Books required per pupil

	Exercise books	Text books	Rough books	
	3	2	2	French
	3	3	3	German
	2	4	3	Latin

=

Total number of books

	Exercise books	Text books	Rough books	
...	...	...	4th year
...	...	...	5th year

180

Combining rows and columns

19 Julie and Sandra McPherson save all their exercise books. After five years at school they have the books shown in the first matrix. The second matrix gives the number of pages and the cost of the different books.

Find how many pages the girls filled and the cost of their books.

Number of books — Maths, English, Science, History, Art, French

	Maths	English	Science	History	Art	French
Julie	20	16	12	15	5	10
Sandra	18	20	15	12	4	10

	Pages per book	Cost per book, pence	
	20	15	Maths
	25	10	English
	20	10	Science
	25	12	History
	25	40	Art
	20	10	French

	Total pages	Total cost pence	
	...	...	Julie
	...	...	Sandra

20 During one day, two shops, Lectrix and Coopers, sell several household goods as shown in the first matrix. Their prices are given in the second matrix.

Calculate the total amounts needed at each shop to buy and sell these goods.

Number of articles — Kettles, Clocks, Lamps, TVs

	Kettles	Clocks	Lamps	TVs
Lectrix	10	8	20	2
Coopers	15	10	10	8

	Cost price, £	Cash price, £	HP price, £	
	20	25	30	each Kettle
	12	15	20	each Clock
	8	10	12	each Lamp
	50	60	65	each TV

Total amounts

	Cost price, £	Cash price, £	HP price, £	
	...	...	...	Lectrix
	...	...	...	Coopers

Matrix multiplication

Part 1

The process of combining the rows and columns of two matrices, as in the previous exercises, is known as **matrix multiplication**.

1 Multiply these matrices together, and notice how your answers build up.

a $\begin{pmatrix} 2 & 5 & 1 \end{pmatrix} \begin{pmatrix} 3 \\ 2 \\ 4 \end{pmatrix} = (\ldots)$

b $\begin{pmatrix} 2 & 5 & 1 \\ 3 & 1 & 2 \end{pmatrix} \begin{pmatrix} 3 \\ 2 \\ 4 \end{pmatrix} = \begin{pmatrix} \cdots \\ \cdots \end{pmatrix}$

c $\begin{pmatrix} 2 & 5 & 1 \\ 3 & 1 & 2 \\ 0 & 3 & 5 \end{pmatrix} \begin{pmatrix} 3 \\ 2 \\ 4 \end{pmatrix} = \begin{pmatrix} \cdots \\ \cdots \\ \cdots \end{pmatrix}$

d $\begin{pmatrix} 2 & 5 & 1 \\ 3 & 1 & 2 \\ 0 & 3 & 5 \\ 4 & 4 & 0 \end{pmatrix} \begin{pmatrix} 3 \\ 2 \\ 4 \end{pmatrix} = \begin{pmatrix} \cdots \\ \cdots \\ \cdots \\ \cdots \end{pmatrix}$

2 Multiply these matrices together, and notice how your answers build up.

a $\begin{pmatrix} 3 & 2 & 5 & 1 \end{pmatrix} \begin{pmatrix} 2 \\ 1 \\ 3 \\ 6 \end{pmatrix} = (\ldots)$

b $\begin{pmatrix} 3 & 2 & 5 & 1 \\ 1 & 4 & 2 & 3 \end{pmatrix} \begin{pmatrix} 2 \\ 1 \\ 3 \\ 6 \end{pmatrix} = \begin{pmatrix} \cdots \\ \cdots \end{pmatrix}$

c $\begin{pmatrix} 3 & 2 & 5 & 1 \\ 1 & 4 & 2 & 3 \\ 6 & 2 & 0 & 1 \end{pmatrix} \begin{pmatrix} 2 \\ 1 \\ 3 \\ 6 \end{pmatrix} = \begin{pmatrix} \cdots \\ \cdots \\ \cdots \end{pmatrix}$

d $\begin{pmatrix} 3 & 2 & 5 & 1 \\ 1 & 4 & 2 & 3 \\ 6 & 2 & 0 & 1 \\ 5 & 0 & 2 & 0 \end{pmatrix} \begin{pmatrix} 2 \\ 1 \\ 3 \\ 6 \end{pmatrix} = \begin{pmatrix} \cdots \\ \cdots \\ \cdots \\ \cdots \end{pmatrix}$

3 Multiply these matrices together.

a $\begin{pmatrix} 2 & 1 & 3 \\ 4 & 3 & 5 \end{pmatrix} \begin{pmatrix} 3 \\ 5 \\ 1 \end{pmatrix} = \begin{pmatrix} \cdots \\ \cdots \end{pmatrix}$

b $\begin{pmatrix} 2 & 1 & 3 \\ 4 & 3 & 5 \end{pmatrix} \begin{pmatrix} 3 & 2 \\ 5 & 2 \\ 1 & 4 \end{pmatrix} = \begin{pmatrix} \cdots & \cdots \\ \cdots & \cdots \end{pmatrix}$

c $\begin{pmatrix} 2 & 1 & 3 \\ 4 & 3 & 5 \\ 0 & 3 & 0 \end{pmatrix} \begin{pmatrix} 3 & 2 \\ 5 & 2 \\ 1 & 4 \end{pmatrix} = \begin{pmatrix} \cdots & \cdots \\ \cdots & \cdots \\ \cdots & \cdots \end{pmatrix}$

d $\begin{pmatrix} 2 & 1 & 3 \\ 4 & 3 & 5 \\ 0 & 3 & 0 \\ 5 & 1 & 0 \end{pmatrix} \begin{pmatrix} 3 & 2 \\ 5 & 2 \\ 1 & 4 \end{pmatrix} = \begin{pmatrix} \cdots & \cdots \\ \cdots & \cdots \\ \cdots & \cdots \\ \cdots & \cdots \end{pmatrix}$

Matrix multiplication

4   Multiply these matrices together.

a $\begin{pmatrix} 8 & 2 & 0 & 1 \\ 6 & 3 & 1 & 5 \end{pmatrix} \begin{pmatrix} 3 \\ 4 \\ 0 \\ 0 \end{pmatrix} = \begin{pmatrix} \cdots \\ \cdots \end{pmatrix}$

b $\begin{pmatrix} 8 & 2 & 0 & 1 \\ 6 & 3 & 1 & 5 \end{pmatrix} \begin{pmatrix} 3 & 0 \\ 4 & 3 \\ 0 & 5 \\ 0 & 4 \end{pmatrix} = \begin{pmatrix} \cdots & \cdots \\ \cdots & \cdots \end{pmatrix}$

c $\begin{pmatrix} 8 & 2 & 0 & 1 \\ 6 & 3 & 1 & 5 \end{pmatrix} \begin{pmatrix} 3 & 0 & 1 \\ 4 & 3 & 1 \\ 0 & 5 & 0 \\ 0 & 4 & 2 \end{pmatrix} = \begin{pmatrix} \cdots & \cdots & \cdots \\ \cdots & \cdots & \cdots \end{pmatrix}$

d $\begin{pmatrix} 8 & 2 & 0 & 1 \\ 6 & 3 & 1 & 5 \\ 0 & 2 & 2 & 1 \end{pmatrix} \begin{pmatrix} 3 & 0 & 1 \\ 4 & 3 & 1 \\ 0 & 5 & 0 \\ 0 & 4 & 2 \end{pmatrix} = \begin{pmatrix} \cdots & \cdots & \cdots \\ \cdots & \cdots & \cdots \\ \cdots & \cdots & \cdots \end{pmatrix}$

5   $A = \begin{pmatrix} 1 & 3 \\ 2 & 4 \end{pmatrix}$ $B = \begin{pmatrix} 2 & 0 \\ 1 & 1 \end{pmatrix}$ $C = \begin{pmatrix} 1 & 4 & 2 \\ 3 & 0 & 2 \end{pmatrix}$

$D = \begin{pmatrix} 2 & 0 & 0 \\ 0 & 1 & 0 \\ 0 & 0 & 3 \end{pmatrix}$ $E = \begin{pmatrix} 3 & 0 \\ 4 & 2 \\ 5 & 2 \end{pmatrix}$ $F = \begin{pmatrix} 2 & 0 & 3 \\ 1 & 4 & 1 \\ 2 & 0 & 1 \end{pmatrix}$ $G = \begin{pmatrix} 3 & 1 \\ 0 & 4 \end{pmatrix}$

Use these matrices A to G to perform the following multiplications. If any are impossible, then say so.

a CE	b AB	c DF	d EC	e BA	f FD	g AG
h GA	i FG	j BG	k GB	l CA	m AC	n BC
o CB	p GE	q EG	r CD	s DC	t ED	u DE

Part 2   With negative numbers

1   Multiply these matrices together.

a $\begin{pmatrix} 4 & -2 \\ 3 & -3 \end{pmatrix} \begin{pmatrix} 5 \\ 3 \end{pmatrix} = \begin{pmatrix} \cdots \\ \cdots \end{pmatrix}$ b $\begin{pmatrix} -2 & 3 \\ -5 & 1 \end{pmatrix} \begin{pmatrix} -3 \\ 4 \end{pmatrix} = \begin{pmatrix} \cdots \\ \cdots \end{pmatrix}$

c $\begin{pmatrix} 4 & -3 & 1 \\ 5 & -2 & 2 \end{pmatrix} \begin{pmatrix} 2 \\ -3 \\ 1 \end{pmatrix} = \begin{pmatrix} \cdots \\ \cdots \end{pmatrix}$

d $\begin{pmatrix} 2 & 0 & -3 \\ 5 & -1 & 1 \end{pmatrix} \begin{pmatrix} 5 & 6 \\ 4 & 8 \\ -4 & -7 \end{pmatrix} = \begin{pmatrix} \cdots & \cdots \\ \cdots & \cdots \end{pmatrix}$

Matrix multiplication

e $\begin{pmatrix} 4 & 8 & -5 \\ -2 & 0 & 3 \end{pmatrix} \begin{pmatrix} 6 & 4 \\ 0 & 1 \\ 5 & 2 \end{pmatrix} = \begin{pmatrix} \cdots & \cdots \\ \cdots & \cdots \end{pmatrix}$

f $\begin{pmatrix} 3 & -2 \\ -4 & 5 \end{pmatrix} \begin{pmatrix} 6 & -4 & 3 \\ 9 & -6 & -2 \end{pmatrix} = \begin{pmatrix} \cdots & \cdots & \cdots \\ \cdots & \cdots & \cdots \end{pmatrix}$

g $\begin{pmatrix} 2 & -3 \\ 1 & -2 \end{pmatrix} \begin{pmatrix} 9 & -3 & 0 \\ 6 & -2 & -5 \end{pmatrix} = \begin{pmatrix} \cdots & \cdots & \cdots \\ \cdots & \cdots & \cdots \end{pmatrix}$

h $\begin{pmatrix} 6 & -2 \end{pmatrix} \begin{pmatrix} 3 & 5 \\ 9 & -2 \end{pmatrix} = \begin{pmatrix} \cdots & \cdots \end{pmatrix}$

i $\begin{pmatrix} -4 & -1 & 5 \end{pmatrix} \begin{pmatrix} -6 & 2 \\ 0 & 3 \\ -5 & -1 \end{pmatrix} = \begin{pmatrix} \cdots & \cdots \end{pmatrix}$

j $\begin{pmatrix} 2 & -1 & 3 \\ -4 & 0 & 5 \\ 6 & -2 & 2 \end{pmatrix} \begin{pmatrix} 3 & 4 & 2 \\ 0 & 1 & -2 \\ -1 & 5 & -4 \end{pmatrix} = \begin{pmatrix} \cdots & \cdots & \cdots \\ \cdots & \cdots & \cdots \\ \cdots & \cdots & \cdots \end{pmatrix}$

k $\begin{pmatrix} 2 & -3 \end{pmatrix} \begin{pmatrix} 8 \\ -4 \end{pmatrix} = \begin{pmatrix} \cdots \end{pmatrix}$

l $\begin{pmatrix} 8 \\ -4 \end{pmatrix} \begin{pmatrix} 2 & -3 \end{pmatrix} = \begin{pmatrix} \cdots & \cdots \\ \cdots & \cdots \end{pmatrix}$

2 $V = \begin{pmatrix} -2 & 0 \\ 3 & -4 \end{pmatrix}$ $W = \begin{pmatrix} -5 \\ 2 \end{pmatrix}$ $X = \begin{pmatrix} 6 & -2 \\ 4 & 7 \end{pmatrix}$

$Y = \begin{pmatrix} -5 & 2 \end{pmatrix}$ $Z = \begin{pmatrix} 3 \\ -3 \end{pmatrix}$

Use these matrices to perform the following multiplications. If any are impossible, then say so.

a VW	b VX	c VY	d VZ	e XW	f XY
g XZ	h WV	i XV	j YZ	k YW	l WY

3 Find the value of each letter in these matrix equations.

a $\begin{pmatrix} 3 & 4 \end{pmatrix} \begin{pmatrix} a \\ 2 \end{pmatrix} = \begin{pmatrix} 14 \end{pmatrix}$ b $\begin{pmatrix} 5 & 3 \end{pmatrix} \begin{pmatrix} b \\ 4 \end{pmatrix} = \begin{pmatrix} 37 \end{pmatrix}$

c $\begin{pmatrix} 2 & -4 \end{pmatrix} \begin{pmatrix} c \\ 3 \end{pmatrix} = \begin{pmatrix} 4 \end{pmatrix}$ d $\begin{pmatrix} 3 & -1 \end{pmatrix} \begin{pmatrix} d \\ 7 \end{pmatrix} = \begin{pmatrix} 2 \end{pmatrix}$

e $\begin{pmatrix} 5 & -2 \end{pmatrix} \begin{pmatrix} e \\ 8 \end{pmatrix} = \begin{pmatrix} -6 \end{pmatrix}$ f $\begin{pmatrix} 7 & f \end{pmatrix} \begin{pmatrix} 2 \\ 3 \end{pmatrix} = \begin{pmatrix} 20 \end{pmatrix}$

Matrix multiplication

g $\begin{pmatrix} 2 & g \end{pmatrix} \begin{pmatrix} 4 \\ -1 \end{pmatrix} = \begin{pmatrix} 7 \end{pmatrix}$

h $\begin{pmatrix} h & 3 \\ i & 5 \end{pmatrix} \begin{pmatrix} 2 \\ 4 \end{pmatrix} = \begin{pmatrix} 16 \\ 24 \end{pmatrix}$

i $\begin{pmatrix} j & 10 \\ k & -2 \end{pmatrix} \begin{pmatrix} 5 \\ 2 \end{pmatrix} = \begin{pmatrix} 35 \\ 6 \end{pmatrix}$

j $\begin{pmatrix} 3 & l \\ -1 & m \end{pmatrix} \begin{pmatrix} 8 \\ 2 \end{pmatrix} = \begin{pmatrix} 30 \\ -2 \end{pmatrix}$

k $\begin{pmatrix} 4 & n \\ -2 & p \end{pmatrix} \begin{pmatrix} 5 \\ 3 \end{pmatrix} = \begin{pmatrix} 32 \\ 5 \end{pmatrix}$

l $\begin{pmatrix} -6 & r \\ q & -3 \end{pmatrix} \begin{pmatrix} 2 \\ 5 \end{pmatrix} = \begin{pmatrix} 8 \\ -1 \end{pmatrix}$

m $\begin{pmatrix} s & 3 & 1 \\ 4 & 1 & t \end{pmatrix} \begin{pmatrix} 2 \\ 4 \\ 5 \end{pmatrix} = \begin{pmatrix} 20 \\ 17 \end{pmatrix}$

n $\begin{pmatrix} 3 & u & -1 \\ v & 5 & -4 \end{pmatrix} \begin{pmatrix} 2 \\ 2 \\ 4 \end{pmatrix} = \begin{pmatrix} 8 \\ 2 \end{pmatrix}$

o $\begin{pmatrix} 5 & -2 \\ 2 & x \end{pmatrix} \begin{pmatrix} w \\ 3 \end{pmatrix} = \begin{pmatrix} 9 \\ 12 \end{pmatrix}$

p $\begin{pmatrix} 6 & -8 \\ -4 & z \end{pmatrix} \begin{pmatrix} y \\ 2 \end{pmatrix} = \begin{pmatrix} -4 \\ 1 \end{pmatrix}$

Square matrices

Introduction

1 a Multiply these matrices. $\begin{pmatrix} 1 & 2 & 5 \\ 0 & 3 & 2 \end{pmatrix} \begin{pmatrix} 4 \\ 2 \\ 0 \end{pmatrix}$

  b Now reverse the order. $\begin{pmatrix} 4 \\ 2 \\ 0 \end{pmatrix} \begin{pmatrix} 1 & 2 & 5 \\ 0 & 3 & 2 \end{pmatrix}$

Is it possible to multiply them now? Give your reasons.

2 a Multiply these matrices. $\begin{pmatrix} 4 & 2 \\ 1 & 5 \end{pmatrix} \begin{pmatrix} 3 \\ 2 \end{pmatrix}$

  b Now reverse the order. $\begin{pmatrix} 3 \\ 2 \end{pmatrix} \begin{pmatrix} 4 & 2 \\ 1 & 5 \end{pmatrix}$

Is it possible to multiply them now? Give your reasons.

3 a Multiply these matrices. $\begin{pmatrix} 4 & 2 \\ 1 & 5 \end{pmatrix} \begin{pmatrix} 3 & 0 \\ 2 & 1 \end{pmatrix}$

  b Now reverse the order. $\begin{pmatrix} 3 & 0 \\ 2 & 1 \end{pmatrix} \begin{pmatrix} 4 & 2 \\ 1 & 5 \end{pmatrix}$

Is it possible to multiply them now? Give your reasons.

4 Answer these questions *yes* or *no*.
  a Is it always possible to multiply two rectangular matrices in either order?
  b Is it always possible to multiply two square matrices in either order?

Part 1 The order matters

In each multiplication there are two square matrices.
In parts **a** and **b**, the order of the multiplication is changed.
Multiply them together and see if your answers are the same or different.

1 a $\begin{pmatrix} 1 & 2 \\ 3 & 4 \end{pmatrix} \begin{pmatrix} 0 & 2 \\ 2 & 5 \end{pmatrix}$ b $\begin{pmatrix} 0 & 2 \\ 2 & 5 \end{pmatrix} \begin{pmatrix} 1 & 2 \\ 3 & 4 \end{pmatrix}$

2 a $\begin{pmatrix} 2 & 2 \\ 3 & 4 \end{pmatrix} \begin{pmatrix} 0 & 5 \\ 5 & 1 \end{pmatrix}$ b $\begin{pmatrix} 0 & 5 \\ 5 & 1 \end{pmatrix} \begin{pmatrix} 2 & 2 \\ 3 & 4 \end{pmatrix}$

3 a $\begin{pmatrix} 1 & 1 \\ 2 & 2 \end{pmatrix} \begin{pmatrix} 3 & 2 \\ 4 & 2 \end{pmatrix}$ b $\begin{pmatrix} 3 & 2 \\ 4 & 2 \end{pmatrix} \begin{pmatrix} 1 & 1 \\ 2 & 2 \end{pmatrix}$

4 a $\begin{pmatrix} 0 & 2 \\ 1 & 6 \end{pmatrix} \begin{pmatrix} 7 & 2 \\ 3 & 3 \end{pmatrix}$ b $\begin{pmatrix} 7 & 2 \\ 3 & 3 \end{pmatrix} \begin{pmatrix} 0 & 2 \\ 1 & 6 \end{pmatrix}$

5 a $\begin{pmatrix} 1 & 2 & 3 \\ 4 & 0 & 1 \\ 2 & 3 & 4 \end{pmatrix} \begin{pmatrix} 2 & 2 & 0 \\ 0 & 2 & 3 \\ 1 & 0 & 5 \end{pmatrix}$ b $\begin{pmatrix} 2 & 2 & 0 \\ 0 & 2 & 3 \\ 1 & 0 & 5 \end{pmatrix} \begin{pmatrix} 1 & 2 & 3 \\ 4 & 0 & 1 \\ 2 & 3 & 4 \end{pmatrix}$

6 a $\begin{pmatrix} 2 & 1 & 4 \\ 4 & 1 & 2 \\ 1 & 4 & 2 \end{pmatrix} \begin{pmatrix} 3 & 0 & 0 \\ 1 & 5 & 2 \\ 0 & 0 & 1 \end{pmatrix}$ b $\begin{pmatrix} 3 & 0 & 0 \\ 1 & 5 & 2 \\ 0 & 0 & 1 \end{pmatrix} \begin{pmatrix} 2 & 1 & 4 \\ 4 & 1 & 2 \\ 1 & 4 & 2 \end{pmatrix}$

Square matrices

7 Answer these questions *yes* or *no*.
   a When you reverse the order of the multiplication, does the answer stay the same?
   b Does the order of the multiplication matter?

Part 2 The exceptions

In each multiplication below, there are two square matrices.
Parts **a** and **b** have them in a different order.
Multiply them together and compare your answers.

Exception 1   The identity matrix, I

1 a $\begin{pmatrix} 1 & 0 \\ 0 & 1 \end{pmatrix}\begin{pmatrix} 2 & 3 \\ 4 & 5 \end{pmatrix}$ b $\begin{pmatrix} 2 & 3 \\ 4 & 5 \end{pmatrix}\begin{pmatrix} 1 & 0 \\ 0 & 1 \end{pmatrix}$

2 a $\begin{pmatrix} 1 & 0 \\ 0 & 1 \end{pmatrix}\begin{pmatrix} 9 & 8 \\ 7 & 7 \end{pmatrix}$ b $\begin{pmatrix} 9 & 8 \\ 7 & 7 \end{pmatrix}\begin{pmatrix} 1 & 0 \\ 0 & 1 \end{pmatrix}$

3 a $\begin{pmatrix} 1 & 0 \\ 0 & 1 \end{pmatrix}\begin{pmatrix} 6 & 4 \\ 8 & 2 \end{pmatrix}$ b $\begin{pmatrix} 6 & 4 \\ 8 & 2 \end{pmatrix}\begin{pmatrix} 1 & 0 \\ 0 & 1 \end{pmatrix}$

4 a $\begin{pmatrix} 1 & 0 & 0 \\ 0 & 1 & 0 \\ 0 & 0 & 1 \end{pmatrix}\begin{pmatrix} 1 & 2 & 3 \\ 4 & 5 & 6 \\ 7 & 8 & 9 \end{pmatrix}$ b $\begin{pmatrix} 1 & 2 & 3 \\ 4 & 5 & 6 \\ 7 & 8 & 9 \end{pmatrix}\begin{pmatrix} 1 & 0 & 0 \\ 0 & 1 & 0 \\ 0 & 0 & 1 \end{pmatrix}$

5 a $\begin{pmatrix} 1 & 0 & 0 \\ 0 & 1 & 0 \\ 0 & 0 & 1 \end{pmatrix}\begin{pmatrix} -6 & 0 & -7 \\ 2 & 1 & 0 \\ 5 & 8 & -3 \end{pmatrix}$ b $\begin{pmatrix} -6 & 0 & -7 \\ 2 & 1 & 0 \\ 5 & 8 & -3 \end{pmatrix}\begin{pmatrix} 1 & 0 & 0 \\ 0 & 1 & 0 \\ 0 & 0 & 1 \end{pmatrix}$

Note that the answer in each case is identical to one of the matrices.

The matrix $\begin{pmatrix} 1 & 0 \\ 0 & 1 \end{pmatrix}$ or $\begin{pmatrix} 1 & 0 & 0 \\ 0 & 1 & 0 \\ 0 & 0 & 1 \end{pmatrix}$ is called the **identity matrix, *I*.**

Exception 2   The zero matrix, 0

6 a $\begin{pmatrix} 0 & 0 \\ 0 & 0 \end{pmatrix}\begin{pmatrix} 1 & 2 \\ 3 & 4 \end{pmatrix}$ b $\begin{pmatrix} 1 & 2 \\ 3 & 4 \end{pmatrix}\begin{pmatrix} 0 & 0 \\ 0 & 0 \end{pmatrix}$

7 a $\begin{pmatrix} 0 & 0 \\ 0 & 0 \end{pmatrix}\begin{pmatrix} -7 & 3 \\ 6 & -5 \end{pmatrix}$ b $\begin{pmatrix} -7 & 3 \\ 6 & -5 \end{pmatrix}\begin{pmatrix} 0 & 0 \\ 0 & 0 \end{pmatrix}$

8 a $\begin{pmatrix} 0 & 0 \\ 0 & 0 \end{pmatrix}\begin{pmatrix} 3 & 0 \\ 0 & 6 \end{pmatrix}$ b $\begin{pmatrix} 3 & 0 \\ 0 & 6 \end{pmatrix}\begin{pmatrix} 0 & 0 \\ 0 & 0 \end{pmatrix}$

9 a $\begin{pmatrix} 0 & 0 & 0 \\ 0 & 0 & 0 \\ 0 & 0 & 0 \end{pmatrix}\begin{pmatrix} 1 & 2 & 3 \\ -4 & 5 & -6 \\ 7 & 8 & 9 \end{pmatrix}$ b $\begin{pmatrix} 1 & 2 & 3 \\ -4 & 5 & -6 \\ 7 & 8 & 9 \end{pmatrix}\begin{pmatrix} 0 & 0 & 0 \\ 0 & 0 & 0 \\ 0 & 0 & 0 \end{pmatrix}$

Note that the answer matrix in every case has only noughts in it.

The matrix $\begin{pmatrix} 0 & 0 \\ 0 & 0 \end{pmatrix}$ or $\begin{pmatrix} 0 & 0 & 0 \\ 0 & 0 & 0 \\ 0 & 0 & 0 \end{pmatrix}$ is called the **zero matrix, *0*.**

Square matrices

Exception 3   The inverse matrix, A^{-1}

10 a $\begin{pmatrix} 3 & 4 \\ 2 & 3 \end{pmatrix}\begin{pmatrix} 3 & -4 \\ -2 & 3 \end{pmatrix}$ b $\begin{pmatrix} 3 & -4 \\ -2 & 3 \end{pmatrix}\begin{pmatrix} 3 & 4 \\ 2 & 3 \end{pmatrix}$

11 a $\begin{pmatrix} 1 & 3 \\ 2 & 7 \end{pmatrix}\begin{pmatrix} 7 & -3 \\ -2 & 1 \end{pmatrix}$ b $\begin{pmatrix} 7 & -3 \\ -2 & 1 \end{pmatrix}\begin{pmatrix} 1 & 3 \\ 2 & 7 \end{pmatrix}$

12 a $\begin{pmatrix} 5 & 3 \\ 3 & 2 \end{pmatrix}\begin{pmatrix} 2 & -3 \\ -3 & 5 \end{pmatrix}$ b $\begin{pmatrix} 2 & -3 \\ -3 & 5 \end{pmatrix}\begin{pmatrix} 5 & 3 \\ 3 & 2 \end{pmatrix}$

13 a $\begin{pmatrix} 4 & 3 \\ 2 & 2 \end{pmatrix}\begin{pmatrix} 1 & -1\frac{1}{2} \\ -1 & 2 \end{pmatrix}$ b $\begin{pmatrix} 1 & -1\frac{1}{2} \\ -1 & 2 \end{pmatrix}\begin{pmatrix} 4 & 3 \\ 2 & 2 \end{pmatrix}$

14 a $\begin{pmatrix} 1 & 2 & 0 \\ -1 & 3 & 2 \\ 1 & 4 & 1 \end{pmatrix}\begin{pmatrix} -5 & -2 & 4 \\ 3 & 1 & -2 \\ -7 & -2 & 5 \end{pmatrix}$

   b $\begin{pmatrix} -5 & -2 & 4 \\ 3 & 1 & -2 \\ -7 & -2 & 5 \end{pmatrix}\begin{pmatrix} 1 & 2 & 0 \\ -1 & 3 & 2 \\ 1 & 4 & 1 \end{pmatrix}$

15 a $\begin{pmatrix} 2 & 0 & 1 \\ 2 & -1 & 0 \\ 1 & 3 & 3 \end{pmatrix}\begin{pmatrix} -3 & 3 & 1 \\ -6 & 5 & 2 \\ 7 & -6 & -2 \end{pmatrix}$

   b $\begin{pmatrix} -3 & 3 & 1 \\ -6 & 5 & 2 \\ 7 & -6 & -2 \end{pmatrix}\begin{pmatrix} 2 & 0 & 1 \\ 2 & -1 & 0 \\ 1 & 3 & 3 \end{pmatrix}$

Note that each answer is the identity matrix, I.
One matrix has the opposite effect of the other matrix, so that the answer is always I.
If one matrix is labelled A, its **inverse matrix** is written A^{-1}.

Transformations and Matrices

Transformations and matrices

Part 1

For each matrix, draw and label both axes from 0 to 16
copy and complete the tables below
draw all three objects and their images onto the one diagram
and answer any questions which are asked.

1 The matrix $\begin{pmatrix} 2 & 0 \\ 0 & 2 \end{pmatrix}$

a *First shape*

Object point		Image point
(1, 1)	$\begin{pmatrix} 2 & 0 \\ 0 & 2 \end{pmatrix}\begin{pmatrix} 1 \\ 1 \end{pmatrix} = \begin{pmatrix} \\ \end{pmatrix}$	(,)
(2, 1)	$\begin{pmatrix} 2 & 0 \\ 0 & 2 \end{pmatrix}\begin{pmatrix} 2 \\ 1 \end{pmatrix} = \begin{pmatrix} \\ \end{pmatrix}$	(,)
(2, 2)	$\begin{pmatrix} 2 & 0 \\ 0 & 2 \end{pmatrix}\begin{pmatrix} 2 \\ 2 \end{pmatrix} = \begin{pmatrix} \\ \end{pmatrix}$	(,)
(1, 2)	$\begin{pmatrix} 2 & 0 \\ 0 & 2 \end{pmatrix}\begin{pmatrix} 1 \\ 2 \end{pmatrix} = \begin{pmatrix} \\ \end{pmatrix}$	(,)

Find the area of the object and the area of the image.

b *Second shape*

Object point		Image point
(5, 2)	$\begin{pmatrix} 2 & 0 \\ 0 & 2 \end{pmatrix}\begin{pmatrix} 5 \\ 2 \end{pmatrix} = \begin{pmatrix} \\ \end{pmatrix}$	(,)
(8, 2)	$\begin{pmatrix} 2 & 0 \\ 0 & 2 \end{pmatrix}\begin{pmatrix} 8 \\ 2 \end{pmatrix} = \begin{pmatrix} \\ \end{pmatrix}$	(,)
(8, 5)	$\begin{pmatrix} 2 & 0 \\ 0 & 2 \end{pmatrix}\begin{pmatrix} 8 \\ 5 \end{pmatrix} = \begin{pmatrix} \\ \end{pmatrix}$	(,)

Find the area of the object and the area of the image.

c *Third shape*

Object point		Image point
(2, 7)	$\begin{pmatrix} 2 & 0 \\ 0 & 2 \end{pmatrix}\begin{pmatrix} 2 \\ 7 \end{pmatrix} = \begin{pmatrix} \\ \end{pmatrix}$	(,)
(4, 8)	$\begin{pmatrix} 2 & 0 \\ 0 & 2 \end{pmatrix}\begin{pmatrix} 4 \\ 8 \end{pmatrix} = \begin{pmatrix} \\ \end{pmatrix}$	(,)
(0, 8)	$\begin{pmatrix} 2 & 0 \\ 0 & 2 \end{pmatrix}\begin{pmatrix} 0 \\ 8 \end{pmatrix} = \begin{pmatrix} \\ \end{pmatrix}$	(,)

Find the area of the object and the area of the image.

d What kind of transformation has taken place?
What is the centre, the length scale factor and the area scale factor of the transformation?

Transformations and matrices
Transformations and matrices

2 The matrix $\begin{pmatrix} 3 & 0 \\ 0 & 3 \end{pmatrix}$.

a *First shape*

Object point		Image point
(1, 2)	$\begin{pmatrix} 3 & 0 \\ 0 & 3 \end{pmatrix}\begin{pmatrix} 1 \\ 2 \end{pmatrix} = \begin{pmatrix} \\ \end{pmatrix}$	(,)
(1, 4)	$\begin{pmatrix} 3 & 0 \\ 0 & 3 \end{pmatrix}\begin{pmatrix} 1 \\ 4 \end{pmatrix} = \begin{pmatrix} \\ \end{pmatrix}$	(,)
(0, 4)	$\begin{pmatrix} 3 & 0 \\ 0 & 3 \end{pmatrix}\begin{pmatrix} 0 \\ 4 \end{pmatrix} = \begin{pmatrix} \\ \end{pmatrix}$	(,)
(0, 2)	$\begin{pmatrix} 3 & 0 \\ 0 & 3 \end{pmatrix}\begin{pmatrix} 0 \\ 2 \end{pmatrix} = \begin{pmatrix} \\ \end{pmatrix}$	(,)

Find the area of the object and the area of the image.

b *Second shape*

Object point		Image point
(2, 5)	$\begin{pmatrix} 3 & 0 \\ 0 & 3 \end{pmatrix}\begin{pmatrix} 2 \\ 5 \end{pmatrix} = \begin{pmatrix} \\ \end{pmatrix}$	(,)
(4, 5)	$\begin{pmatrix} 3 & 0 \\ 0 & 3 \end{pmatrix}\begin{pmatrix} 4 \\ 5 \end{pmatrix} = \begin{pmatrix} \\ \end{pmatrix}$	(,)
(4, 3)	$\begin{pmatrix} 3 & 0 \\ 0 & 3 \end{pmatrix}\begin{pmatrix} 4 \\ 3 \end{pmatrix} = \begin{pmatrix} \\ \end{pmatrix}$	(,)

Find the area of the object and the area of the image.

c *Third shape*

Object point		Image point
(4, 2)	$\begin{pmatrix} 3 & 0 \\ 0 & 3 \end{pmatrix}\begin{pmatrix} 4 \\ 2 \end{pmatrix} = \begin{pmatrix} \\ \end{pmatrix}$	(,)
(4, 0)	$\begin{pmatrix} 3 & 0 \\ 0 & 3 \end{pmatrix}\begin{pmatrix} 4 \\ 0 \end{pmatrix} = \begin{pmatrix} \\ \end{pmatrix}$	(,)
(5, 0)	$\begin{pmatrix} 3 & 0 \\ 0 & 3 \end{pmatrix}\begin{pmatrix} 5 \\ 0 \end{pmatrix} = \begin{pmatrix} \\ \end{pmatrix}$	(,)

Find the area of the object and the area of the image.

d What kind of transformation has taken place?
What is the centre, the length scale factor and the area scale factor of the transformation?

Transformations and matrices

3 The matrix $\begin{pmatrix} 0 & 1 \\ 1 & 0 \end{pmatrix}$

a *First shape*

Object point		Image point
(9, 4)	$\begin{pmatrix} 0 & 1 \\ 1 & 0 \end{pmatrix}\begin{pmatrix} 9 \\ 4 \end{pmatrix} = \begin{pmatrix} \\ \end{pmatrix}$	(,)
(10, 4)	$\begin{pmatrix} 0 & 1 \\ 1 & 0 \end{pmatrix}\begin{pmatrix} 10 \\ 4 \end{pmatrix} = \begin{pmatrix} \\ \end{pmatrix}$	(,)
(10, 9)	$\begin{pmatrix} 0 & 1 \\ 1 & 0 \end{pmatrix}\begin{pmatrix} 10 \\ 9 \end{pmatrix} = \begin{pmatrix} \\ \end{pmatrix}$	(,)
(9, 9)	$\begin{pmatrix} 0 & 1 \\ 1 & 0 \end{pmatrix}\begin{pmatrix} 9 \\ 9 \end{pmatrix} = \begin{pmatrix} \\ \end{pmatrix}$	(,)

b *Second shape*

Object point		Image point
(6, 1)	$\begin{pmatrix} 0 & 1 \\ 1 & 0 \end{pmatrix}\begin{pmatrix} 6 \\ 1 \end{pmatrix} = \begin{pmatrix} \\ \end{pmatrix}$	(,)
(6, 4)	$\begin{pmatrix} 0 & 1 \\ 1 & 0 \end{pmatrix}\begin{pmatrix} 6 \\ 4 \end{pmatrix} = \begin{pmatrix} \\ \end{pmatrix}$	(,)
(8, 4)	$\begin{pmatrix} 0 & 1 \\ 1 & 0 \end{pmatrix}\begin{pmatrix} 8 \\ 4 \end{pmatrix} = \begin{pmatrix} \\ \end{pmatrix}$	(,)

c *Third shape*

Object point		Image point
(12, 10)	$\begin{pmatrix} 0 & 1 \\ 1 & 0 \end{pmatrix}\begin{pmatrix} 12 \\ 10 \end{pmatrix} = \begin{pmatrix} \\ \end{pmatrix}$	(,)
(12, 13)	$\begin{pmatrix} 0 & 1 \\ 1 & 0 \end{pmatrix}\begin{pmatrix} 12 \\ 13 \end{pmatrix} = \begin{pmatrix} \\ \end{pmatrix}$	(,)
(16, 13)	$\begin{pmatrix} 0 & 1 \\ 1 & 0 \end{pmatrix}\begin{pmatrix} 16 \\ 13 \end{pmatrix} = \begin{pmatrix} \\ \end{pmatrix}$	(,)

d What kind of transformation has taken place?
Draw the *mirror line* of the transformation on your diagram.

Transformations and matrices

4 The matrix $\begin{pmatrix} 1 & 1 \\ 0 & 1 \end{pmatrix}$

a *First shape*

Object point		Image point
(1, 0)	$\begin{pmatrix} 1 & 1 \\ 0 & 1 \end{pmatrix}\begin{pmatrix} 1 \\ 0 \end{pmatrix} = \begin{pmatrix} \\ \end{pmatrix}$	(,)
(3, 0)	$\begin{pmatrix} 1 & 1 \\ 0 & 1 \end{pmatrix}\begin{pmatrix} 3 \\ 0 \end{pmatrix} = \begin{pmatrix} \\ \end{pmatrix}$	(,)
(3, 6)	$\begin{pmatrix} 1 & 1 \\ 0 & 1 \end{pmatrix}\begin{pmatrix} 3 \\ 6 \end{pmatrix} = \begin{pmatrix} \\ \end{pmatrix}$	(,)
(1, 6)	$\begin{pmatrix} 1 & 1 \\ 0 & 1 \end{pmatrix}\begin{pmatrix} 1 \\ 6 \end{pmatrix} = \begin{pmatrix} \\ \end{pmatrix}$	(,)

b *Second shape*

Object point		Image point
(8, 0)	$\begin{pmatrix} 1 & 1 \\ 0 & 1 \end{pmatrix}\begin{pmatrix} 8 \\ 0 \end{pmatrix} = \begin{pmatrix} \\ \end{pmatrix}$	(,)
(9, 0)	$\begin{pmatrix} 1 & 1 \\ 0 & 1 \end{pmatrix}\begin{pmatrix} 9 \\ 0 \end{pmatrix} = \begin{pmatrix} \\ \end{pmatrix}$	(,)
(9, 3)	$\begin{pmatrix} 1 & 1 \\ 0 & 1 \end{pmatrix}\begin{pmatrix} 9 \\ 3 \end{pmatrix} = \begin{pmatrix} \\ \end{pmatrix}$	(,)
(11, 3)	$\begin{pmatrix} 1 & 1 \\ 0 & 1 \end{pmatrix}\begin{pmatrix} 11 \\ 3 \end{pmatrix} = \begin{pmatrix} \\ \end{pmatrix}$	(,)
(11, 4)	$\begin{pmatrix} 1 & 1 \\ 0 & 1 \end{pmatrix}\begin{pmatrix} 11 \\ 4 \end{pmatrix} = \begin{pmatrix} \\ \end{pmatrix}$	(,)
(8, 4)	$\begin{pmatrix} 1 & 1 \\ 0 & 1 \end{pmatrix}\begin{pmatrix} 8 \\ 4 \end{pmatrix} = \begin{pmatrix} \\ \end{pmatrix}$	(,)

c *Third shape*

Object point		Image point
(1, 8)	$\begin{pmatrix} 1 & 1 \\ 0 & 1 \end{pmatrix}\begin{pmatrix} 1 \\ 8 \end{pmatrix} = \begin{pmatrix} \\ \end{pmatrix}$	(,)
(1, 12)	$\begin{pmatrix} 1 & 1 \\ 0 & 1 \end{pmatrix}\begin{pmatrix} 1 \\ 12 \end{pmatrix} = \begin{pmatrix} \\ \end{pmatrix}$	(,)
(4, 12)	$\begin{pmatrix} 1 & 1 \\ 0 & 1 \end{pmatrix}\begin{pmatrix} 4 \\ 12 \end{pmatrix} = \begin{pmatrix} \\ \end{pmatrix}$	(,)
(4, 8)	$\begin{pmatrix} 1 & 1 \\ 0 & 1 \end{pmatrix}\begin{pmatrix} 4 \\ 8 \end{pmatrix} = \begin{pmatrix} \\ \end{pmatrix}$	(,)

d What kind of transformation has taken place?
Which line has stayed unchanged under this transformation?
In which direction has all movement taken place?

Transformations and matrices

Part 2 All quadrants

For each matrix, draw and label both axes from 0 to 16

plot points and draw each object shape on the axes

transform each object and draw its image on the same diagram

use *one* word to describe the transformation which has taken place

and answer any further questions.

1 The matrix $\begin{pmatrix} \frac{1}{2} & 0 \\ 0 & \frac{1}{2} \end{pmatrix}$ *First object* (0, 16), (4, 12), (8, 16)
Second object (8, 6), (8, 10), (10, 10), (10, 6)
Third object (16, 0), (16, 4), (14, 4), (14, 2), (12, 2), (12, 0)

What is the centre and length scale factor of this transformation?

2 The matrix $\begin{pmatrix} 2 & 0 \\ 0 & 1 \end{pmatrix}$ *First object* (1, 2), (4, 1), (4, 3)
Second object (2, 4), (6, 4), (2, 8)
Third object (3, 10), (5, 10), (3, 12), (5, 14), (3, 14), (0, 12)

In which direction has motion taken place?

3 The matrix $\begin{pmatrix} 1 & 0 \\ 0 & 3 \end{pmatrix}$ *First object* (1, 1), (3, 1), (2, 4)
Second object (5, 1), (5, 3), (7, 2), (11, 3), (11, 1)
Third object (14, 1), (12, 3), (14, 5), (16, 3)

In which direction has motion taken place?

4 The matrix $\begin{pmatrix} 1 & 0 \\ 1 & 1 \end{pmatrix}$ *First object* (0, 2), (0, 4), (3, 4), (3, 2)
Second object (1, 9), (1, 11), (4, 11), (4, 12), (6, 10), (4, 8), (4, 9)
Third object (5, 1), (6, 3), (10, 2), (12, 4), (11, 2), (12, 0), (10, 1), (7, 0)

One line on your diagram has been unchanged by the transformation. Which line is it?
In which direction have all other points moved?

For all further matrices in this section, label both your axes from -8 to 8.

5 The matrix $\begin{pmatrix} -1 & 0 \\ 0 & 1 \end{pmatrix}$ *First object* (3, 6), (4, 8), (0, 8)
Second object (1, 4), (4, 6), (4, 3), (8, 4), (7, 1), (4, 1), (3, 4)
Third object (2, -3), (4, -5), (2, -7), (-2, -5)

Which line is the *mirror line* of this transformation?
Draw this line on your diagram.

6 The matrix $\begin{pmatrix} 1 & 0 \\ 0 & -1 \end{pmatrix}$ *First object* (2, 0), (6, 0), (6, 5), (5, 5), (5, 4), (4, 5), (2, 3)
Second object (2, 4), (0, 6), (2, 8), (-4, 6)
Third object (-8, 3), (-6, 4), (-4, 3), (-6, -2)

Which line is the *mirror line* of this transformation?
Draw this line on your diagram.

Transformations and matrices

7 The matrix $\begin{pmatrix} 0 & 1 \\ -1 & 0 \end{pmatrix}$ *First object*   (0, 8), (6, 8), (5, 5)

Second object   (0, 0), (1, 2), (7, 2), (7, 1), (2, 1)

Third object   (−2, −1), (−4, −4), (−7, −4), (−7, −7), (−5, −7), (−3, −6)

About which point and in which direction has all the motion taken place?
What angle have objects been turned through?

8 The matrix $\begin{pmatrix} 0 & -1 \\ 1 & 0 \end{pmatrix}$ *First object*   (0, 0), (4, 1), (2, 3), (2, 1)

Second object   (0, 0), (−6, −2), (−6, −5), (−1, −5), (−1, −2), (−4, −2)

Third object   (7, 2), (7, 7), (8, 8), (2, 7), (4, 4), (6, 6)

About which point and in which direction has all the motion taken place?
What angle have objects been turned through?

9 The matrix $\begin{pmatrix} 0 & -1 \\ -1 & 0 \end{pmatrix}$ *First object*   (3, 5), (3, 4), (1, 1), (−3, 1), (−3, 5)

Second object   (−6, 7), (−6, 6), (−1, 6), (−1, 7)

Third object   (8, −1), (5, −1), (5, −4), (7, −2), (8, −4)

Which line is the *mirror line* of this transformation?
Draw this line on your diagram.

10 The matrix $\begin{pmatrix} -2 & 0 \\ 0 & -2 \end{pmatrix}$ *First object*   (2, 0), (2, 1), (4, 1), (4, 3), (2, 3), (2, 4), (1, 2)

Second object   (4, −1), (4, −3), (3, −3), (3, −4), (1, −4), (1, −3), (0, −3)

What is the centre and length scale factor of this transformation?

11 The matrix $\begin{pmatrix} 0 & 1 \\ -1 & 2 \end{pmatrix}$ *First object*   (1, 1), (2, 2), (0, 4), (−1, 3)

Second object   (3, 3), (4, 4), (6, 2), (7, 3), (8, 2), (5, −1), (4, 0), (5, 1)

Third object   (−6, −6), (−5, −5), (−6, −4), (−5, −3), (−8, −3), (−8, −6), (−7, −5)

One line stays unchanged under this transformation. Draw it on your diagram
and give its equation.
In which direction have all other points moved?

12 The matrix $\begin{pmatrix} 0.7 & 0.7 \\ -0.7 & 0.7 \end{pmatrix}$ *First object*   (0, 0), (4, 4), (6, 0), (4, 1)

Second object   (0, 0), (−8, 0), (−6, 1), (−8, 2), (−2, 2)

Third object   (1, −3), (3, −5), (1, −7), (1, −6), (−1, −6), (−1, −4), (1, −4)

About which point and in which direction has all the motion taken place?
What angle have the objects been turned through?

Transformations and matrices

Part 3 Two transformations combined

Two simple transformations can be combined and given by *one* matrix.

For each matrix below, draw and label both axes from -8 to 8

calculate the position of the image shape

draw both object and image shapes on the same diagram

and name the two simple transformations which have taken place.

	Matrix	Object shape
1	$\begin{pmatrix} 2 & 2 \\ 0 & 2 \end{pmatrix}$	$(1, 0), (2, 0), (2, 2), (1, 2)$
2	$\begin{pmatrix} 2 & 0 \\ 0 & -2 \end{pmatrix}$	$(4, 1), (4, 4), (0, 4), (0, 2), (3, 3)$
3	$\begin{pmatrix} 0 & 2 \\ -2 & 0 \end{pmatrix}$	$(3, 2), (3, 3), (1, 3), (1, 4), (-2, 3), (1, 2)$
4	$\begin{pmatrix} 1 & 1 \\ -1 & 0 \end{pmatrix}$	$(2, 1), (2, 3), (4, 3), (4, 4), (0, 4), (0, 1)$
5	$\begin{pmatrix} 1 & 0 \\ 0 & -3 \end{pmatrix}$	$(3, 0), (3, 2), (-5, 2), (-5, 0), (-4, 0), (-3, 1), (2, 1)$
6	$\begin{pmatrix} -2 & 0 \\ 0 & -2 \end{pmatrix}$	$(1, 1), (1, 4), (3, 4), (3, 3), (2, 3)$
7	$\begin{pmatrix} -2 & 0 \\ 0 & 1 \end{pmatrix}$	$(2, 4), (4, -4), (2, -2), (1, -2), (1, -4), (0, -4)$
8	$\begin{pmatrix} 1 & -1 \\ 1 & 1 \end{pmatrix}$	$(-2, 2), (-1, 2), (2, -1), (5, -1), (5, -3), (3, -3)$

Successive transformations

Part 1

All diagrams for these problems need both axes labelled from -7 to 7.

1   a   The triangle with corners $A(2, 1)$, $B(3, 1)$, $C(1, 3)$ is transformed using the matrix $\begin{pmatrix} 1 & 0 \\ 0 & -1 \end{pmatrix}$ onto the triangle $A'B'C'$.
Calculate the positions of A', B' and C'. Draw the triangle ABC and its image on the same diagram.

     b   The triangle $A'B'C'$ is now transformed onto $A''B''C''$ using the matrix $\begin{pmatrix} 2 & 0 \\ 0 & 2 \end{pmatrix}$.
Calculate the positions of A'', B'' and C''. Draw the new image on the same diagram.

     c   Describe in words the two transformations which have taken place, giving full details. Find *one* matrix which will map triangle ABC *directly* onto triangle $A''B''C''$ in one step.

2   a   A rectangle has corners $P(1, 0)$, $Q(3, 0)$, $R(3, 3)$, $S(1, 3)$. It is transformed using the matrix $\begin{pmatrix} 1 & 1 \\ 0 & 1 \end{pmatrix}$ onto the image $P'Q'R'S'$.
Calculate the positions of the corners of the image; and draw both the rectangle $PQRS$ and its image on one diagram.

     b $P'Q'R'S'$ is now transformed onto $P''Q''R''S''$ using the matrix $\begin{pmatrix} 0 & 1 \\ -1 & 0 \end{pmatrix}$.
Calculate the positions of P'', Q'', R'' and S''. Draw this new image onto the same diagram.

     c   Describe, giving full details, the two transformations which have occurred. Calculate the matrix which maps $PQRS$ *directly* onto $P''Q''R''S''$ in one step.

3   a   Triangle $L(2, 0)$, $M(4, 0)$, $N(2, 2)$ is transformed by the matrix $\begin{pmatrix} 1 & 0 \\ 0 & 3 \end{pmatrix}$ onto triangle $L'M'N'$.
Calculate the co-ordinates of L', M' and N'; and draw both triangles LMN and $L'M'N'$ onto one diagram.
Describe fully the transformation which has taken place.

     b   The matrix $\begin{pmatrix} -1 & 0 \\ 0 & -1 \end{pmatrix}$ transforms triangle $L'M'N'$ onto $L''M''N''$.
Calculate the co-ordinates of the corners of this new image, and then draw it on the same diagram.
Describe fully the transformation which has occurred.

     c   Calculate the matrix which will map triangle LMN *directly* onto triangle $L''M''N''$ in one step.

4   a   A five-sided shape has corners $A(1, 2)$, $B(6, 2)$, $C(2, 4)$, $D(2, 5)$, $E(1, 5)$. It is transformed by the matrix $\begin{pmatrix} 0 & -1 \\ 1 & 0 \end{pmatrix}$ onto $A'B'C'D'E'$.
Calculate the co-ordinates of the corners of the image; and draw both the object shape $ABCDE$ and its image on the same diagram.
Describe fully the transformation which has taken place.

     b   The matrix $\begin{pmatrix} 0 & 1 \\ 1 & 0 \end{pmatrix}$ transforms the shape $A'B'C'D'E'$ onto a new image $A''B''C''D''E''$.
Calculate the position of this new image and draw it on the same diagram.
Describe fully the transformation given by this matrix.

     c   Calculate the matrix which will transform $ABCDE$ onto $A''B''C''D''E''$ directly in one step. Describe in words the transformation involved.

Successive transformations

5 a The square S with corners (4, 0), (6, 2), (4, 4), (2, 2) is mapped onto S' by the
   matrix $\begin{pmatrix} 0 & 1 \\ -1 & 2 \end{pmatrix}$.
   Calculate the corners of the image S' and draw both S and S' on the same
   diagram.
   Describe this transformation in words, giving full details.

  b S' is now mapped onto S'' by the matrix $\begin{pmatrix} 0 & 1 \\ 1 & 0 \end{pmatrix}$.
   Calculate the position of S'' and draw it on the same diagram.
   Describe this transformation fully.

  c Find the matrix which will map S directly onto S''.

6 a The shape L with corners (2, 2), (2, 1), (3, 1), (3, 3), (0, 3), (0, 2) is mapped
   onto L' by the matrix $\begin{pmatrix} 1 & 0 \\ 1 & 1 \end{pmatrix}$.
   Calculate the position of the image L' and draw both shape L and its image
   L' on one diagram.

  b The matrix $\begin{pmatrix} 0 & -1 \\ -1 & 0 \end{pmatrix}$ now transforms L' onto L''.
   Calculate the position of this new image L'', and draw it on the same diagram.

  c Describe fully the two transformations which have taken place; and find *one*
   matrix which will map L directly onto L''.

7 a The points (− 2, 1), (1, 2), (2, − 1) and (− 1, − 2) are the corners of a square S
   which is transformed by the matrix $\begin{pmatrix} 3 & 0 \\ 0 & 3 \end{pmatrix}$ onto its image S'.
   Calculate the co-ordinates of the corners of S'; and draw both S and S' onto
   the same diagram.
   Describe fully the transformation which has occurred.

  b S' is now transformed onto S'' under a transformation given by the matrix
   $\begin{pmatrix} 0.7 & -0.7 \\ 0.7 & 0.7 \end{pmatrix}$.
   Calculate the position of S'' and draw it on the same diagram.
   Describe this transformation fully.

  c Find the matrix which will map S onto S'' in one step.

8 a The triangle T with corners (− 4, 4), (− 2, 2), (1, 5) is mapped onto the
   triangle T' by the matrix $\begin{pmatrix} 2 & 1 \\ -1 & 0 \end{pmatrix}$.
   Calculate the positions of the corners of T'; and draw both T and T' on one
   diagram.
   Describe, with full details, the transformation which has occurred.

  b The matrix $\begin{pmatrix} 1 & 0 \\ 0 & -1 \end{pmatrix}$ transforms triangle T' onto T''.
   Calculate the position of T'' and draw it on the same diagram.
   Describe this transformation fully.

  c T'' is now mapped onto T''' by the matrix $\begin{pmatrix} 0 & 1 \\ -1 & 2 \end{pmatrix}$.
   Calculate the position of T''' and draw it on the same diagram.
   Describe this transformation fully.

  d What transformation will map T directly onto T''' in *one* step?
   Find the matrix for this transformation.

Successive transformations

Part 2   Letters for transformations

All diagrams for these problems need both axes labelling from -7 to 7.

1   **M** represents the transformation given by the matrix $\begin{pmatrix} 1 & 0 \\ 1 & 1 \end{pmatrix}$.

   N represents the transformation given by the matrix $\begin{pmatrix} -1 & 0 \\ 0 & -1 \end{pmatrix}$.

   The rectangle R has corners $(0, 1)$, $(0, 3)$, $(3, 3)$, $(3, 1)$.
   a   The rectangle R is mapped onto its image R' where $R' = \mathbf{M}(R)$.
       Calculate the corners of R', and draw both R and R' onto the same diagram.
       Label R and R', and describe transformation **M**.
   b R' is now mapped onto R'' where $R'' = \mathbf{N}(R')$.
       Calculate the corners of R'', and draw it on the same diagram.
       Describe the transformation **N**.
   c   Calculate the matrix **NM** which maps R onto R'' in *one* step.

2   **X** represents the transformation given by the matrix $\begin{pmatrix} 1 & 0 \\ 0 & -1 \end{pmatrix}$.

   Y represents the transformation given by the matrix $\begin{pmatrix} -1 & 0 \\ 0 & 1 \end{pmatrix}$.

   The quadrilateral Q has corners $(2, 1)$, $(2, 4)$, $(4, 3)$, $(3, 3)$ joined in this order.
   a Q is mapped onto Q' where $Q' = \mathbf{X}(Q)$.
       Calculate the position of Q', and draw both Q and Q' on one diagram.
       Describe the transformation **X**.
   b Q' is now transformed onto Q'' where $Q'' = \mathbf{Y}(Q')$.
       Calculate the position of Q'' and draw it on the same diagram.
       Describe the transformation **Y**.
   c   Find the matrix **YX** which maps Q directly onto Q'' in one step.

3   Transformation **G** is given by the matrix $\begin{pmatrix} 1 & 0 \\ 0 & 3 \end{pmatrix}$; and transformation **H** is given by the matrix $\begin{pmatrix} 3 & 0 \\ 0 & 1 \end{pmatrix}$.
   The square S has corners $(1, 1)$, $(2, 1)$, $(2, 2)$, $(1, 2)$.
   a S' is the image of S where $S' = \mathbf{G}(S)$.
       Calculate the position of S' and draw both S and S' on the same diagram.
       Describe the transformation **G**.
   b S' is now mapped onto S'' where $S'' = \mathbf{H}(S')$.
       Calculate the position of S'' and draw it on the same diagram.
       Describe the transformation **H**.
   c   Find the matrix **HG** which maps S directly onto S'', and describe this
       transformation.

4   The two transformations **R** and **E** are given by the matrices $\begin{pmatrix} 0 & 1 \\ 1 & 0 \end{pmatrix}$ and $\begin{pmatrix} 2 & 0 \\ 0 & 2 \end{pmatrix}$ respectively. The points $(2, 2)$, $(2, 3)$, $(-1, 3)$ are the corners of triangle T.
   a   Calculate the corners of the image T' of triangle T where $T' = \mathbf{R}(T)$. Draw T
       and T' on one diagram, and describe the transformation which has taken
       place.

Successive transformations

b T' is now transformed onto T'' such that $T'' = E(T')$.
   Calculate the corners of T'' and draw T'' on the same diagram.
   Describe the transformation **E**.

c Calculate the single matrix **ER** which will map T directly onto T''.

5 The two matrices $\begin{pmatrix} 1 & 0 \\ 0 & -1 \end{pmatrix}$ and $\begin{pmatrix} 0 & -1 \\ 1 & 0 \end{pmatrix}$ give the two transformations **A** and **B** respectively.

The shape S has corners $(3, 4)$, $(3, 6)$, $(-2, 6)$, $(-2, 4)$, $(-1, 4)$ and $(-1, 5)$ joined in this order.

a Find the position of the image S' of S where $S' = A(S)$. Draw S and S' on one diagram and describe the transformation **A**.

b S' is now transformed onto S'' where $S'' = B(S')$. Find the position of S'' and draw it on the same diagram.
   Describe the transformation **B**.

c Calculate the single matrix **BA** which maps S directly onto S'', and describe it.

6 a The matrix $\begin{pmatrix} 1 & -\frac{1}{2} \\ 1 & 0 \end{pmatrix}$ defines the transformation **K**; and the matrix $\begin{pmatrix} 2 & -2 \\ 0 & -1 \end{pmatrix}$ defines the transformation **L**. An object shape P with vertices $(4, 2)$, $(5, 2)$, $(5, 4)$, $(6, 4)$, $(4, 6)$ has an image P' where $P' = K(P)$.
   Calculate the positions of the vertices of P' and draw both P and P' on one diagram.

b If $P'' = L(P')$, calculate the positions of the vertices of P'' and draw P'' on the same diagram.

c Find the single matrix which transforms P directly onto P'', and describe this transformation.

7 a The transformation **Y** given by the matrix $\begin{pmatrix} -1 & -1 \\ -2 & 0 \end{pmatrix}$ maps the shape S onto its image S' where $S' = Y(S)$.
   If S has vertices $(3, 0)$, $(3, 2)$, $(2, 2)$, $(2, 3)$, $(1, 3)$, $(1, 2)$ joined in this order, find the position of S' and draw one diagram showing S and S'.

b If $S'' = M(S')$, where **M** is the transformation given by the matrix $\begin{pmatrix} 0 & -1 \\ -2 & 1 \end{pmatrix}$, find and draw S'' on the same diagram.

c Calculate the single matrix which maps S directly onto S'', and describe it in words.

8 a The object shape A $(0, 0)$, $(2, 2)$, $(3, 2)$, $(3, 3)$, $(2, 3)$ is transformed onto its image A' where $A' = M(A)$ and **M** is the transformation given by the matrix $\begin{pmatrix} 1 & -1 \\ 1 & 1 \end{pmatrix}$.
   Calculate the vertices of A' and draw A and A' on one diagram.
   Describe the transformation **M**.

b A' is now mapped onto A'' such that $A'' = M(A')$. Find A'' and draw it on the same diagram.
   Describe the transformation which maps A directly onto A'' and calculate the matrix M^2 for this transformation.

Area scale factors and determinants

Part 1

For each matrix below, draw and label axes as indicated
transform the object shape
draw both object and image on your axes
calculate the areas of the object and the image
and write down the **area scale factor**.

	Matrix	Object shape	Axes
1	$\begin{pmatrix} 2 & 1 \\ 0 & 1 \end{pmatrix}$	(1, 2), (1, 5), (3, 5), (3, 2)	
2	$\begin{pmatrix} 1 & 0 \\ 1 & 1 \end{pmatrix}$	(1, 1), (1, 2), (4, 2), (4, 1)	
3	$\begin{pmatrix} -2 & 0 \\ 0 & -2 \end{pmatrix}$	(1, 3), (3, 1), (3, −2), (1, −2)	
4	$\begin{pmatrix} 2 & 1 \\ -2 & 1 \end{pmatrix}$	(0, 2), (2, 2), (3, 4), (1, 4)	
5	$\begin{pmatrix} 2 & 2 \\ -2 & 2 \end{pmatrix}$	(2, 1), (2, 2), (0, 2), (0, 1)	
6	$\begin{pmatrix} 1 & -1 \\ 1 & 1 \end{pmatrix}$	(2, 1), (4, 1), (4, 5), (2, 5)	
7	$\begin{pmatrix} 3 & 0 \\ 1 & 2 \end{pmatrix}$	(1, 1), (1, 3), (3, 3), (3, 1)	
8	$\begin{pmatrix} 1 & -2 \\ 2 & 1 \end{pmatrix}$	(1, 1), (3, 1), (3, 2), (1, 2)	

9   Copy and complete this table with your results for the eight transformations.

	1	2	3	4	5	6	7	8
Object area								
Image area								
Area scale factor								
Matrix	$\begin{pmatrix} 2 & 1 \\ 0 & 1 \end{pmatrix}$	$\begin{pmatrix} 1 & 0 \\ 1 & 1 \end{pmatrix}$	$\begin{pmatrix} -2 & 0 \\ 0 & -2 \end{pmatrix}$	$\begin{pmatrix} 2 & 1 \\ -2 & 1 \end{pmatrix}$	$\begin{pmatrix} 2 & 2 \\ -2 & 2 \end{pmatrix}$	$\begin{pmatrix} 1 & -1 \\ 1 & 1 \end{pmatrix}$	$\begin{pmatrix} 3 & 0 \\ 1 & 2 \end{pmatrix}$	$\begin{pmatrix} 1 & -2 \\ 2 & 1 \end{pmatrix}$

Can you see a pattern linking the area scale factors and the matrices?
Look closely at the numbers on the two diagonals of each matrix.

Area scale factors and determinants

10 The area scale factor of a transformation can be found directly from its matrix. It is called the **determinant** of the matrix, and is given the symbol Δ.

For the matrix $\begin{pmatrix} a & b \\ c & d \end{pmatrix}$, the determinant $\Delta = ad - bc$.

Find the determinant of each matrix in the table of problem **9** above and check that it gives the area scale factor of the transformation.

11 Find the determinant, Δ, of these matrices.

a $\begin{pmatrix} 3 & 1 \\ 0 & 2 \end{pmatrix}$ b $\begin{pmatrix} 3 & 4 \\ 2 & 5 \end{pmatrix}$ c $\begin{pmatrix} 5 & 1 \\ 3 & 2 \end{pmatrix}$ d $\begin{pmatrix} 3 & 5 \\ 4 & 7 \end{pmatrix}$

e $\begin{pmatrix} 4 & 2 \\ 0 & 3 \end{pmatrix}$ f $\begin{pmatrix} 1 & 0 \\ -3 & 5 \end{pmatrix}$ g $\begin{pmatrix} 3 & 0 \\ 0 & 3 \end{pmatrix}$ h $\begin{pmatrix} 0 & 2 \\ -3 & 5 \end{pmatrix}$

i $\begin{pmatrix} 2 & 4 \\ -1 & 0 \end{pmatrix}$ j $\begin{pmatrix} 1 & -1 \\ 2 & 2 \end{pmatrix}$ k $\begin{pmatrix} 3 & 3 \\ -2 & 1 \end{pmatrix}$ l $\begin{pmatrix} -2 & 6 \\ -1 & 2 \end{pmatrix}$

m $\begin{pmatrix} 3 & -2 \\ 6 & -3 \end{pmatrix}$ n $\begin{pmatrix} -1 & 3 \\ -3 & 2 \end{pmatrix}$ o $\begin{pmatrix} 4 & 9 \\ -1 & -2 \end{pmatrix}$ p $\begin{pmatrix} -4 & 2 \\ 1 & -3 \end{pmatrix}$

q $\begin{pmatrix} -5 & 3 \\ 3 & -2 \end{pmatrix}$ r $\begin{pmatrix} -1 & 3 \\ -2 & -8 \end{pmatrix}$ s $\begin{pmatrix} 4 & -6 \\ -3 & 5 \end{pmatrix}$ t $\begin{pmatrix} 4 & -5 \\ -2 & 4 \end{pmatrix}$

u $\begin{pmatrix} -2 & 4 \\ -3 & 5 \end{pmatrix}$

12 An object has an area of 3 cm² and it is transformed using the matrix $\begin{pmatrix} 3 & 4 \\ 1 & 3 \end{pmatrix}$.

Find
a   the area scale factor of the transformation   b   the area of the image.

13 An object with an area of 5 cm² is transformed using the matrix $\begin{pmatrix} 2 & 2 \\ 4 & 6 \end{pmatrix}$.

Find
a   the area scale factor of the transformation   b   the area of the image.

14 The matrix $\begin{pmatrix} 3 & 4 \\ 0 & 2 \end{pmatrix}$ transforms an object of area $\frac{1}{2}$ cm².
Find the area of its image.

15 An object of area 8 cm² is transformed by the matrix $\begin{pmatrix} \frac{1}{2} & 1 \\ 0 & 1 \end{pmatrix}$.

Find the area of its image.

16 If an object of area 12 cm² is transformed by the matrix $\begin{pmatrix} \frac{1}{2} & 0 \\ 0 & \frac{1}{2} \end{pmatrix}$, what is the area of its image?

Area scale factors and determinants

17 This object shape is transformed by the matrix $\begin{pmatrix} 3 & 5 \\ 2 & 4 \end{pmatrix}$.
Without drawing any diagrams, find
a the area of the object
b the area of the image.

18 The matrix $\begin{pmatrix} 2 & -3 \\ 1 & 2 \end{pmatrix}$ is used to transform the object shape drawn here.
Without drawing any diagrams, find
a the area of this object
b the area of its image.

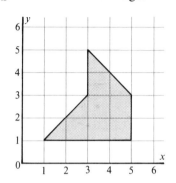
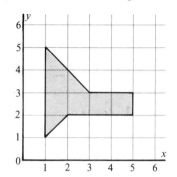

19 The matrix $\begin{pmatrix} 3 & 6 \\ 2 & 5 \end{pmatrix}$ transforms an object so that its image has an area of 15 cm². What is the area of the object?

20 The matrix $\begin{pmatrix} 1 & 4 \\ -1 & 2 \end{pmatrix}$ transforms an object so that its image has an area of 18 cm². What is the area of the object?

21 If an object maps onto its image, under a transformation given by the matrix $\begin{pmatrix} 1 & 1 \\ -2 & 3 \end{pmatrix}$, so that the area of the image is 30 cm², what is the area of the object?

22 The matrix $\begin{pmatrix} \frac{1}{3} & 1 \\ 0 & 1 \end{pmatrix}$ maps an object onto an image of area 2 cm². Find the area of the object.

23 The matrix $\begin{pmatrix} \frac{1}{2} & 1 \\ -\frac{1}{2} & 1 \end{pmatrix}$ produces an image of area 5 cm². What is the area of the object?

24 Copy and complete this table.

	a	b	c	d	e	f	g	h
Matrix	$\begin{pmatrix} 4 & 3 \\ 1 & 2 \end{pmatrix}$	$\begin{pmatrix} 2 & 3 \\ 3 & 5 \end{pmatrix}$	$\begin{pmatrix} 0 & 2 \\ -3 & 4 \end{pmatrix}$	$\begin{pmatrix} 5 & 1 \\ -4 & 0 \end{pmatrix}$	$\begin{pmatrix} 2 & 2 \\ -1 & 3 \end{pmatrix}$	$\begin{pmatrix} 5 & -2 \\ 2 & 1 \end{pmatrix}$	$\begin{pmatrix} -3 & -2 \\ 7 & 4 \end{pmatrix}$	$\begin{pmatrix} 2 & 3 \\ -4 & -2 \end{pmatrix}$
Determinant, Δ								
Object area	3 cm²	7 cm²	2 cm²	$\frac{1}{2}$ cm²				
Image area					24 cm²	18 cm²	6 cm²	4 cm²

203

Area scale factors and determinants

25 This parallelogram with corners
(1, 0), (− 1, 4), (1, 2), (3, − 2) is transformed

by the matrix $\begin{pmatrix} 1 & \frac{1}{2} \\ 1 & 1 \end{pmatrix}$.

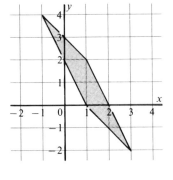

   a Find the positions of the corners of its image
      and draw the image on squared paper.
   b Find the area scale factor of the
      transformation and hence find the area of the
      original parallelogram.

26 A parallelogram with corners (0, 2), (− 2, 4), (− 4, 8),

   (− 2, 6) is transformed by the matrix $\begin{pmatrix} 4 & 2 \\ 2 & 2 \end{pmatrix}$.

   a Calculate the corners of its image, and draw both the parallelogram and its
      image on the same diagram.
   b Find the area scale factor of the transformation, and hence find the area of
      the parallelogram.

Part 2 $\Delta \leqslant 0$

1 The parallelogram (1, 1), (0, 2), (1, 2), (2, 1) is transformed by the matrix $\begin{pmatrix} 2 & 1 \\ 4 & 2 \end{pmatrix}$.

   a Calculate the corners of its image. Labelling the x-axis from 0 to 5 and the y-axis
      from 0 to 10, draw both the parallelogram and its image on the same diagram.
   b What is the area of the parallelogram, the area of its image and the area
      scale factor of the transformation?
   c Find the determinant of the matrix.
   d This transformation could be called a **collapse**. What is the equation of the
      line on which the image lies?

2 The triangle (1, 0), (1, 1), (0, 1) is transformed by the matrix $\begin{pmatrix} 2 & 1 \\ 6 & 3 \end{pmatrix}$.

   a Calculate the corners of its image. Draw the triangle and its image on axes
      labelled as in number **1** above.
   b What is the area of the triangle, the area of its image and the area scale
      factor of the transformation?
   c Find the determinant of the matrix.
   d What is the equation of the line on which the image lies?

3 The triangle (1, 1), (2, 1), (1, 2) is transformed by the matrix $\begin{pmatrix} 2 & 4 \\ 1 & 2 \end{pmatrix}$.

   a Labelling the x-axis from 0 to 10 and the y-axis from 0 to 5, draw both the
      triangle and its image on the same diagram.
   b What is the area scale factor of the transformation? What is the determinant
      of the matrix?
   c Find the equation of the line on which the image lies.

4 The rectangle (1, 1), (3, 1), (3, 2), (1, 2) is transformed by the matrix $\begin{pmatrix} -1 & 1 \\ 2 & -2 \end{pmatrix}$.

   a Draw both the rectangle and its image onto axes labelled from − 5 to 5.
   b What is the area scale factor of the transformation, and the determinant of
      the matrix?
   c Find the equation of the line on which the image lies.

Area scale factors and determinants

5 A matrix which has a zero determinant is said to be **singular**.
Which of these matrices are singular?

a $\begin{pmatrix} 6 & 4 \\ 3 & 2 \end{pmatrix}$ b $\begin{pmatrix} 8 & 3 \\ 5 & 2 \end{pmatrix}$ c $\begin{pmatrix} 0 & 1 \\ -1 & 0 \end{pmatrix}$ d $\begin{pmatrix} 8 & 4 \\ 4 & 2 \end{pmatrix}$

e $\begin{pmatrix} 3 & 6 \\ 4 & 8 \end{pmatrix}$ f $\begin{pmatrix} 6 & -10 \\ -3 & 5 \end{pmatrix}$ g $\begin{pmatrix} 4 & 8 \\ -2 & 4 \end{pmatrix}$ h $\begin{pmatrix} 0 & -1 \\ 2 & 2 \end{pmatrix}$

i $\begin{pmatrix} -1 & 3 \\ -2 & 6 \end{pmatrix}$ j $\begin{pmatrix} 2 & 1 \\ 4 & -2 \end{pmatrix}$ k $\begin{pmatrix} -3 & -9 \\ 2 & 6 \end{pmatrix}$ l $\begin{pmatrix} -4 & 8 \\ 3 & -6 \end{pmatrix}$

6 Which of these matrices represent transformations which give a *collapse*?

a $\begin{pmatrix} 9 & 3 \\ 3 & 1 \end{pmatrix}$ b $\begin{pmatrix} 7 & 5 \\ 0 & 1 \end{pmatrix}$ c $\begin{pmatrix} 3 & 1 \\ 6 & 2 \end{pmatrix}$ d $\begin{pmatrix} -2 & 1 \\ 8 & -4 \end{pmatrix}$

e $\begin{pmatrix} 3 & 12 \\ -2 & 8 \end{pmatrix}$ f $\begin{pmatrix} -4 & 10 \\ -2 & 5 \end{pmatrix}$ g $\begin{pmatrix} 9 & -5 \\ -7 & 4 \end{pmatrix}$ h $\begin{pmatrix} 4 & 2 \\ 0 & \frac{1}{2} \end{pmatrix}$

7 Each of these matrices represents a collapse.
Find the equation of the line of the collapse
either by drawing the image of the unit square $(0, 0)$, $(1, 0)$, $(1, 1)$, $(0, 1)$ on a
   diagram
or by using algebra.

a $\begin{pmatrix} 2 & \frac{1}{2} \\ 4 & 1 \end{pmatrix}$ b $\begin{pmatrix} 1 & 2 \\ 3 & 6 \end{pmatrix}$ c $\begin{pmatrix} 3 & 1 \\ 3 & 1 \end{pmatrix}$ d $\begin{pmatrix} 4 & 2 \\ 2 & 1 \end{pmatrix}$

e $\begin{pmatrix} 2 & 3 \\ -4 & -6 \end{pmatrix}$ f $\begin{pmatrix} 1 & 2 \\ -1 & -2 \end{pmatrix}$ g $\begin{pmatrix} 4 & -2 \\ -2 & 1 \end{pmatrix}$ h $\begin{pmatrix} 2 & -1 \\ -6 & 3 \end{pmatrix}$

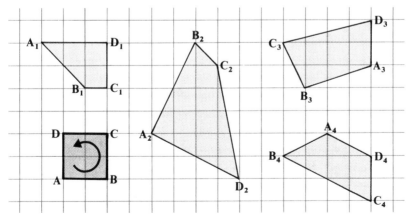

8 This diagram shows an object square $ABCD$ and four images $A_1B_1C_1D_1$,
$A_2B_2C_2D_2$, etc.
Going round the corners of the square in order gives an anticlockwise direction
as shown by the arrow.
Go round the corners of each image in order, and say whether the direction is
the same as or different from that of the object.

Area scale factors and determinants

9 a Find the determinant Δ of these three matrices:
$$M_1 = \begin{pmatrix} 2 & 1 \\ 2 & 2 \end{pmatrix} \quad M_2 = \begin{pmatrix} 2 & 1 \\ 2 & 1 \end{pmatrix} \quad \text{and} \quad M_3 = \begin{pmatrix} 2 & 1 \\ 2 & 0 \end{pmatrix}.$$
Note which determinant is positive, which is negative and which is zero.

b Draw the object square $A(1, 1)$, $B(1, 2)$, $C(2, 2)$, $D(2, 1)$ on axes from 0 to 8, and label its corners.
Find the image of this square using each of the three matrices. Draw these three images on the same diagram, labelling their corners $A_1B_1C_1D_1$, $A_2B_2C_2D_2$, $A_3B_3C_3D_3$.

c As you visit the four corners of the square in the order A, B, C and D, are you going round clockwise or anticlockwise?
As you visit the four corners of each image in order, which direction do you go round?
Do you suspect a connection between the sign of the determinant and the direction around the image?

10 a Find the determinant of each of these matrices:
$$N_1 = \begin{pmatrix} 2 & 1 \\ 0 & 1 \end{pmatrix} \quad N_2 = \begin{pmatrix} 2 & 1 \\ 0 & 0 \end{pmatrix} \quad N_3 = \begin{pmatrix} 2 & 1 \\ 0 & -1 \end{pmatrix}.$$

b Draw the object rectangle $A(1, 1)$, $B(2, 1)$, $C(2, 3)$, $D(1, 3)$ on axes from -4 to 6, and label the corners.
Find the images of this rectangle using each matrix; and draw the three images on the same diagram with their corners labelled.

c Has the direction round the shapes altered under any of these transformations?

11 For each transformation given by these matrices, state whether the direction round an object shape will be the *same* as or *different* from that round its image.

a $\begin{pmatrix} 4 & 3 \\ 1 & 2 \end{pmatrix}$ b $\begin{pmatrix} 2 & 1 \\ 5 & 2 \end{pmatrix}$ c $\begin{pmatrix} 3 & 2 \\ 1 & 0 \end{pmatrix}$ d $\begin{pmatrix} 6 & 3 \\ 3 & 2 \end{pmatrix}$

e $\begin{pmatrix} 5 & 4 \\ 2 & 0 \end{pmatrix}$ f $\begin{pmatrix} 1 & 2 \\ -2 & 1 \end{pmatrix}$ g $\begin{pmatrix} 4 & -5 \\ 1 & 1 \end{pmatrix}$ h $\begin{pmatrix} 4 & 6 \\ 3 & 4 \end{pmatrix}$

12 Under which of these transformations will the direction round a shape be changed?
a a rotation   b an enlargement   c a shear
d a reflection   e a stretch   f a translation

Inverse matrices

Introduction   A comparison

1   Copy and complete these multiplications.

    a $3 \times \ldots = 3$ b $7 \times \ldots = 7$ c $\frac{1}{2} \times \ldots = \frac{1}{2}$

    Note that the number 1 leaves these numbers unchanged after multiplication. 1 is called the *identity* for multiplication.

2   Copy and complete these multiplications.

    a $\frac{1}{2} \times \ldots = 1$ b $\frac{1}{4} \times \ldots = 1$ c $\frac{1}{3} \times \ldots = 1$

    When two numbers multiply to give the identity 1, then one number is the *inverse* of the other.

3   Multiply these matrices.

    a $\begin{pmatrix} 3 & 4 \\ 5 & 6 \end{pmatrix}\begin{pmatrix} 1 & 0 \\ 0 & 1 \end{pmatrix}$ b $\begin{pmatrix} 6 & 7 \\ 3 & 2 \end{pmatrix}\begin{pmatrix} 1 & 0 \\ 0 & 1 \end{pmatrix}$ c $\begin{pmatrix} 2 & 5 \\ 3 & 8 \end{pmatrix}\begin{pmatrix} 1 & 0 \\ 0 & 1 \end{pmatrix}$

    Note that the matrix $\begin{pmatrix} 1 & 0 \\ 0 & 1 \end{pmatrix}$ leaves the other matrices unchanged.

    $\begin{pmatrix} 1 & 0 \\ 0 & 1 \end{pmatrix}$ is the *identity matrix, I*.

4   Multiply these matrices.

    a $\begin{pmatrix} 3 & 5 \\ 1 & 2 \end{pmatrix}\begin{pmatrix} 2 & -5 \\ -1 & 3 \end{pmatrix}$ b $\begin{pmatrix} 2 & 3 \\ 3 & 5 \end{pmatrix}\begin{pmatrix} 5 & -3 \\ -3 & 2 \end{pmatrix}$ c $\begin{pmatrix} 2 & 1 \\ 7 & 4 \end{pmatrix}\begin{pmatrix} 4 & -1 \\ -7 & 2 \end{pmatrix}$

    When two matrices multiply to give the identity matrix, I, then one matrix is the *inverse* of the other.

Part 1   Finding inverse matrices

1   For each pair of matrices, show that one is the inverse of the other by multiplying them together.

    a $\begin{pmatrix} 3 & 5 \\ 4 & 7 \end{pmatrix}$ and $\begin{pmatrix} 7 & -5 \\ -4 & 3 \end{pmatrix}$ b $\begin{pmatrix} 9 & 4 \\ 2 & 1 \end{pmatrix}$ and $\begin{pmatrix} 1 & -4 \\ -2 & 9 \end{pmatrix}$

    c $\begin{pmatrix} 11 & 3 \\ 7 & 2 \end{pmatrix}$ and $\begin{pmatrix} 2 & -3 \\ -7 & 11 \end{pmatrix}$ d $\begin{pmatrix} 3 & 7 \\ 2 & 5 \end{pmatrix}$ and $\begin{pmatrix} 5 & -7 \\ -2 & 3 \end{pmatrix}$

    e $\begin{pmatrix} 7 & -4 \\ 2 & -1 \end{pmatrix}$ and $\begin{pmatrix} -1 & 4 \\ -2 & 7 \end{pmatrix}$ f $\begin{pmatrix} -5 & 3 \\ -2 & 1 \end{pmatrix}$ and $\begin{pmatrix} 1 & -3 \\ 2 & -5 \end{pmatrix}$

2   The above pattern, connecting a matrix A with its inverse A^{-1}, changes the *position* of numbers on the leading diagonal, and the *signs* of numbers on the other diagonal.

    Write down the inverse matrix for each of these, and show that $A^{-1}A = I$ in each case.

    a $\begin{pmatrix} 7 & 5 \\ 4 & 3 \end{pmatrix}$ b $\begin{pmatrix} 4 & 11 \\ 1 & 3 \end{pmatrix}$ c $\begin{pmatrix} 5 & 3 \\ 3 & 2 \end{pmatrix}$ d $\begin{pmatrix} 5 & 1 \\ 9 & 2 \end{pmatrix}$

    e $\begin{pmatrix} 4 & 5 \\ 7 & 9 \end{pmatrix}$ f $\begin{pmatrix} 5 & 4 \\ 6 & 5 \end{pmatrix}$ g $\begin{pmatrix} 8 & 7 \\ 9 & 8 \end{pmatrix}$ h $\begin{pmatrix} -2 & 1 \\ -3 & 1 \end{pmatrix}$

    i $\begin{pmatrix} -5 & 7 \\ -3 & 4 \end{pmatrix}$ j $\begin{pmatrix} 2 & -7 \\ 1 & -3 \end{pmatrix}$ k $\begin{pmatrix} -3 & -5 \\ 2 & 3 \end{pmatrix}$ l $\begin{pmatrix} -9 & 11 \\ 4 & -5 \end{pmatrix}$

Inverse matrices

3 See how the above method breaks down with these matrices. Notice that you do *not* get the identity matrix, I, after multiplying the two matrices.

a $\begin{pmatrix} 2 & 4 \\ 2 & 5 \end{pmatrix}$
b $\begin{pmatrix} 3 & 8 \\ 2 & 6 \end{pmatrix}$
c $\begin{pmatrix} 9 & 3 \\ 5 & 2 \end{pmatrix}$

d $\begin{pmatrix} 4 & 10 \\ 2 & 6 \end{pmatrix}$
e $\begin{pmatrix} -2 & 2 \\ -4 & 3 \end{pmatrix}$
f $\begin{pmatrix} -3 & 10 \\ -2 & 5 \end{pmatrix}$

g $\begin{pmatrix} 2 & 4 \\ -4 & -5 \end{pmatrix}$
h $\begin{pmatrix} 8 & -4 \\ -6 & 2 \end{pmatrix}$
i $\begin{pmatrix} 4 & -7 \\ -3 & 7 \end{pmatrix}$

4 To find the inverse of any 2×2 matrix, you must
      (i) change the *positions* of numbers on the leading diagonal
      (ii) change the *signs* of numbers on the other diagonal
and (iii) divide by the determinant $\Delta = ad - bc$.
Find the inverses of these matrices, and check your answers by multiplying each matrix by its inverse.

a $\begin{pmatrix} 6 & 5 \\ 2 & 2 \end{pmatrix}$
b $\begin{pmatrix} 3 & 2 \\ 5 & 4 \end{pmatrix}$
c $\begin{pmatrix} 4 & 3 \\ 6 & 5 \end{pmatrix}$
d $\begin{pmatrix} 3 & 5 \\ 3 & 6 \end{pmatrix}$

e $\begin{pmatrix} 3 & 3 \\ 9 & 10 \end{pmatrix}$
f $\begin{pmatrix} 4 & 7 \\ 4 & 8 \end{pmatrix}$
g $\begin{pmatrix} 4 & -6 \\ -5 & 8 \end{pmatrix}$
h $\begin{pmatrix} 9 & -10 \\ -6 & 7 \end{pmatrix}$

i $\begin{pmatrix} -5 & -8 \\ -6 & -10 \end{pmatrix}$
j $\begin{pmatrix} -2 & 2 \\ -4 & 3 \end{pmatrix}$
k $\begin{pmatrix} -4 & -2 \\ 11 & 5 \end{pmatrix}$
l $\begin{pmatrix} 5 & 10 \\ -5 & -9 \end{pmatrix}$

m $\begin{pmatrix} 6 & 8 \\ 4 & 7 \end{pmatrix}$
n $\begin{pmatrix} 10 & -12 \\ -5 & 7 \end{pmatrix}$
o $\begin{pmatrix} 9 & -10 \\ -8 & 9 \end{pmatrix}$
p $\begin{pmatrix} 2 & 4 \\ 4 & 7 \end{pmatrix}$

q $\begin{pmatrix} 2 & 4 \\ 6 & 11 \end{pmatrix}$
r $\begin{pmatrix} 4 & 2 \\ -1 & 0 \end{pmatrix}$
s $\begin{pmatrix} 0 & -1 \\ 3 & 9 \end{pmatrix}$
t $\begin{pmatrix} -7 & -2 \\ 9 & 3 \end{pmatrix}$

u $\begin{pmatrix} 9 & 7 \\ -6 & -5 \end{pmatrix}$
v $\begin{pmatrix} -1 & 4 \\ 2 & 2 \end{pmatrix}$

5 Show that each of these matrices does not have an inverse. Explain why the method of finding them breaks down.

a $\begin{pmatrix} 3 & 2 \\ 6 & 4 \end{pmatrix}$
b $\begin{pmatrix} 3 & 9 \\ 2 & 6 \end{pmatrix}$
c $\begin{pmatrix} 4 & -6 \\ -6 & 9 \end{pmatrix}$

d $\begin{pmatrix} -4 & 5 \\ -8 & 10 \end{pmatrix}$
e $\begin{pmatrix} -3 & -8 \\ 6 & 16 \end{pmatrix}$

6 The method of finding the inverse of a 3×3 or even larger matrix is much more complicated and is not given here.
However, each square matrix, no matter how large, will always multiply with its inverse to give the identity matrix, I.
Multiply these pairs of matrices and show that one is the inverse of the other.

a $\begin{pmatrix} 0 & 1 & 2 \\ -1 & 0 & 2 \\ 1 & 1 & 1 \end{pmatrix}$ and $\begin{pmatrix} -2 & 1 & 2 \\ 3 & -2 & -2 \\ -1 & 1 & 1 \end{pmatrix}$

Inverse matrices

b $\begin{pmatrix} 1 & 4 & 4 \\ 2 & 0 & 1 \\ 2 & -1 & 0 \end{pmatrix}$ and $\begin{pmatrix} 1 & -4 & 4 \\ 2 & -8 & 7 \\ -2 & 9 & -8 \end{pmatrix}$

c $\begin{pmatrix} -5 & -2 & 4 \\ 3 & 1 & -2 \\ -7 & -2 & 5 \end{pmatrix}$ and $\begin{pmatrix} 1 & 2 & 0 \\ -1 & 3 & 2 \\ 1 & 4 & 1 \end{pmatrix}$

d $\begin{pmatrix} 0 & 1 & 2 \\ 2 & -1 & 3 \\ 1 & 1 & 4 \end{pmatrix}$ and $\begin{pmatrix} -7 & -2 & 5 \\ -5 & -2 & 4 \\ 3 & 1 & -2 \end{pmatrix}$

e $\begin{pmatrix} -3 & 3 & 1 \\ -6 & 5 & 2 \\ 7 & -6 & -2 \end{pmatrix}$ and $\begin{pmatrix} 2 & 0 & 1 \\ 2 & -1 & 0 \\ 1 & 3 & 3 \end{pmatrix}$

f $\begin{pmatrix} -9 & 3 & -1 \\ 16 & -5 & 2 \\ 1 & 0 & 0 \end{pmatrix}$ and $\begin{pmatrix} 0 & 0 & 1 \\ 2 & 1 & 2 \\ 5 & 3 & -3 \end{pmatrix}$

g $\begin{pmatrix} 1 & 1\frac{1}{2} & 0 \\ 1 & 2 & 0 \\ -1 & 3 & 2 \end{pmatrix}$ and $\begin{pmatrix} 4 & -3 & 0 \\ -2 & 2 & 0 \\ 5 & -4\frac{1}{2} & \frac{1}{2} \end{pmatrix}$

h $\begin{pmatrix} 1 & 0 & 2 & 0 \\ 3 & -1 & -4 & 2 \\ 0 & 1 & 2 & 0 \\ 2 & 0 & \frac{1}{2} & 1 \end{pmatrix}$ and $\begin{pmatrix} 3 & 2 & 2 & -4 \\ 2 & 2 & 3 & -4 \\ -1 & -1 & -1 & 2 \\ -5\frac{1}{2} & -3\frac{1}{2} & -3\frac{1}{2} & 8 \end{pmatrix}$

7 To show that the inverse A^{-1} of a matrix has the opposite effect to the matrix A itself,
(i) find the inverse A^{-1} of the given matrix A
(ii) perform the two multiplications.

a If $A = \begin{pmatrix} 2 & 5 \\ 1 & 3 \end{pmatrix}$ find $A\begin{pmatrix} 4 \\ 1 \end{pmatrix}$ and $A^{-1}\begin{pmatrix} 13 \\ 7 \end{pmatrix}$.

b If $A = \begin{pmatrix} 3 & 10 \\ 2 & 7 \end{pmatrix}$ find $A\begin{pmatrix} 2 \\ 0 \end{pmatrix}$ and $A^{-1}\begin{pmatrix} 6 \\ 4 \end{pmatrix}$.

c If $A = \begin{pmatrix} 2 & 2 \\ 2 & 3 \end{pmatrix}$ find $A\begin{pmatrix} 1 \\ 3 \end{pmatrix}$ and $A^{-1}\begin{pmatrix} 8 \\ 11 \end{pmatrix}$.

d If $A = \begin{pmatrix} 4 & 5 \\ 6 & 8 \end{pmatrix}$ find $A\begin{pmatrix} 1 \\ 1 \end{pmatrix}$ and $A^{-1}\begin{pmatrix} 9 \\ 14 \end{pmatrix}$.

e If $A = \begin{pmatrix} 4 & 8 \\ 4 & 9 \end{pmatrix}$ find $A\begin{pmatrix} 3 \\ 0 \end{pmatrix}$ and $A^{-1}\begin{pmatrix} 12 \\ 12 \end{pmatrix}$.

f If $A = \begin{pmatrix} 6 & -9 \\ -5 & 8 \end{pmatrix}$ find $A\begin{pmatrix} 3 \\ 2 \end{pmatrix}$ and $A^{-1}\begin{pmatrix} 0 \\ 1 \end{pmatrix}$.

g If $A = \begin{pmatrix} 3 & -5 \\ -2 & 4 \end{pmatrix}$ find $A\begin{pmatrix} 6 \\ 4 \end{pmatrix}$ and $A^{-1}\begin{pmatrix} -2 \\ 4 \end{pmatrix}$.

h If $A = \begin{pmatrix} -7 & 4 \\ -4 & 2 \end{pmatrix}$ find $A\begin{pmatrix} 0 \\ -2 \end{pmatrix}$ and $A^{-1}\begin{pmatrix} -8 \\ -4 \end{pmatrix}$.

Inverse matrices

Part 2   Simultaneous equations

1   The simultaneous equations $\begin{array}{l} 2x + y = 7 \\ 3x + 2y = 1 \end{array}$ can be written as the

matrix equation $\begin{pmatrix} 2 & 1 \\ 3 & 2 \end{pmatrix}\begin{pmatrix} x \\ y \end{pmatrix} = \begin{pmatrix} 7 \\ 1 \end{pmatrix}$.

   a   Find the inverse of $\begin{pmatrix} 2 & 1 \\ 3 & 2 \end{pmatrix}$.

   b   Pre-multiply both sides of the matrix equation by this inverse and hence solve the equation for x and y.

2   Use this method to solve these simultaneous equations.

   a $4x + y = 6$
       $7x + 2y = 11$

   b $3x + 4y = 10$
       $2x + 3y = 7$

   c $4x + 3y = 7$
       $5x + 4y = 9$

   d $5x + 3y = 11$
       $3x + 2y = 7$

   e $4x - 3y = 5$
       $7x - 5y = 9$

   f $2x - 3y = 8$
       $3x - 4y = 11$

   g $5x + 8y = 3$
       $3x + 5y = 2$

   h $2x - 3y = 1$
       $-7x + 11y = -3\frac{1}{2}$

3   Solve these simultaneous equations (where $\Delta > 1$).

   a $6x + 4y = 10$
       $4x + 3y = 7$

   b $3x + 5y = 6$
       $5x + 9y = 10$

   c $3x - 8y = 5$
       $-2x + 7y = 0$

   d $x - 2y = 9$
       $3x + y = 13$

   e $5x - 8y = 2$
       $x - 2y = 0$

   f $4x + 3y = 8$
       $6x + 5y = 16$

   g $5x - 3y = 18$
       $2x + y = 5$

   h $7x - 5y = 12$
       $3x - 2y = 5$

   i $x + 2y = 4$
       $3x - 2y = 0$

   j $4x + 2y = 9$
       $-x + 2y = -1$

4   Solve these simultaneous equations (where $\Delta < 0$).

   a $x + 4y = 1$
       $2x + 5y = 5$

   b $2x + y = 4$
       $5x + 2y = 9$

   c $3x + 4y = 5$
       $7x + 6y = 10$

   d $3x + 4y = 2$
       $2x - y = 5$

   e $4x + 9y = 7$
       $2x - 3y = 1$

   f $2x - 3y = 6$
       $3x - 7y = 9$

   g $-x + 2y = 9$
       $3x + y = 1$

   h $3x + 4y = 5$
       $7x + 8y = 11$

   i $9x - 2y = 12$
       $3x - y = 4$

   j $5x - 8y = 7$
       $4x - 7y = 5$

5   Write these three simultaneous equations as *one* matrix equation.
   $3x - 3y - z = 0$
   $6x - 5y - 2z = 2$
   $-7x + 6y + 2z = -4$

   Given that the inverse of $\begin{pmatrix} 3 & -3 & -1 \\ 6 & -5 & -2 \\ -7 & 6 & 2 \end{pmatrix}$ is $\begin{pmatrix} -2 & 0 & -1 \\ -2 & 1 & 0 \\ -1 & -3 & -3 \end{pmatrix}$, solve

   this matrix equation to find the values of x, y and z.

Inverse matrices

6 If the inverse of $\begin{pmatrix} -2 & 1 & 2 \\ 3 & -2 & -2 \\ -1 & 1 & 1 \end{pmatrix}$ is $\begin{pmatrix} 0 & 1 & 2 \\ -1 & 0 & 2 \\ 1 & 1 & 1 \end{pmatrix}$, solve

these simultaneous equations $\begin{array}{rcl} -2x + y + 2z &=& 3 \\ 3x - 2y - 2z &=& -5 \\ -x + y + z &=& 2. \end{array}$

7 Multiply together these two matrices $\begin{pmatrix} 1 & 2 & 0 \\ -1 & 3 & 2 \\ 1 & 4 & 1 \end{pmatrix}\begin{pmatrix} -5 & -2 & 4 \\ 3 & 1 & -2 \\ -7 & -2 & 5 \end{pmatrix}$, and

hence solve the simultaneous equations $\begin{array}{rcl} -5x - 2y + 4z &=& 6 \\ 3x + y - 2z &=& -4 \\ -7x - 2y + 5z &=& 9. \end{array}$

Part 3 Inverse transformations

1 An *inverse* operation has the opposite effect to the original operation.
What are the inverse operations of
a opening a book
b taking two paces forward
c adding 5
d multiplying by 3
e turning left
f rotating 45° clockwise
g switching the light on
h reflecting in the x-axis
i squaring a number
j rotating a half-turn clockwise?
Which *two* of these operations are their own inverses?

2 Describe the inverse transformations of
a a rotation about the origin through 90° clockwise
b an enlargement, centre the origin with length scale factor of 2
c a reflection in the y-axis.

In problems **3** to **6**, any diagrams should have both axes labelled from 0 to 6.

3 a Draw the square with corners (1, 1), (1, 2), (2, 2), (2, 1) and transform it using the matrix $A = \begin{pmatrix} 1 & 2 \\ 0 & 1 \end{pmatrix}$. Draw the image of the square on the same diagram.

 b On a new diagram, draw the parallelogram with corners (3, 1), (5, 2), (6, 2), (4, 1). Transform this parallelogram using the matrix $B = \begin{pmatrix} 1 & -2 \\ 0 & 1 \end{pmatrix}$, and draw the image on the same diagram.

 c What do you notice about your two diagrams?
 Prove that B is the inverse of A by showing that $AB = I$.

4 a Draw the square with corners (1, 1), (1, 2), (2, 2), (2, 1) and transform it using the matrix $M = \begin{pmatrix} 2 & -1 \\ 2 & 0 \end{pmatrix}$. Draw the image of the square on the same diagram.

 b On a new diagram, draw the parallelogram with corners (1, 2), (0, 2), (2, 4), (3, 4). Transform this parallelogram using the matrix $N = \begin{pmatrix} 0 & \frac{1}{2} \\ -1 & 1 \end{pmatrix}$, and draw the image on the same diagram.

 c Make a deduction from your diagrams about the matrices M and N; and show by multiplication that $MN = I$.

211

Inverse matrices

5 a The parallelogram (0, 4), (2, 6), (4, 6), (2, 4) is transformed by the matrix
$P = \begin{pmatrix} 0 & 1 \\ -1 & 1 \end{pmatrix}$. Draw both the parallelogram and its image on the same diagram.

b The square (4, 4), (6, 4), (6, 2), (4, 2) is transformed by the matrix
$Q = \begin{pmatrix} 1 & -1 \\ 1 & 0 \end{pmatrix}$. Draw both the square and its image on another diagram.

c What do you deduce about the matrices P and Q from your diagrams? Show by multiplication that $PQ = I$.

6 a The matrix $U = \begin{pmatrix} 3 & -1 \\ 1 & 0 \end{pmatrix}$ transforms the rectangle (2, 1), (1, 1), (1, 3), (2, 3) onto a parallelogram. Draw both rectangle and parallelogram on the same diagram.

b The matrix $V = \begin{pmatrix} 0 & 1 \\ -1 & 3 \end{pmatrix}$ transforms the parallelogram (5, 2), (2, 1), (0, 1), (3, 2). Draw both this parallelogram and its image on another diagram.

c Confirm by multiplication that $UV = I$.

7 The matrix $A = \begin{pmatrix} 4 & 2 \\ 3 & 2 \end{pmatrix}$ has an inverse
$A^{-1} = \begin{pmatrix} 1 & -1 \\ -1\frac{1}{2} & 2 \end{pmatrix}$.
Show that
a the matrix A maps the point $P(1, 1)$ onto Q as in this diagram
b the matrix A^{-1} maps the point Q back onto P.

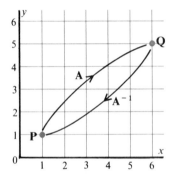

8

The matrix $M = \begin{pmatrix} 3 & 5 \\ 1 & 2 \end{pmatrix}$ has an inverse
$M^{-1} = \begin{pmatrix} 2 & -5 \\ -1 & 3 \end{pmatrix}$.
The point P maps onto Q under matrix M.
Hence Q maps back onto P under the matrix M^{-1}.
Find
a Q if P is (2, 1)   b Q if P is (2, −1)
c Q if P is (0, 3)   d P if Q is (3, 0)
e P if Q is (4, 1)   f P if Q is (3, −2).

9 The point P maps onto its image P' under a transformation given by the matrix
$N = \begin{pmatrix} 4 & 2 \\ 3 & 2 \end{pmatrix}$. P' maps back onto P under the inverse transformation.
Find
a the inverse matrix N^{-1} b P' when P is (0, 2)
c P' when P is (3, −2)   d P when P' is (4, 0)
e P when P' is (−2, 3).

Inverse matrices

10 A transformation is given by the matrix $T = \begin{pmatrix} 3 & 5 \\ -2 & -3 \end{pmatrix}$.

The image of a point P is given by $P' = T(P)$.

Find

a the inverse matrix T^{-1} b P' when P is $(2, 1)$
c P' when P is $(5, 2)$ d P when P' is $(0, 4)$
e P when P' is $(-2, 1)$.

11 Copy and complete this table where the image P' of point P is given by $P' = M(P)$.

		a	b	c	d	e	f	g	h
Matrix	M	$\begin{pmatrix} 2 & 1 \\ 3 & 2 \end{pmatrix}$	$\begin{pmatrix} 4 & 3 \\ 6 & 5 \end{pmatrix}$	$\begin{pmatrix} 3 & 2 \\ 5 & 4 \end{pmatrix}$	$\begin{pmatrix} 2 & 5 \\ 3 & 9 \end{pmatrix}$	$\begin{pmatrix} 10 & -4 \\ -4 & 2 \end{pmatrix}$	$\begin{pmatrix} 3 & -5 \\ -4 & 7 \end{pmatrix}$	$\begin{pmatrix} 2 & 2 \\ -2 & 3 \end{pmatrix}$	$\begin{pmatrix} 5 & -3 \\ 2 & 2 \end{pmatrix}$
Inverse matrix	M^{-1}								
Object point	P	$(4, 0)$	$(1, -1)$	$(2, 2)$	$(3, 0)$				
Image point	P'					$(0, 2)$	$(3, -2)$	$(6, -1)$	$(9, 10)$

12 The point $P(x, y)$ maps onto $P'(6, 5)$ under a transformation given by the matrix

$M = \begin{pmatrix} 7 & 8 \\ 6 & 7 \end{pmatrix}$. In short, $\begin{pmatrix} 7 & 8 \\ 6 & 7 \end{pmatrix}\begin{pmatrix} x \\ y \end{pmatrix} = \begin{pmatrix} 6 \\ 5 \end{pmatrix}$.

Finding the values of x and y for point P is then the same problem as solving the simultaneous equations

$7x + 8y = 6$
$6x + 7y = 5$.

The method used in this problem is essentially the same as that used in part **2** for solving simultaneous equations.

Find

a the inverse matrix, M^{-1} b the values of x and y.

13 The point $P(x, y) \rightarrow P'(7, 6)$ under the matrix $\begin{pmatrix} 9 & 10 \\ 8 & 9 \end{pmatrix}$.

Find the values of x and y.

14 The point $R(x, y) \rightarrow R'(2, 3)$ under the matrix $\begin{pmatrix} 5 & 4 \\ 7 & 6 \end{pmatrix}$.

Find the values of x and y.

15 The matrix $\begin{pmatrix} 6 & 2 \\ -1 & 0 \end{pmatrix}$ maps the point (x, y) onto the point $(8, -1)$.
Find the values of x and y.

Inverse matrices

16 Here is a list of transformations and their matrices.
For each matrix (i) find the inverse matrix
(ii) decide whether the transformation is its own inverse.

a a reflection in the x-axis; $\begin{pmatrix} 1 & 0 \\ 0 & -1 \end{pmatrix}$

b a reflection in the y-axis; $\begin{pmatrix} -1 & 0 \\ 0 & 1 \end{pmatrix}$

c an enlargement, centre the origin and scale factor 2; $\begin{pmatrix} 2 & 0 \\ 0 & 2 \end{pmatrix}$

d a stretch parallel to the y-axis; $\begin{pmatrix} 1 & 0 \\ 0 & 3 \end{pmatrix}$

e a reflection in the line $y = x$; $\begin{pmatrix} 0 & 1 \\ 1 & 0 \end{pmatrix}$

f a reflection in the line $y = -x$; $\begin{pmatrix} 0 & -1 \\ -1 & 0 \end{pmatrix}$

g a rotation of a half-turn about the origin; $\begin{pmatrix} -1 & 0 \\ 0 & -1 \end{pmatrix}$

h a rotation of 90° clockwise about the origin; $\begin{pmatrix} 0 & 1 \\ -1 & 0 \end{pmatrix}$

17 These problems involve multiplying a matrix by itself to find its *square*.
For each of these matrices, find (i) the square of the matrix
(ii) the inverse matrix.
What do you notice?

a $\begin{pmatrix} -2 & -3 \\ 1 & 1 \end{pmatrix}$ b $\begin{pmatrix} 2 & 7 \\ -1 & -3 \end{pmatrix}$ c $\begin{pmatrix} 1 & -3 \\ 1 & -2 \end{pmatrix}$

18 If $M = \begin{pmatrix} 0 & 1 \\ -1 & -1 \end{pmatrix}$, prove that $M^2 = M^{-1}$.

19 Find the square M^2 of each of these matrices M, and use your answer to write down, without any further calculation, the inverse M^{-1}.

a $\begin{pmatrix} 4 & 7 \\ -2 & -4 \end{pmatrix}$ b $\begin{pmatrix} 3 & 1 \\ -6 & -3 \end{pmatrix}$ c $\begin{pmatrix} -2 & 2 \\ 3 & 2 \end{pmatrix}$

20 If $M = \begin{pmatrix} 5 & -2 \\ 10 & -5 \end{pmatrix}$, find the value of M^2 and hence write down M^{-1}.

Finding a transformation matrix

1 Combine these matrices: a $\begin{pmatrix} 1 & 2 \\ 3 & 4 \end{pmatrix}\begin{pmatrix} 1 \\ 0 \end{pmatrix}$ and $\begin{pmatrix} 1 & 2 \\ 3 & 4 \end{pmatrix}\begin{pmatrix} 0 \\ 1 \end{pmatrix}$

 b $\begin{pmatrix} 5 & 6 \\ 7 & 8 \end{pmatrix}\begin{pmatrix} 1 \\ 0 \end{pmatrix}$ and $\begin{pmatrix} 5 & 6 \\ 7 & 8 \end{pmatrix}\begin{pmatrix} 0 \\ 1 \end{pmatrix}$

 c $\begin{pmatrix} 9 & 0 \\ 1 & 2 \end{pmatrix}\begin{pmatrix} 1 \\ 0 \end{pmatrix}$ and $\begin{pmatrix} 9 & 0 \\ 1 & 2 \end{pmatrix}\begin{pmatrix} 0 \\ 1 \end{pmatrix}$.

What do you notice about your answers and the columns of the matrices?

2 Combine these matrices: $\begin{pmatrix} a & b \\ c & d \end{pmatrix}\begin{pmatrix} 1 \\ 0 \end{pmatrix}$ and $\begin{pmatrix} a & b \\ c & d \end{pmatrix}\begin{pmatrix} 0 \\ 1 \end{pmatrix}$.

Notice that the point $(1, 0)$ maps onto the point (a, c)
 and the point $(0, 1)$ maps onto the point (b, d).

3 These diagrams show the unit square $OIKJ$ and its image $OI'K'J'$ after certain transformations.

For each diagram, write the co-ordinates of the points I' and J'; and hence write the matrix for the transformation.

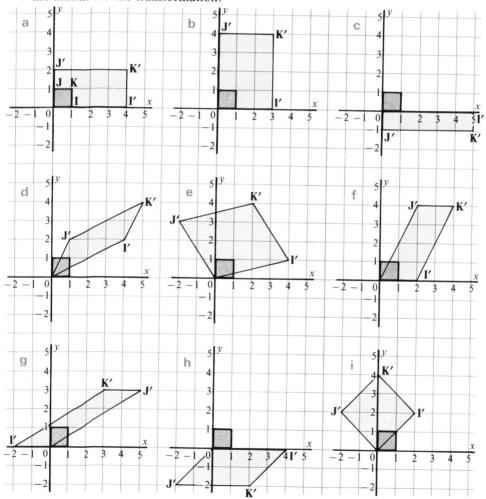

Finding a transformation matrix

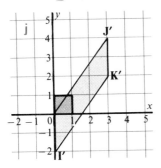

4   Here is a list of transformations.
    Find the matrix for each transformation by
      (i) drawing the unit square $0IKJ$ and its image $0I'K'J'$
      (ii) labelling the corners of the unit square and its image
      (iii) writing the co-ordinates of the image points I' and J'
      (iv) filling in the columns of the matrix.
    a   an enlargement, centre the origin and length scale factor 2
    b   an enlargement, centre the origin and length scale factor 3
    c   an enlargement, centre the origin and length scale factor -2
    d   an enlargement, centre the origin and length scale factor $\frac{1}{2}$
    e   a reflection in the x-axis
    f   a reflection in the y-axis
    g   a reflection in the line $y = x$
    h   a reflection in the line $y = -x$
    i   a rotation about the origin through 90° clockwise
    j   a rotation about the origin through 90° anticlockwise
    k   a half-turn rotation about the origin
    l   a stretch parallel to the y-axis in which the x-axis is invariant and the point
        (0, 1) maps onto (0, 2)
    m   a stretch parallel to the x-axis in which the y-axis is invariant and the point
        (1, 0) maps onto (3, 0)
    n   a shear in which the x-axis is invariant and the point (0, 1) maps onto (2, 1)
    o   a shear in which the y-axis is invariant and the point (1, 0) maps onto (1, 3)
    p   the identity transformation in which the unit square maps onto itself

5   Here is a list of more complicated transformations.
    Use the same method to find the matrix for each one.
    a   a rotation about the origin of 45° anticlockwise
    b   a rotation about the origin of 45° clockwise
    c   a rotation about the origin of 60° clockwise
    d   a rotation about the origin of 60° anticlockwise
    e   a reflection in the line $y = 2x$
    f   a reflection in the line $y = \frac{1}{2}x$
    g   a reflection in the line $y = -2x$